A COMMUTATIVE HYPERCOMPLEX CALCULUS WITH APPLICATIONS TO SPECIAL RELATIVITY

CLYDE M. DAVENPORT

Printed and bound in the United States of America.

ISBN 0-9623837-0-8

Library of Congress Cataloging
in Publication Data 89-90348

Dedicated to the memory of:

Sir William Rowan Hamilton (1805–1865)
Hermann Günther Grassman (1809–1877)
Josiah Willard Gibbs (1839–1903)
Oliver W. Heaviside (1850–1925),

And to scientists and engineers in the mathematical trenches, everywhere.

CONTENTS

	PREFACE	***vii***
	ACKNOWLEDGEMENTS	***ix***
I.	**INTRODUCTION**	**1**
II.	**A SYSTEM OF HYPERCOMPLEX ANALYSIS**	**7**
	2.1 A Four-Dimensional Real Basis Algebra	7
	2.2 Properties of the Basis Algebra 𝔻	17
	2.3 A Function Theory and System of Analysis	37
III.	**𝔻-SPACE OPERATIONS RELATED TO CLASSICAL VECTOR ANALYSIS**	**63**
	3.1 Classical Vector Operator Analogues in 𝔻	63
	3.2 Maxwell's Equations in 𝔻-Space Notation	95
	3.3 Some Ramifications for the Theory of Partial Differential Equations	102
IV.	**APPLICATIONS TO RELATIVITY PHYSICS**	**139**
	4.1 Motivation for Relativity Applications	139
	4.2 Relativity Aspects of the Hypercomplex Algebra	140
	4.3 Construction of a 𝔻-Space Relativity Transformation Group	146
	4.4 Additional Effects Are Postulated	170
	4.5 Transformation Effects for the Field Equations of Physics	189
V.	**CONCLUSIONS**	**203**
	REFERENCES	**207**
	INDEX	**211**

PREFACE

The mathematical ideas presented in this work may be viewed collectively as a classical-looking algebra and calculus of four-dimensional vectors, or of *commutative* hypercomplex numbers in four dimensions. It has significant potential value as a computational tool replacing or complementing the classical vector analysis. Its construction was motivated by the author's desire to see something in four dimensions that is analogous to the classical complex analysis of two dimensions. The book is organized into two main subject areas. The first develops the hypercomplex algebra and system of analysis, and the second explores applications to physics, particularly to relativity. The underlying algebra, itself, exhibits certain aspects of relativity, and may represent a useful view of the space-time continuum.

The casual reader who would like a browsing overview should read Section 2.1.5 (definition of the basis algebra) and Section 2.2.2 (definition of the vector canonical notation). The vector canonical form of a hypercomplex function is given in (2.96), with a conventional vector expansion in (2.99). The four-dimensional Cauchy-Riemann conditions are given in (2.156), and some of their consequences are given in (3.62), (3.67), (3.72), (3.82), and (3.87). This small amount of extremely direct material presents the central ideas of the mathematics chapter. An understanding of the applications chapters will require a more in-depth reading of most of the book.

The material is written in an expository style at the upper-division undergraduate level, hence is relatively easy to read and will be accessible to a wide range of readers. I occasionally repeat formulas or ideas so that the development will flow more straightforwardly and the reader will not have to be constantly referring back to earlier pages; moreover, so that a browsing reader, who is likely to jump over some of the earlier sections, will at least have some minimal lead-in.

A professional mathematician may find little of interest in the present material. The work is based on elementary group algebra and classical complex variable concepts, even the most elementary concepts as are found in any upper-division applied text on the subject, such as R. V. Churchill's *Complex Variables and Applications.* What is new is the use and reinterpretation of existing axioms and concepts to synthesize a four-dimensional *analogue* of the complex analysis, taking into account the fact that there is no such thing as a field of four-dimensional numbers. The work includes very few theorems or proofs, because there is little which requires proof beyond that already existent in the theory of group algebras and complex variables.

The physics reader, however, will be presented a new formulation of Einstein's special relativity, couched in terms of the mathematical system developed earlier in the book. A few differences from existing theory occur, centered about the relativistic transformation. Current physics uses the four-dimensional group of Lorentz transformations, usually stated in terms of 4 X 4 matrices. I have developed a group of transformations that meets the requirements of Einstein's special relativity postulates, but is not reducible to the Lorentz group. All of the special relativistic effects in one space dimension and time are reproduced, but the four-dimensional effects suggest some extensions of current theory.

Clyde M. Davenport
June 21, 1986

ACKNOWLEDGEMENTS

This work is an expanded, revised, and more-expository version of a thesis presented by the author for an MS degree in mathematics from the University of Tennessee in June, 1978. The thesis was done under the guidance of Professor David E. Dobbs. I appreciate the substantial help and forebearance extended by Dr. Dobbs and the University to me as a working student.

Dr. Zane W. Bell reviewed the manuscript and suggested many improvements throughout, from a physicist's viewpoint. His considerable efforts are appreciated. Mr. Steven A. Wallace, a co-worker at Martin Marietta Energy Systems, served as the author's sole confidant and sounding board during the long gestation period of this work. His interest and encouragements were a great help. Dr. V. A. Protopopescu of the Oak Ridge National Laboratory reviewed Section 3.3, finding several errors that have been corrected, and offered other constructive comments.

I. INTRODUCTION

The aim of this book is to present an algebra, calculus, function theory, and system of analysis for a hypercomplex variable of the form $\mathbf{1}x + \mathbf{i}y + \mathbf{j}z + \mathbf{k}ct$ (non-quaternionic), where $\mathbf{1},\mathbf{i},\mathbf{j},\mathbf{k}$ are unit vectors and c is the speed of light, and to apply the results in the area of relativity physics and electromagnetics. The most straightforward extension of the system of applied complex analysis will be presented: one that admits an interpretation in four dimensions of any expression in the complex plane, and one in which manipulations of vectors in a four-dimensional space obey axioms analogous to those for the real or complex variables. The hypercomplex analysis will be presented and illustrated as an alternative to the classical vector analysis.

We begin by reviewing the literature, specifically the historical antecedents, inasmuch as there is no concerted research presently being carried out in this particular applications area. There are two main historical areas to be considered: classical complex variable theory, and linear vector spaces as applied in physics. In the first, the complex numbers $z = x + \mathrm{i}y$, as one interpretation, make up a linear vector space of two dimensions. The classical three-dimensional linear vector space used in science and engineering merely tacks on one more dimension, but does so in a way that does not allow a vector to be carried forward as a three-dimensional complex variable. Specifically, commutativity of multiplication is not preserved. Let us suspend conventional thinking for a moment and consider: what if one *could* create a four-dimensional linear vector space whose elements could be manipulated as field elements, using the axioms and function theory of the classical complex variables? The computational advantages would be enormous, due to simplified notation, commutativity, existence of vector inverses, and the vast range of complex analysis techniques. In the following, we will examine why this line of thought has not been pursued. The discussion is needed to set the scene for the present work and put it in perspective with today's vector analysis. The reader is referred to Michael J. Crowe's *History of Vector Analysis*[1] for a detailed account of the development of vector analysis. The interpretations, conclusions, and opinions in the following will be due to the present author.

In the early decades of the nineteenth century, the developmental state of physical science and engineering applications was running ahead of the then-existent mathematical systems' ability to clearly and concisely describe the physical principles. The four main tools (vector analysis, complex analysis, matrix analysis, and group theory) either were not yet in existence or were not widely understood. In the 1830s, Sir W. R. Hamilton, a physicist, undertook to create an algebra of three-dimensional vectors that could be used to codify physical principles and simplify calculations, particularly in the fields of mechanics and optics. He sought a system of multi-dimensioned quantities that could be manipulated using the axioms of the real number system. Not having group theory, he tried by trial and error to find basis vectors i,j,k which would produce a closed system and which would allow all quantities of the form $\mathrm{i}x + \mathrm{j}y + \mathrm{k}z$, where not all of the coefficients x,y,z are zero, to have a nonsingular inverse. He found that, to get closure, he would have to add another dimension to his basic quantities, with basis vectors now 1,i,j,k.

Probably very quickly, Hamilton must have found that it was not going to be easy to satisfy a requirement for the general existence of inverses, while retaining all the other axioms of the real and complex algebras. After several years of struggle with the problem, he found a system that met his requirements except for one detail: multiplication was not commutative. While this killed any hopes for treating his four-dimensional quantities, which he called *quaternions*, as anything like real or complex numbers, Hamilton realized that what he had was sufficient for the main problem areas of his time, those being mechanics and optics. He saw that the vector properties of his algebra would allow him to state the principles of mechanics, both celestial and mundane, in a very concise fashion compared to any previous formulation. Hamilton presented his initial results in 1843 in a paper given before the Royal Irish Academy, followed by partial publication of the paper in 1844[2].

The quaternions of Hamilton were well-suited to the physics of his day, by comparison with anything else at the time, but were never ardently embraced by the physics community. The commonest complaint was that the notation was hard to learn, read, and understand. It was said that Hamilton's books[3] on the subject, his definitive statements, were written in a too-abstract style without sufficient examples. Nevertheless, the quaternions became the basis for today's linear vector analysis with its **i,j,k** notation.

During the mid-nineteenth century, science and engineering relied mainly on the older coordinate-component methods, with some matrix analysis. Matrix analysis was new, and it was in this time period that it was developed into the modern form. A far-reaching scientific discovery occurred, however, which was to force the issue of mathematical notation. James Clerk Maxwell, by 1865, had published his four major papers on the theory of electromagnetism[4]. He used mainly component notation. In 1873, however, Maxwell published his *Treatise on Electricity and Magnetism*[5], in which he again used mostly component notation, but additionally stated certain key results in quaternion form. It is reasonable to say that Maxwell made his discoveries without the aid of quaternions, and only employed them later to gain a more concise and understandable formulation from a physics viewpoint. The overwhelming importance of Maxwell's work to the field of physics, and its heavily mathematical nature, influenced the physics community to study and reevaluate quaternion notation. Once again, quaternions were not embraced.

Possibly, one of the obstacles was that physicists wanted to work within a system of three-dimensional vectors, but quaternions are inherently four-dimensional. Even if one begins a calculation with all quaternions of three dimensions (one element consistently zeroed), say of the form $ix + jy + kz$, the result is still likely to be four-dimensional. A good example is the quaternion product $\nabla\mathbf{E}$, where ∇ is the three-dimensional gradient operator of vector analysis, and **E** is a vector function of three dimensions. The result is $-div(\mathbf{E}) + curl(\mathbf{E})$, which is the sum of a scalar and a three-dimensional vector quantity; i.e., is four-dimensional. The quantities $div(\mathbf{E})$ and $curl(\mathbf{E})$ are very important in the theory of electromagnetism, but physicists like to treat them as separate entities because they describe two distinct aspects of physical reality.

After the appearance of Maxwell's theory of electromagnetism, J. W. Gibbs[6] in America and O. W. Heaviside[7] in Britain, both physicists, separately took quaternion theory and extracted the parts that are most specific to three-dimensional field analysis, and created what they called *vector analysis*. It took substantially the form that is taught in science and engineering classes today. Gibbs and Heaviside eliminated any direct reference to four-dimensional quantities, instead redefining operations such as multiplication (*curl*) in a way that all results stay in the original three-dimensional domain. Crowe[8] provides a thorough analysis of this aspect of the evolution of vector analysis from quaternion analysis. Stephenson[9], also, reviewed this particular set of developments and came to substantially the same conclusions as did Crowe about the fundamental role of quaternions.

A considerable discussion, at times criticizing principal individuals more than the ideas presented, was set off in the scientific community in the late

1800s over which notation should be used [10]. The quaternion purists maintained that quaternion analysis provided the most concise and illuminating, mathematically-pure notation, and held that vector analysis was an unconscionable desecration. Vector analysts, however, felt that they had extracted the axioms, concepts, and mathematical forms which were of the most direct value in scientific applications, especially in electromagnetism. By the early 1900s, the conflict had resolved in favor of the vector analysts, and nothing since then has even nudged that consensus.

Before continuing, we acknowledge Hermann Grassman, who, in 1844, published a book [11] which contained a large part of modern vector analysis concepts and results. His work went almost entirely unnoticed, however, until late in the century. His notation was said to be difficult to understand, but almost certainly would have been more influential had it been more widely known.

We now return briefly to the first item in our review agenda: the question of why higher-dimensional complex variables were not constructed. Hamilton probably diminished many hopes by his extensive research which resulted in a noncommutative system. The controversy which erupted after the publication of Maxwell's theories of electromagnetism, however, generated a need to reinvestigate the issue. In 1877, Frobenius [12] proved that a commutative division algebra (i.e., a field) of vectors in four real dimensions cannot exist. In 1893, Scheffers [13] proved that one cannot construct a function theory which satisfies conventional complex-analytic properties (such as those involving derivatives or integrals) over a noncommutative algebra, hence quaternions could not be the basis of any conventional function theory in four dimensions. Frobenius and Scheffers did *not*, however, eliminate the possibility of something analogous to the classical complex properties in higher dimensions, and that is one of the main subjects of this book.

In the years since 1900, some study of function theories for higher-dimensional systems has occurred. That work, for example the study of the properties of higher-dimensional analytic functions, was carried out by means of very general expansions over algebraic bases of arbitrary dimensionality. In this way, most of the results of the complex function theory, such as Weierstrass' theorems on analytic functions and Cauchy's integral theorem, were extended to spaces of higher dimension. As representative of this approach, we mention Hausdorff [14], Ward [15], Agmon and Bers [16], Douglis [17], Vekua [18], and Ketchum [19].

The above-mentioned works treated the general properties of arbitrary analytic functions by manipulating infinite expansions and subsequently by showing that suitable conditions could be developed on the terms of the expansions to give the desired results. They did not emphasize particular functions, such as the elementary transcendental functions, in spaces of higher dimension; nor did they develop the notions of derivative and integral in the usual notation, as applied to a higher-dimensional variable. The usual notations for complex analysis were not carried over into the more general case.

There was at least one attempt to develop a function theory for a commutative four-dimensional variable. In 1928, Futagawa[20] presented results which contained some of the ideas of the present work. In particular, he obtained a generalization of the Cauchy-Riemann equations that differs from those in the present work in minor-appearing (but significant) ways: his z-axis is apparently defined in the reverse direction from the present, he has some sign differences, and in two places he takes partial derivatives with respect to a different combination of the independent variables than is done in the present work.

In the 1880s, the theory of linear associative algebras was developed, and all algebras of elements up to dimensionality six, including the algebra that will be used in the present work, were elucidated[47]. The concept of *group algebra*, which we shall use, was developed. There are five distinct group algebras of four-dimensional elements, including the quaternion case. In the author's opinion, it is strange that only the quaternion algebra was considered for physical applications, the only question being about which notation to use. Might some of the others be as good, perhaps even better, than the quaternion algebra for theoretical and engineering calculations? We shall investigate one alternative and let the reader be the judge. We shall place the present work into precise historical perspective, below, after we have stated its algebraic structure.

At the end of all this, the vector analysis of Gibbs and Heaviside was firmly entrenched in science and engineering somewhat by default because, in the opinion of the author, it was the least inconvenient of the notational tools then being considered. Its noncommutativity creates all sorts of computational difficulty. There is nothing intrinsic in vector analysis that makes it the exclusive mode of expression for science, as witness the fact that coordinate-component, matrix, and tensor notations also apply. Vector analysis was derived from the quaternion algebra, which is only one of several possible algebras based on groups of order eight, and there has been no great effort to evaluate and apply the alternative algebras. It is the author's opinion that we have continued on our present path because of, first, the undeniable usefulness and success of vector analysis, but secondly, an unquestioning acceptance of something of longstanding usage, something which was devised before group/ring theory and modern physics considerations were at hand to provide insight. In the following work, an alternative will be presented in the form of a system of hypercomplex analysis of four-dimensional numbers, that is at the same time a complete vector analysis of four-dimensional vectors.

Its computational advantages will be demonstrated in two applications chapters, and further comments will be made on why it may have been considered and rejected in the past, as far back as Hamilton.

A recent postscript: G. L. Shpil'ker of the Schmidt Institute of Physics of the Earth, Moscow, published a paper[42] in 1985 giving the **1,i,j,k** basis of this book, including the matrix representations, and the fundamental ring operations.

II. A SYSTEM OF HYPERCOMPLEX ANALYSIS

The topics in Chapter II start with elementary group and ring concepts, leading into elementary applied complex analysis. We will be constructing our new system of analysis from existing building blocks, hence there are no deep theorems to prove. Our task is to merely state the mathematical elements of the new analysis. We shall see that a new viewpoint is being presented for a collection of very old, very familiar concepts.

2.1 A FOUR-DIMENSIONAL REAL BASIS ALGEBRA

This section will define the **1,i,j,k** basis elements and their multiplicative group table. The algebraic element $\mathbf{1}x + \mathbf{i}y + \mathbf{j}z + \mathbf{k}t$ will be constructed, and conditions will be developed on the real values x,y,z,t such that those elements with singular inverses (zero divisors) can be identified and characterized. The set of zero divisors, rather than being a liability, will be seen to play a key role all the way through to the physics applications. A 4 X 4 real matrix representation of the basis elements and the general algebraic element will be developed and applied to help define the hypercomplex algebra. We will conclude with a statement of a hypercomplex algebra which, it will be easy to discern, has all the properties of the algebra of the classical complex variables.

2.1.1 Definition Of The Four-Dimensional Element And The $\mathbb{D}$-Space

The classical complex variable is of the form $z = x + \mathrm{i}y$, where x,y are real and i is the pure imaginary. Considered from a two-dimensional vector viewpoint, they are of the form $\mathbf{z} = \mathbf{1}x + \mathbf{i}y$, where **1**,**i** could be considered as unit basis vectors and x,y are real. This leads us naturally to define the *element* in our proposed algebra to be of the form:

$$\mathbf{Z} = \mathbf{1}x + \mathbf{i}y + \mathbf{j}z + \mathbf{k}t,$$

where x,y,z,t are real and **1**,**i**,**j**,**k** are *unit basis vectors*. The basis vectors will be given a more concrete representation below, and will be thoroughly examined. One should not overemphasize the vector interpretation, however, because these elements will ultimately be treated as hypercomplex variables.

During the development of the algebra, function theory, and fundamental analysis techniques, an element with a **k**-component denoted by "t" will be used, for convenience. In the applications sections, the **k**-component will be denoted by "ct," where c is the speed of light and t is time, in accordance with physical reality.

For convenience in later discussion, $\mathbb{D}$ will denote the set of all points (x,y,z,t) in a four-dimensional real space:

$$\mathbb{D} = \{(x,y,z,t) \mid x,y,z,t \ \textit{real}\},$$

and will refer to this set in the context of the present work as a $\mathbb{D}$-*Space* (or Duplex-space), for reasons which will become apparent later. Certain other conditions which will be developed on the elements of $\mathbb{D}$ will differentiate it from the real four-space R^4. Because of the one-to-one correspondence between points (x,y,z,t) and vectors **Z** as defined above, one may also write

$$\mathbb{D} = \{\mathbf{Z} \mid x,y,z,t \ \textit{real}\}.$$

2.1.2 Development Of The Basis Group $\mathbb{G}$

The program for this section will be precisely that addressed by William Hamilton in the 1830s: How to define multiplication on a set of basis vectors **1**,**i**,**j**,**k** such that the result may always be expressed in terms of the same set of basis vectors (closure) and such that vectors, or numbers, constructed over the basis obey the same axioms as do the real and complex numbers. Hamilton was unable to meet the latter objective because of his insistence that every nonzero vector (those having not all components equal to zero) should have an inverse. We, however, shall take advantage of the considerable mathematical insights which have occurred since his time and will develop a different line of reasoning.

■ *A Unit Vector Representation Of The Basis*—The *multiplicative basis group* $\mathbb{G}$ will be denoted by

$$\mathbb{G} = \{\mathbf{1}, \mathbf{i}, \mathbf{j}, \mathbf{k}, -\mathbf{1}, -\mathbf{i}, -\mathbf{j}, -\mathbf{k}\}, \qquad (2.1)$$

with multiplication given by Table 1. From the symmetry of the table, it is evident that multiplication is commutative, hence **1,i,j,k** are *not quaternion* elements. Table 1 establishes the group properties more or less by inspection, except for associativity. For that, a real matrix representation for the basis elements, to be given below, will yield associativity from known matrix properties in general, without the pain of writing everything out. From the table, it is evident that the group identity element is **1** (not by accident) and the respective inverses of **1,i,j,k,–1,–i,–j,–k** must be **1,–i,–j,k,–1,i,j,–k**.

	1	**i**	**j**	**k**	**-1**	**-i**	**-j**	**-k**
1	**1**	**i**	**j**	**k**	**-1**	**-i**	**-j**	**-k**
i	**i**	**-1**	**k**	**-j**	**-i**	**1**	**-k**	**j**
j	**j**	**k**	**-1**	**-i**	**-j**	**-k**	**1**	**i**
k	**k**	**-j**	**-i**	**1**	**-k**	**j**	**i**	**-1**
-1	**-1**	**-i**	**-j**	**-k**	**1**	**i**	**j**	**k**
-i	**-i**	**1**	**-k**	**j**	**i**	**-1**	**k**	**-j**
-j	**-j**	**-k**	**1**	**i**	**j**	**k**	**-1**	**-i**
-k	**-k**	**j**	**i**	**-1**	**k**	**-j**	**-i**	**1**

Table 1. Multiplication Table For The Basis Group $\mathbb{G}$.

■ *A 4 X 4 Real Matrix Representation Of The Basis Vectors*—Enough information now exists to define addition, subtraction, and multiplication of elements of $\mathbb{D}$, but it is not yet apparent how to define division by an element in $\mathbb{D}$. In order to overcome the problem about how to define division, we state the following matrix representation for the basis group $\mathbb{G}$:

$$E_1 = \begin{bmatrix} 1 & 0 & 0 & 0 \\ 0 & 1 & 0 & 0 \\ 0 & 0 & 1 & 0 \\ 0 & 0 & 0 & 1 \end{bmatrix} \qquad E_3 = \begin{bmatrix} 0 & 0 & -1 & 0 \\ 0 & 0 & 0 & -1 \\ 1 & 0 & 0 & 0 \\ 0 & 1 & 0 & 0 \end{bmatrix}$$

$$E_2 = \begin{bmatrix} 0 & -1 & 0 & 0 \\ 1 & 0 & 0 & 0 \\ 0 & 0 & 0 & -1 \\ 0 & 0 & 1 & 0 \end{bmatrix} \qquad E_4 = \begin{bmatrix} 0 & 0 & 0 & 1 \\ 0 & 0 & -1 & 0 \\ 0 & -1 & 0 & 0 \\ 1 & 0 & 0 & 0 \end{bmatrix} \tag{2.2}$$

Now it is simple to show that the set

$$\mathbb{E} = \{E_1, E_2, E_3, E_4, -E_1, -E_2, -E_3, -E_4\} \tag{2.3}$$

is an Abelian multiplicative group that is isomorphic to $\mathbb{G}$. One may do so by making the correspondences $\mathbf{1}\rightarrow E_1$, $\mathbf{i}\rightarrow E_2$, $\mathbf{j}\rightarrow E_3$, $\mathbf{k}\rightarrow E_4$ then by repeating all the multiplications of Table 1, which will not be shown here. The task is made simpler if 2 X 2 block multiplications are used. Now, having the same multiplication table, the general matrix multiplication theory asserts associativity for the **1,i,j,k** forms.

The E matrices are all nonsingular and of rank four; but for later purposes it is more important that they are *orthogonal*, inasmuch as all have determinant +1 and mutually orthogonal column vectors. The structure of the group $\mathbb{G}$ will be examined in a later section, and we will show why we chose this particular group over others.

2.1.3 A Real Matrix Representation Of An Algebraic Element

It follows from the previous section that the typical element in $\mathbb{D}$ can be represented in *matrix* form as

$$\mathbf{Z} = x\mathrm{E}_1 + y\mathrm{E}_2 + z\mathrm{E}_3 + t\mathrm{E}_4$$

$$= \begin{bmatrix} x & -y & -z & t \\ y & x & -t & -z \\ z & -t & x & -y \\ t & z & y & x \end{bmatrix} . \tag{2.4}$$

■ *The Nested Complex Algebra Property*—Recall that the complex variable $z = x+\mathbf{i}y$ may be represented in matrix form as follows:

$$z = \begin{bmatrix} x & -y \\ y & x \end{bmatrix} , \tag{2.5}$$

and all the operations of the complex algebra can be stated in the matrix form. If one examines the four-dimensional matrix form (2.4) for elements $\mathbf{Z}$, it is evident that it can be partitioned into four complex variable submatrices:

$$\left[\begin{array}{cc|cc} x & -y & -z & t \\ y & x & -t & -z \\ \hline z & -t & x & -y \\ t & z & y & x \end{array}\right] , \tag{2.6}$$

which is of the form

$$\begin{bmatrix} z_1 & -z_2 \\ z_2 & z_1 \end{bmatrix} , \tag{2.7}$$

where z_1 and z_2 are complex variables. Evidently, this is a complex algebra nested within another complex algebra. This observation will be used later, in showing how to extend the results of the present work to even higher, 2^n-order algebras. Under the complex-matrix representation, the basis matrices are:

$$\mathrm{E}_1 \rightarrow \begin{bmatrix} 1 & 0 \\ 0 & 1 \end{bmatrix} \quad \mathrm{E}_3 \rightarrow \begin{bmatrix} 0 & -1 \\ 1 & 0 \end{bmatrix}$$
$$\mathrm{E}_2 \rightarrow \begin{bmatrix} \mathrm{i} & 0 \\ 0 & \mathrm{i} \end{bmatrix} \quad \mathrm{E}_4 \rightarrow \begin{bmatrix} 0 & -\mathrm{i} \\ \mathrm{i} & 0 \end{bmatrix} \tag{2.8}$$

where "i" is the pure imaginary of complex variable theory, distinct from the hypercomplex element, **i**.

■ *Comparison With The Quaternion Matrix Representation*—This is a good place to show the similarities and differences of the algebra which is being constructed here, with that for the quaternions. The quaternion basis matrices are:

$$\mathrm{Q}_1 = \begin{bmatrix} 1 & 0 & 0 & 0 \\ 0 & 1 & 0 & 0 \\ 0 & 0 & 1 & 0 \\ 0 & 0 & 0 & 1 \end{bmatrix} \quad \mathrm{Q}_3 = \begin{bmatrix} 0 & 0 & 1 & 0 \\ 0 & 0 & 0 & 1 \\ -1 & 0 & 0 & 0 \\ 0 & -1 & 0 & 0 \end{bmatrix}$$
$$\mathrm{Q}_2 = \begin{bmatrix} 0 & 1 & 0 & 0 \\ -1 & 0 & 0 & 0 \\ 0 & 0 & 0 & -1 \\ 0 & 0 & 1 & 0 \end{bmatrix} \quad \mathrm{Q}_4 = \begin{bmatrix} 0 & 0 & 0 & 1 \\ 0 & 0 & -1 & 0 \\ 0 & 1 & 0 & 0 \\ -1 & 0 & 0 & 0 \end{bmatrix} \tag{2.9}$$

$$\mathbf{Z} = \begin{bmatrix} x & y & z & t \\ -y & x & -t & z \\ -z & t & x & -y \\ -t & -z & y & x \end{bmatrix}. \tag{2.10}$$

These forms were given by Frazer[21] et. al. in 1938. The Q matrices form a group, of course (the quaternion group), and all are orthogonal. They have a strong similarity to the E matrix forms for the group $\mathbb{G}$, with merely sign changes here and there. The changes are drastically significant because they result in a non-Abelian group, upon which is constructed a noncommutative algebra.

Perhaps the clearest comparison with the group basis of $\mathbb{D}$ is given in the complex-matrix representation:

$$Q_1 \rightarrow \begin{bmatrix} 1 & 0 \\ 0 & 1 \end{bmatrix} \quad Q_3 \rightarrow \begin{bmatrix} 0 & 1 \\ -1 & 0 \end{bmatrix}$$

$$Q_2 \rightarrow \begin{bmatrix} -i & 0 \\ 0 & i \end{bmatrix} \quad Q_4 \rightarrow \begin{bmatrix} 0 & -i \\ -i & 0 \end{bmatrix} \tag{2.11}$$

In this form, the basis matrices for the two systems are the same except for only three differences in sign: one each in Q_2, Q_3, and Q_4. That is enough, however, to preclude commutativity. Note that Q_2 and Q_4 cannot be interpreted as classical complex variable forms, even if the "i"s were replaced with "1"s. A slight variant of these forms was given by Turnbull[22] in 1928.

2.1.4 Definition Of The Algebraic Operations On $\mathbb{D}$

Before one can define an algebra on the set $\mathbb{D}$, certain algebraic entities and operations must be defined. In particular, "identity," "inverse," addition, and multiplication must be given form. These will be stated in the basis matrix form because that is the most familiar and concrete representation, one in which all the needed operations are well understood. For this discussion, let

$$\mathbf{Z}_1 = x_1 E_1 + y_1 E_2 + z_1 E_3 + t_1 E_4$$

and

$$\mathbf{Z}_2 = x_2 E_1 + y_2 E_2 + z_2 E_3 + t_2 E_4$$

be two elements of $\mathbb{D}$. Then by *addition* is meant

$$\mathbf{Z}_1 + \mathbf{Z}_2 = (x_1+x_2)E_1 + (y_1+y_2)E_2 + (z_1+z_2)E_3 + (t_1+t_2)E_4. \tag{2.12}$$

The *additive identity* is the element (0,0,0,0). The *additive inverse* of an element $\mathbf{Z}$ is the negative of the element:

$$\begin{aligned} \mathbf{Z} &= x\mathrm{E}_1 + y\mathrm{E}_2 + z\mathrm{E}_3 + t\mathrm{E}_4 \\ -\mathbf{Z} &= (-x)\mathrm{E}_1 + (-y)\mathrm{E}_2 + (-z)\mathrm{E}_3 + (-t)\mathrm{E}_4 \\ \mathbf{Z} + (-\mathbf{Z}) &= (x-x)\mathrm{E}_1 + (y-y)\mathrm{E}_2 + (z-z)\mathrm{E}_3 + (t-t)\mathrm{E}_4 = (0,0,0,0) \end{aligned} \tag{2.13}$$

Clearly, *subtraction* is a special case of addition. *Multiplication* is merely a term-by term multiplication followed by a collection of similar terms, exactly as for the classical complex variables:

$$\begin{aligned} \mathbf{Z}_1\mathbf{Z}_2 &= (x_1\mathrm{E}_1+y_1\mathrm{E}_2+z_1\mathrm{E}_3+t_1\mathrm{E}_4)\ (x_2\mathrm{E}_1+y_2\mathrm{E}_2+z_2\mathrm{E}_3+t_2\mathrm{E}_4) \\ &= (x_1x_2-y_1y_2-z_1z_2+t_1t_2)\ \mathrm{E}_1 \\ &+ (y_1x_2+x_1y_2-t_1z_2-z_1t_2)\ \mathrm{E}_2 \\ &+ (z_1x_2-t_1y_2+x_1z_2-y_1t_2)\ \mathrm{E}_3 \\ &+ (t_1x_2+z_1y_2+y_1z_2+x_1t_2)\ \mathrm{E}_4. \end{aligned} \tag{2.14}$$

The *multiplicative identity* is the identity matrix:

$$\mathrm{E}_1 = \begin{bmatrix} 1 & 0 & 0 & 0 \\ 0 & 1 & 0 & 0 \\ 0 & 0 & 1 & 0 \\ 0 & 0 & 0 & 1 \end{bmatrix}.$$

The *multiplicative inverse* of the typical element in $\mathbb{D}$ is given by

$$\mathrm{Z}^{-1} = \begin{bmatrix} x & -y & -z & t \\ y & x & -t & -z \\ z & -t & x & -y \\ t & z & y & x \end{bmatrix}^{-1} \tag{2.15}$$

$$= (\mathrm{A}_{11}\mathrm{E}_1 + \mathrm{A}_{12}\mathrm{E}_2 + \mathrm{A}_{13}\mathrm{E}_3 + \mathrm{A}_{14}\mathrm{E}_4)/\,det\,(\mathbf{Z}),$$

where the A_{ij} are the signed minors of the first row of the matrix form of the element $\mathbf{Z}$, with

$$
\begin{aligned}
A_{11} &= \ \ x\,(x^2+y^2+z^2+t^2) - 2t\,(xt-yz)\\
A_{12} &= -y\,(x^2+y^2+z^2+t^2) - 2z\,(xt-yz)\\
A_{13} &= -z\,(x^2+y^2+z^2+t^2) - 2y\,(xt-yz)\\
A_{14} &= \ \ t\,(x^2+y^2+z^2+t^2) - 2x\,(xt-yz)
\end{aligned}
\qquad (2.16)
$$

$$
det(\mathbf{Z}) = [(x-t)^2 + (y+z)^2]\,[(x+t)^2 + (y-z)^2]. \qquad (2.17)
$$

Here is the first indication that something is going to be different: the multiplicative inverse is not defined under the conditions

$$
\begin{aligned}
&(x-t)^2 + (y+z)^2 = 0\\
\text{or}\quad &(x+t)^2 + (y-z)^2 = 0.
\end{aligned}
\qquad (2.18)
$$

This is the point at which W. R. Hamilton may have rejected this particular basis **1,i,j,k** with its commutative multiplication rules. He had no grounds for hypothesizing that any nonzero point in the four-space should have any different status than another (i.e., some having inverses, others not). Evidently, there are infinitely many zero divisors in the set $\mathbb{D}$, but we merely continue here with a promise to show that not only is this no problem in applications, but is extremely significant and useful in a relativity physics context.

2.1.5 Statement Of The Basis Algebra $\mathbb{D}$

For completeness, all the key elements and algebraic operations will be stated in the **1,i,j,k** notation. Let the algebraic element (or vector or hypercomplex variable) in $\mathbb{D}$ be denoted by

$$
\mathbf{Z} = \mathbf{1}x + \mathbf{i}y + \mathbf{j}z + \mathbf{k}t,
$$

where x,y,z,t are real and **1,i,j,k** are basis vectors obeying the (commutative) multiplication rules:

$$
\begin{aligned}
&\mathbf{i}^2 = \mathbf{j}^2 = -\mathbf{1}, \quad \mathbf{1}^2 = \mathbf{k}^2 = \mathbf{1}, \quad \mathbf{1ijk} = \mathbf{1},\\
&\mathbf{ij} = \mathbf{k}, \quad \mathbf{jk} = -\mathbf{i}, \quad \mathbf{ki} = -\mathbf{j} \qquad \text{(per Table 1).}
\end{aligned}
\qquad (2.19)
$$

Further, let

$$
\mathbf{Z}_1 = \mathbf{1}x_1 + \mathbf{i}y_1 + \mathbf{j}z_1 + \mathbf{k}t_1
$$

and

$$\mathbf{Z}_2 = \mathbf{1}x_2 + \mathbf{i}y_2 + \mathbf{j}z_2 + \mathbf{k}t_2$$

be in $\mathbb{D}$; then

$$\mathbf{Z} = \mathbf{1}0 + \mathbf{i}0 + \mathbf{j}0 + \mathbf{k}0 = (0,0,0,0) \qquad \text{(Additive unity)} \qquad (2.20)$$

$$\mathbf{Z}_1 + \mathbf{Z}_2 = \mathbf{1}(x_1+ x_2) + \mathbf{i}(y_1+y_2) + \mathbf{j}(z_1+z_2) + \mathbf{k}(t_1+t_2) \qquad \text{(Addition)} \qquad (2.21)$$

$$\mathbf{Z}_1 - \mathbf{Z}_2 = \mathbf{1}(x_1-x_2) + \mathbf{i}(y_1-y_2) + \mathbf{j}(z_1-z_2) + \mathbf{k}(t_1-t_2) \qquad \text{(Subtraction)} \qquad (2.22)$$

$$-\mathbf{Z} = \mathbf{1}(-x) + \mathbf{i}(-y) + \mathbf{j}(-z) + \mathbf{k}(-t) \qquad \text{(Additive inverse)} \qquad (2.23)$$

$$\mathbf{Z} = \mathbf{1}(1) \qquad \text{(Multiplicative unity)} \qquad (2.24)$$

$$\begin{aligned}\mathbf{Z}_1\mathbf{Z}_2 = \mathbf{1}\,&(x_1x_2 - y_1y_2 - z_1z_2 + t_1t_2)\\ +\, \mathbf{i}\,&(y_1x_2 + x_1y_2 - t_1z_2 - z_1t_2)\\ +\, \mathbf{j}\,&(z_1x_2 - t_1y_2 + x_1z_2 - y_1t_2)\\ +\, \mathbf{k}\,&(t_1x_2 + z_1y_2 + y_1z_2 + x_1t_2)\end{aligned} \qquad \text{(Multiplication)} \qquad (2.25)$$

$$\begin{aligned}\mathbf{Z}^{-1} = \mathbf{1}&\left[\frac{x\,(x^2 + y^2 + z^2 + t^2) - 2t\,(xt-yz)}{[(x-t)^2 + (y+z)^2]\,[(x+t)^2 + (y-z)^2]}\right]\\ + \mathbf{i}&\left[\frac{-y(x^2 + y^2 + z^2 + t^2) - 2z\,(xt-yz)}{[(x-t)^2 + (y+z)^2]\,[(x+t)^2 + (y-z)^2]}\right]\\ + \mathbf{j}&\left[\frac{-z(x^2 + y^2 + z^2 + t^2) - 2y\,(xt-yz)}{[(x-t)^2 + (y+z)^2]\,[(x+t)^2 + (y-z)^2]}\right]\\ + \mathbf{k}&\left[\frac{t\,(x^2 + y^2 + z^2 + t^2) - 2x\,(xt-yz)}{[(x-t)^2 + (y+z)^2]\,[(x+t)^2 + (y-z)^2]}\right]\end{aligned} \qquad (2.26)$$

(Multiplicative inverse)

$$det(\mathbf{Z}) = [(x-t)^2 + (y+z)^2]\,[(x+t)^2 + (y-z)^2]. \qquad (2.27)$$

(Determinant of matrix form)

The multiplicative inverse is not defined if $det(\mathbf{Z})$ is zero, which it can be for more than one combination of x,y,z,t, hence what we are defining cannot be a field of four-dimensional numbers. It is the next lower mathematical structure: *a commutative ring with unity*. The casual reader should not lose interest over this statement, nor underestimate to what extent a system of analysis can be constructed over the algebra $\mathbb{D}$. From this point on, we will refer to $\mathbb{D}$ as *the Ring* $\mathbb{D}$, where appropriate.

Note that addition and subtraction are the same as for ordinary vectors, and multiplication is similar to quaternion multiplication, hence contains terms similar to those in the vector cross product. These similarities will be examined in depth in the applications sections of the book. The multiplicative inverse, however, is something new. It will be examined in the immediately following sections.

2.2 PROPERTIES OF THE BASIS ALGEBRA $\mathbb{D}$

The ring $\mathbb{D}$ and its basis group $\mathbb{G}$ both have considerable mathematical structure which is not evident from their initial statements of definition. In this section, we will thoroughly investigate both and report certain insights which are extremely useful in later sections.

2.2.1 Structure Of The Basis Group

The basis group $\mathbb{G}$ has been shown to be an Abelian group of order eight. It is known from group theory that there are only five nonisomorphic groups of order eight: three Abelian and two non-Abelian. Which do we have here? The two non-Abelian groups are eliminated. Then, $\mathbf{1}$ and $\mathbf{k}$ are of cyclic order two because $\mathbf{1}^2 = \mathbf{1}$ and $\mathbf{k}^2 = \mathbf{1}$; $\mathbf{i}$ and $\mathbf{j}$ are of cyclic order four because $\mathbf{i}^2 = -\mathbf{1}$, $\mathbf{i}^4 = \mathbf{1}$, and similarly for $\mathbf{j}$. Only one eighth-order Abelian group has elements of cyclic order four, and that is

$$\mathbb{G} = \mathbb{C}_2 \times \mathbb{C}_4, \tag{2.28}$$

where $\mathbb{C}_n$ is the cyclic group of order n.

Some subgroups are: $\{\mathbf{1},\mathbf{k}\}$, $\{\mathbf{1},\mathbf{i},-\mathbf{1},-\mathbf{i}\}$, $\{\mathbf{1},\mathbf{j},-\mathbf{1},-\mathbf{j}\}$, and $\{\mathbf{1},\mathbf{k},-\mathbf{1},-\mathbf{k}\}$.

2.2.2 Algebraic Elements In Vector Canonical Form

Now that a commutative ring has been established over $\mathbb{D}$, one may manipulate elements of $\mathbb{D}$ in all ways consistent with ring theory. One may rearrange and combine the components of the typical vector-form element of $\mathbb{D}$ in ways that will lead to greater understanding of the structure of $\mathbb{D}$. In particular, we want to show that *the typical element*

$$\mathbf{Z} = \mathbf{1}x + \mathbf{i}y + \mathbf{j}z + \mathbf{k}t$$

may be represented in the form

$$\mathbf{Z} = [(x-t) + \mathbf{i}(y+z)]\,\frac{(\mathbf{1}-\mathbf{k})}{2} + [(x+t) + \mathbf{i}(y-z)]\,\frac{(\mathbf{1}+\mathbf{k})}{2}. \tag{2.29}$$

To do so, one may start by separating $\mathbf{Z}$ into two equal parts:

$$\begin{aligned} \mathbf{Z} = {} & \mathbf{1}(x/2) + \mathbf{i}(y/2) + \mathbf{j}(z/2) + \mathbf{k}(t/2) \\ & + \mathbf{1}(x/2) + \mathbf{i}(y/2) + \mathbf{j}(z/2) + \mathbf{k}(t/2). \end{aligned}$$

Now add and subtract $-\mathbf{1}(t/2) + \mathbf{i}(z/2) + \mathbf{j}(y/2) - \mathbf{k}(x/2)$ on the right-hand side and rearrange to get

$$\begin{aligned} \mathbf{Z} = {} & \mathbf{1}(x-t)/2 + \mathbf{i}(y+z)/2 + \mathbf{j}(z+y)/2 + \mathbf{k}(t-x)/2 \\ & + \mathbf{1}(x+t)/2 + \mathbf{i}(y-z)/2 + \mathbf{j}(z-y)/2 + \mathbf{k}(t+x)/2 \\ = {} & (x-t)\ (\mathbf{1}-\mathbf{k})/2 + (y+z)\ (\mathbf{i}+\mathbf{j})/2 \\ + {} & (x+t)\ (\mathbf{1}+\mathbf{k})/2 + (y-z)\ (\mathbf{i}-\mathbf{j})/2 \\ = {} & [(x-t) + \mathbf{i}(y+z)]\ (\mathbf{1}-\mathbf{k})/2 + [(x+t) + \mathbf{i}(y-z)]\ (\mathbf{1}+\mathbf{k})/2. \end{aligned}$$

We have used the facts that $\mathbf{i}+\mathbf{j} = \mathbf{i}(\mathbf{1}-\mathbf{k})$ and $\mathbf{i}-\mathbf{j} = \mathbf{i}(\mathbf{1}+\mathbf{k})$, as may be verified from Table 1. This is the desired form. Now we use the following notation:

$$\xi = (x-t) + \mathbf{i}(y+z) \tag{2.30}$$

$$\eta = (x+t) + \mathbf{i}(y-z)$$

$$\mathbf{e}_1 = (\mathbf{1}-\mathbf{k})/2 \tag{2.31}$$

$$\mathbf{e}_2 = (\mathbf{1}+\mathbf{k})/2$$

and define the *vector canonical form* of $\mathbf{Z} = \mathbf{1}x + \mathbf{i}y + \mathbf{j}z + \mathbf{k}t$ as

$$\mathbf{Z} = \xi\mathbf{e}_1 + \eta\mathbf{e}_2. \tag{2.32}$$

If we must distinguish between the components of vectors $\mathbf{Z}_n$ and $\mathbf{Z}_m$, we will use a subscript to identify the vector:

$$\mathbf{Z}_n = \xi_n \mathbf{e}_1 + \eta_n \mathbf{e}_2 \, .$$

The significance of the canonical form arises from the fact that $\xi,\eta,\mathbf{e}_1,\mathbf{e}_2$ may be manipulated as elements of the ring $\mathbb{D}$ and have the following useful properties:

$$(\mathbf{e}_1)^n = \mathbf{e}_1, \ n \text{ an integer} \tag{2.33}$$

$$(\mathbf{e}_2)^n = \mathbf{e}_2$$

$$\mathbf{e}_1 \ \mathbf{e}_2 = (0,0,0,0)$$

$$\mathbf{e}_1 \bullet \mathbf{e}_2 = 0 \qquad \text{(Vector dot product)}$$

$$\mathbf{e}_1 + \mathbf{e}_2 = \mathbf{1}$$

$$-\mathbf{e}_1 + \mathbf{e}_2 = \mathbf{k}$$

ξ,η have the algebraic properties of complex variables.

Consequently, in the canonical form,

$$\mathbf{Z}_1 + \mathbf{Z}_2 = (\xi_1 + \xi_2)\,\mathbf{e}_1 + (\eta_1 + \eta_2)\,\mathbf{e}_2 \tag{2.34}$$

$$\mathbf{Z}_1 - \mathbf{Z}_2 = (\xi_1 - \xi_2)\,\mathbf{e}_1 + (\eta_1 - \eta_2)\,\mathbf{e}_2 \tag{2.35}$$

$$\mathbf{Z}_1\,\mathbf{Z}_2 = \xi_1\xi_2\,\mathbf{e}_1 + \eta_1\eta_2\,\mathbf{e}_2 \tag{2.36}$$

$$\mathbf{Z}^{-1} = \xi^{-1}\,\mathbf{e}_1 + \eta^{-1}\,\mathbf{e}_2, \tag{2.37}$$

when $det(\mathbf{Z})$ is nonzero.

These forms have great computational advantages over the vector or matrix notations for the fundamental ring operations, and will be seen to have yet more advantages when functions are considered.

2.2.3 Eigenvalues And Eigenvectors Of The Matrix Form

Having the vector canonical form of an element $\mathbf{Z}$, it is now easy to determine the eigenvalues and eigenvectors of the matrix form of $\mathbf{Z}$, because we have

$$\mathbf{Z} = \xi\, \mathbf{e}_1 + \eta\, \mathbf{e}_2,$$
$$\mathbf{Z}\, \mathbf{e}_1 = \xi\, \mathbf{e}_1, \qquad (2.38)$$
$$\mathbf{Z}\, \mathbf{e}_2 = \eta\, \mathbf{e}_2,$$

which are classical eigenvalue relations.

Recall that $\mathbf{e}_1$ and $\mathbf{e}_2$ can be represented as vectors and that ξ and η have the algebraic properties of complex variables. The "**i**" that both contain is a four-dimensional quantity, however, and might require considerable interpretation as part of an eigenvalue of a real-valued matrix, except that $\mathbf{Z}$ is an element of $\mathbb{D}$. The determinant of $\mathbf{Z}$ sheds some light on this question:

$$\begin{aligned} det(\mathbf{Z}) &= [(x-t)^2 + (y+z)^2]\,[(x+t)^2 + (y-z)^2] \\ &= [(x-t) + \mathrm{i}(y+z)]\,[(x-t) - \mathrm{i}(y+z)] \\ &\qquad \times [(x+t) + \mathrm{i}(y-z)]\,[(x+t) - \mathrm{i}(y-z)] \qquad (2.39) \\ &= \text{product of four eigenvalues of } \mathbf{Z}, \end{aligned}$$

where the "i" can be the pure imaginary of complex variables, or could be the hypercomplex "**i**" as well. Apparently, ξ and η are a new category of eigenvalue forms and their complex conjugates are also eigenvalues. That is, they are eigenvalues of a 4 X 4 real matrix, yet may be themselves stated in 4 X 4 real matrix form. We summarize by writing them out explicitly in both forms. For the matrix

$$\mathbf{Z} = \begin{bmatrix} x & -y & -z & t \\ y & x & -t & -z \\ z & -t & x & -y \\ t & z & y & x \end{bmatrix}.$$

which is an element of $\mathbb{D}$, the eigenvalues in $\mathbb{D}$ are:

$$\xi = (x-t) + \mathbf{i}(y+z) \qquad \xi^* = (x-t) - \mathbf{i}(y+z)$$
$$\eta = (x+t) + \mathbf{i}(y-z) \qquad \eta^* = (x+t) - \mathbf{i}(y-z) \qquad \text{(Vector forms)} \qquad (2.40)$$

$$\xi = \begin{bmatrix} (x-t) & -(y+z) & 0 & 0 \\ (y+z) & (x-t) & 0 & 0 \\ 0 & 0 & (x-t) & -(y+z) \\ 0 & 0 & (y+z) & (x-t) \end{bmatrix} \quad \text{(Matrix forms)} \qquad (2.41)$$

$$\xi^* = \begin{bmatrix} (x-t) & (y+z) & 0 & 0 \\ -(y+z) & (x-t) & 0 & 0 \\ 0 & 0 & (x-t) & (y+z) \\ 0 & 0 & -(y+z) & (x-t) \end{bmatrix}$$

$$\eta = \begin{bmatrix} (x+t) & -(y-z) & 0 & 0 \\ (y-z) & (x+t) & 0 & 0 \\ 0 & 0 & (x+t) & -(y-z) \\ 0 & 0 & (y-z) & (x+t) \end{bmatrix}$$

$$\eta^* = \begin{bmatrix} (x+t) & (y-z) & 0 & 0 \\ -(y-z) & (x+t) & 0 & 0 \\ 0 & 0 & (x+t) & (y-z) \\ 0 & 0 & -(y-z) & (x+t) \end{bmatrix},$$

where (*) indicates the complex conjugate.

It is remarkable that any element in the ring $\mathbb{D}$, an infinite ring of real 4 X 4 matrices, can be made to exhibit its eigenvalues almost by inspection, by use of simple formulas.

The eigenvectors are:

$$\mathbf{e}_1 = (1/2)\mathbf{1} - (1/2)\mathbf{k} \quad \text{(Vector forms)} \qquad (2.42)$$

$$\mathbf{e}_2 = (1/2)\mathbf{1} + (1/2)\mathbf{k}$$

$$\mathbf{e}_1 = (1/2)\begin{bmatrix} 1 & 0 & 0 & -1 \\ 0 & 1 & 1 & 0 \\ 0 & 1 & 1 & 0 \\ -1 & 0 & 0 & 1 \end{bmatrix}, \quad \mathbf{e}_2 = (1/2)\begin{bmatrix} 1 & 0 & 0 & 1 \\ 0 & 1 & -1 & 0 \\ 0 & -1 & 1 & 0 \\ 1 & 0 & 0 & 1 \end{bmatrix}$$

(Matrix forms) (2.43)

Note that the eigenvectors $\mathbf{e}_1$ and $\mathbf{e}_2$ are eigenvectors for every element in $\mathbb{D}$, or *absolute invariants*. Of course, the eigenvectors are orthogonal:

$$\mathbf{e}_1 \bullet \mathbf{e}_2 = [\mathbf{1}(1/2) - \mathbf{k}(1/2)] \bullet [\mathbf{1}(1/2) + \mathbf{k}(1/2)] = 0. \quad (2.44)$$

It will be shown in later sections that they lie in orthogonal planes which remain invariant in the real four-space under orthogonal transformations and even under the function operations which will be developed.

In their matrix forms, both $\mathbf{e}_1$ and $\mathbf{e}_2$ are singular: $det(\mathbf{e}_1) = det(\mathbf{e}_2) = 0$, but the definition of the multiplicative inverse of an element in $\mathbb{D}$ does not require the inverse of either $\mathbf{e}_1$ or $\mathbf{e}_2$.

2.2.4 Isomorphism With The Product Ring $\mathbb{C} \times \mathbb{C}$

Consider the product ring $\mathbb{C}^2$ with elements which are ordered pairs of complex numbers (z_1,z_2). The fundamental ring operations are

$$\begin{aligned} Z_1 + Z_2 &= (z_{11},z_{21}) + (z_{12},z_{22}) \\ &= [(z_{11}+ z_{12}),\ (z_{21}+ z_{22})] \end{aligned} \quad (2.45)$$

$$\begin{aligned} Z_1\ Z_2 &= (z_{11},\ z_{21})\ (z_{12},z_{22}) \\ &= (z_{11} z_{12},\ z_{21} z_{22}), \end{aligned} \quad (2.46)$$

where the z_{ij} are complex variables with the first subscript indicating the component of the ordered pair, and the second indicating the particular ordered pair. The additive unity is (0,0) and the multiplicative unity is (1,1).

A one-to-one correspondence of elements and operations can be made as follows:

$$\xi\,\mathbf{e}_1 + \eta\,\mathbf{e}_2 \rightarrow (\xi,\eta)$$
$$\rightarrow (z_1,z_2), \tag{2.47}$$

where

$$\xi = (x-t) + \mathbf{i}(y+z)$$
$$\eta = (x+t) + \mathbf{i}(y-z);$$

then $\mathbb{D}$ *is isomorphic to* $\mathbb{C}^2$. This is the reason for the name $\mathbb{D}$-space: it can be treated as a space composed of pairs (duplexes) of complex numbers.

Several facts are known for the ring $\mathbb{C}^2$ that will be useful in the context of the (isomorphic) ring $\mathbb{D}$. The most important is that $\mathbb{D}$ *is a principal ideal ring* having exactly two maximal ideals: $\{\mathbf{Z} \in \mathbb{D} \mid \xi = (0,0)\}$ and $\{\mathbf{Z} \in \mathbb{D} \mid \eta = (0,0)\}$. Referring to the canonical vector form of the inverse of an element, (2.37), it follows that *the zero divisors in* $\mathbb{D}$ *collectively form two distinct maximal ideals*. Secondly, each ideal is a *field* (of complex numbers), hence $\mathbb{D}$ *is a direct sum of fields*, which we know are complex fields.

The correspondences with classical complex elements are

$$x+\mathrm{i}y \rightarrow x-t+\mathbf{i}(y+z)$$

and

$$x+\mathrm{i}y \rightarrow x+t+\mathbf{i}(y-z)\ .$$

Because of the isomorphism, we are justified in treating ξ and η in all ways as we would the classical complex variables, including the same definitions of functions, derivatives, integrals, and so on. For the reader who is uncomfortable in making this transition (after all, ξ and η are also vectors in the $\mathbb{D}$-space), recall that the entire classical complex algebra, function theory, and system of analysis can be expressed in terms of ordered pairs (x,y) of real numbers, and we could do the same for the $\mathbb{D}$-space elements ξ and η, treating ξ, for example, as ordered pairs of real numbers $(x-t,y+z)$. No reference ever needs to be made to anything geometric.

We now recognize that the $\mathbb{D}$-*space algebra was among those first studied and described by Peirce*[44] in 1881 and Study[45] in 1889. Dedekind[46] published a study of algebras that are direct sums of copies of the complex field, giving the properties (2.33) of the basis elements in a form equivalent to the canonical form as herein defined. B. L. van der Waerden[47] gives an extensive history of the development of algebras, with references to the more important publications and personalities.

■ *The Maximal Ideal Subrings*—The maximal ideals have such importance to the subsequent arguments that we give them names:

$$O^- = \{\mathbf{Z} \in \mathbb{D} \mid \eta = (0,0)\} \tag{2.48}$$

$$O^+ = \{\mathbf{Z} \in \mathbb{D} \mid \xi = (0,0)\}, \tag{2.49}$$

where

$$\xi = (x-t) + \mathbf{i}(y+z)$$

$$\eta = (x+t) + \mathbf{i}(y-z).$$

For our purposes later, it is important to note that each is a closed subspace (a complex field) in $\mathbb{D}$, even though $\mathbb{D}$ is only a ring.

■ *Interpretation Of Ideals As Coordinate Axis Planes*—The maximal ideals O^- and O^+ are complex fields, hence each must lie in a separate plane in the $\mathbb{D}$ four-space. What is the orientation of these planes? From the definition of O^-, we have

$$\eta = (x+t) + \mathbf{i}(y-z) = (0,0),$$

hence

$$x = -t, \; y = z$$

are the defining equations of the O^- plane. Evidently, O^- intersects the real xyz three-space along the line $y = z$, $x = 0$ at time $t = 0$, and the line of intersection moves out along the minus-x direction parallel to the yz-plane as time increases.

Similarly,

$$x = t, \; y = -z$$

define the O^+ plane, which has a line $y = -z$, $x = 0$ of intersection with the real xyz-space at time $t = 0$ that moves out along the plus-x direction as time increases.

At time $t = 0$, the axis planes are orthogonal because the lines $y = z$, $x = 0$ and $y = -z$, $x = 0$ intersect at a right angle. In the more general case, the general vector lying in O^- is

$$\mathbf{Z}^- = \mathbf{1}(-t) + \mathbf{i}z + \mathbf{j}z + \mathbf{k}t, \tag{2.50}$$

and that for O^+ is

$$\mathbf{Z}^+ = \mathbf{1}t + \mathbf{i}(-z) + \mathbf{j}z + \mathbf{k}t. \tag{2.51}$$

By means of the vector dot product, defined in the usual way, we see that

$$\mathbf{Z}^- \bullet \mathbf{Z}^+ = -t^2 - z^2 + z^2 + t^2 = 0,$$

hence O^- and O^+ are mutually orthogonal. Recall that the vector canonical form asserts that every point (vector) in $\mathbb{D}$ can be uniquely specified by a point (eigenvalue) in O^- and one in O^+. We conclude that O^- and O^+ may be considered as *orthogonal axis planes* upon which the $\mathbb{D}$-space may be coordinatized.

When it is recalled that any two orthogonal planes in a real three-space intersect in a line, it may seem strange that O^- *and* O^+ *intersect in a single point:* (0,0,0,0). As proof, we know that at any point of intersection the two eigenvalues are equal:

$$\xi = \eta$$

$$(x-t)+\mathbf{i}(y+z) = (x+t)+\mathbf{i}(y-z)$$

$$\begin{aligned} x-t &= x+t \\ y+z &= y-z, \end{aligned} \tag{2.52}$$

which imply $z = t = 0$, x, y arbitrary; i.e., any intersection occurs in the xy-plane. As we saw above, the intersections of the axis planes with the real xyz-space are orthogonal lines moving away from each other, and neither line lies in the xy-plane. Their intersections with the xy-plane are, consequently, two points moving in opposite directions along the x-axis, and the two points coincide only at $t = 0$, which occurs at the origin, (0,0,0,0). In set notation,

$$O^- \cap O^+ = \{(0,0,0,0)\}. \tag{2.53}$$

2.2.5 The Extended Zero Analogy

The axis planes O^- and O^+ each have properties analogous to those for the *multiplicative zero element* in $\mathbb{C}$. Consider the following: if O is the zero element in $\mathbb{C}$, then

(i) No inverse of O exists in $\mathbb{C}$.
(ii) If $z \in \mathbb{C}$, then $Oz = O$.
(iii) If $z_1,z_2 \in \mathbb{C}$, then $z_1z_2 = O$
implies either
$z_1 = O$ or $z_2 = O$, or both.

These relations can be stated in set notation. Let $\theta = (0,0)$ and $O = \{\theta\}$; then

(i) Elements of O have no multiplicative inverses in $\mathbb{C}$.
(ii) If $z_1 \in O$ and $z_2 \in \mathbb{C}$, then
$z_1z_2 \in O$.

(iii) If $z_1,z_2 \in \mathbb{C}$, then $z_1z_2 \in O$
implies either
$z_1 \in O$ or $z_2 \in O$, or both.

The four-dimensional analogues of the above set relations are as follows. Let O be either O^- or O^+ throughout the following; then

(i) Elements of O have no multiplicative inverses in $\mathbb{D}$.
(ii) If $\mathbf{Z}_1 \in O$ and $\mathbf{Z}_2 \in \mathbb{D}$, then
$\mathbf{Z}_1\mathbf{Z}_2 \in O$.

(iii) If $\mathbf{Z}_1,\mathbf{Z}_2 \in \mathbb{D}$, then $\mathbf{Z}_1\mathbf{Z}_2 \in O$
implies either
$\mathbf{Z}_1 \in O$ or $\mathbf{Z}_2 \in O$, or both.

These statements also hold if one defines $O = O^- \cup O^+$. Moreover, if $\mathbf{Z} \in \mathbb{D}$ and if O is either O^-, O^+, or $O^- \cup O^+$, then in set notation one may write

$$O\mathbf{Z} = \mathbf{Z}O = O. \tag{2.54}$$

This appears to be a very natural extension of the concept of "zero element" to "*zero set.*"

2.2.6 The Number Field Analogy

If the notion of "zero set" is accepted then we have an extension of the concept of "complex field" to four dimensions. We shall call it a *hypercomplex field over the four-dimensional* $\mathbb{D}$ *space*. It will be shown that the zero set (the mathematical union of the axis planes) remains invariant even under orthogonal transformations in $\mathbb{D}$ or function/derivative operations, and behaves in all respects like the zero element in the complex field. Even more, it will be shown later that these "fields" may be generalized to any 2^n-order of dimensions.

2.2.7 Topological Equivalence With R^4

In many places in the book, we will see strange-appearing effects due to the four-dimensional nature of the space in which we will be working. It will help to keep things in perspective if we realize that $\mathbb{C}^2$ *and the* $\mathbb{D}$*-space are topologically equivalent to the real four-space*, R^4. This may be seen as follows: let

$$Z_1 = (z_{11}, z_{21})$$

and

$$Z_2 = (z_{12}, z_{22}),$$

be elements of $\mathbb{C}^2$, with z_{11}, z_{21}, z_{12}, z_{22} complex variables; then the usual Euclidean metric σ on $\mathbb{C}^2$ is, by definition,

$$\sigma(Z_1, Z_2) = [|z_{11} - z_{12}|^2 + |z_{21} - z_{22}|^2]^{1/2}. \tag{2.55}$$

Now let $\mathbf{Z}$, $\mathbf{Z}_1$, and $\mathbf{Z}_2$ be elements of $\mathbb{D}$; then the Euclidean Norm is defined in the usual way:

$$|\mathbf{Z}|^2 = \mathbf{Z} \cdot \mathbf{Z} = x^2 + y^2 + z^2 + t^2 \tag{2.56}$$

$$= \frac{(|\xi|^2 + |\eta|^2)}{2}$$

in the canonical form. If we now make the correspondences

$$\begin{aligned} (z_{11}, z_{21}) &\rightarrow \xi_1 \mathbf{e}_1 + \eta_1 \mathbf{e}_2 \\ (z_{12}, z_{22}) &\rightarrow \xi_2 \mathbf{e}_1 + \eta_2 \mathbf{e}_2, \end{aligned} \tag{2.57}$$

then we can see that the inner product of $\mathbf{Z}_1 - \mathbf{Z}_2$ with itself in $\mathbb{D}$ induces a metric on $\mathbb{D}$ and is directly proportional to σ:

$$(\mathbf{Z}_1 - \mathbf{Z}_2) \bullet (\mathbf{Z}_1 - \mathbf{Z}_2) = |\,\mathbf{Z}_1 - \mathbf{Z}_2|^2 = (|\xi_1 - \xi_2|^2 + |\eta_1 - \eta_2|^2)/2$$

$$= \frac{\sigma^2}{2}. \tag{2.58}$$

Also, the usual metric on R^4 is

$$[(\mathbf{Z}_1 - \mathbf{Z}_2) \bullet (\mathbf{Z}_1 - \mathbf{Z}_2)]^{1/2}$$

$$= [(x_1 - x_2)^2 + (y_1 - y_2)^2 + (z_1 - z_2)^2 + (t_1 - t_2)^2]^{1/2}, \tag{2.59}$$

which is the same as the above metric on $\mathbb{D}$. We have

$$\text{metric}\ (\mathbb{C}^2) = \sqrt{2}\ \text{metric}\ (\mathbb{D}) = \sqrt{2}\ \text{metric}\ (R^4), \tag{2.60}$$

and the proof is concluded.

2.2.8 Reduction To The Complex Algebra In Two Dimensions

If one has a typical element in $\mathbb{D}$,

$$\mathbf{Z} = \mathbf{1}x + \mathbf{i}y + \mathbf{j}z + \mathbf{k}t,$$

and sets $z = t = 0$, then $\mathbf{Z}$ reduces to

$$\mathbf{Z} = \mathbf{1}x + \mathbf{i}y,$$

which behaves like a classical complex variable. Under the same conditions, the canonical form, also, unravels to an ordinary complex variable:

$$\begin{aligned}(\mathbf{Z})_{z=0,\,t=0} &= [(x-0) + \mathbf{i}(y+0)]\,\mathbf{e}_1 + [(x+0) + \mathbf{i}(y-0)]\,\mathbf{e}_2 \\ &= [x + \mathbf{i}y]\,\mathbf{e}_1 + [x + \mathbf{i}y]\,\mathbf{e}_2 \\ &= [x + \mathbf{i}y]\,[\mathbf{e}_1 + \mathbf{e}_2] \\ &= [x + \mathbf{i}y]\,[\,\mathbf{1}\,] = \mathbf{1}x + \mathbf{i}y.\end{aligned} \tag{2.61}$$

2.2.9 The Transposed Elements Partition The $\mathbb{D}$-Space

Consider the typical element in $\mathbb{D}$ in matrix form:

$$\mathbf{Z} = \begin{bmatrix} x & -y & -z & t \\ y & x & -t & -z \\ z & -t & x & -y \\ t & z & y & x \end{bmatrix},$$

and let a superscript "T" denote the matrix transpose operation; then

$$\mathbf{Z}^{\mathrm{T}} = \begin{bmatrix} x & y & z & t \\ -y & x & -t & z \\ -z & -t & x & y \\ t & -z & -y & x \end{bmatrix}, \tag{2.62}$$

In the vector form, this is

$$\mathbf{Z} = \mathbf{1}x + \mathbf{i}y + \mathbf{j}z + \mathbf{k}t$$

$$\mathbf{Z}^{\mathrm{T}} = \mathbf{1}x - \mathbf{i}y - \mathbf{j}z + \mathbf{k}t, \tag{2.63}$$

and in the vector canonical form is

$$\mathbf{Z} = \xi\mathbf{e}_1 + \eta\mathbf{e}_2 \tag{2.64}$$

$$\mathbf{Z}^{\mathrm{T}} = \xi^*\mathbf{e}_1 + \eta^*\mathbf{e}_2. \tag{2.65}$$

That is, transposing an element in the matrix sense merely changes the sign of the y and z components, leaving the result as another element in $\mathbb{D}$. Since the eigenvalue set is ξ,η,ξ^*,η^*, this is an explicit example of the matrix theory assertion that the transpose operation does not affect the eigenvalues per se, but we see that *transposing an element in* $\mathbb{D}$ *takes the complex conjugate of the eigenvalues which are utilized in the vector canonical form.* As a consequence, every element has a mirror image in a complex cojugate, canonical vector sense, which is a partition of the $\mathbb{D}$-space. Perhaps this is why the complex conjugate eigenvalues do not have to appear explicitly in the canonical representation, because they are implicitly represented in the transposed elements.

The eigenvectors are doubly degenerate because ξ and ξ^* have the same eigenvector, $\mathbf{e}_1$, and similarly for η, η^*, and $\mathbf{e}_2$. This is directly opposite the usual case encountered in classical vector applications, wherein a single eigenvalue may have multiple eigenvectors.

Another property of the transpose is that *the product of an element* **Z** *with its transpose is an element in the* **1,k** *plane*:

$$
\begin{aligned}
\mathbf{Z}\,\mathbf{Z}^{\mathrm{T}} &= (\xi\,\mathbf{e}_1 + \eta\,\mathbf{e}_2)\,(\xi^*\,\mathbf{e}_1 + \eta^*\,\mathbf{e}_2) \\
&= \xi\,\xi^*\,\mathbf{e}_1 + \eta\,\eta^*\,\mathbf{e}_2 \qquad (2.66)\\
&= |\xi|^2\,(\mathbf{1}-\mathbf{k})/2 + |\eta|^2\,(\mathbf{1}+\mathbf{k})/2 \\
&= \mathbf{1}\,(|\xi|^2 + |\eta|^2)/2 + \mathbf{k}\,(|\eta|^2 - |\xi|^2)/2 \\
&= \mathbf{1}\,(x^2 + y^2 + z^2 + t^2) - \mathbf{k}\,2(xt - yz).
\end{aligned}
$$

The eigenvalues ξ and η have the properties of complex numbers, and (*) denotes the usual complex conjugate. Another way of saying the same thing is that the transpose of a vector, $\mathbf{Z}^{\mathrm{T}}$, when applied to **Z**, rotates the vector into the **1**,**k** plane. It will be shown later that taking the transpose of an element **Z** in $\mathbb{D}$ corresponds to taking the complex conjugate of **Z**, and that the product $\mathbf{Z}\mathbf{Z}^{\mathrm{T}}$ is the squared modulus function for **Z**.

Finally, *the vector* $\mathbf{Z}\mathbf{Z}^{\mathrm{T}}$ *is an invariant under all orthogonal transformations of the underlying coordinates*. This is established as follows: The magnitude of a vector,

$$|\mathbf{Z}|^2 = x^2 + y^2 + z^2 + t^2\,,$$

is an invariant under orthogonal transformations, as is

$$det(\mathbf{Z}) = (x^2 + y^2 + z^2 + t^2)^2 - 4(xt - yz)^2\,;$$

it follows that the term $(xt - yz)$ is, also. If both components of $\mathbf{Z}\mathbf{Z}^{\mathrm{T}}$ are invariant, then the product $\mathbf{Z}\mathbf{Z}^{\mathrm{T}}$ is invariant under orthogonal transformations.

2.2.10 A Change Of Coordinates Simplifies The Canonical Form

Thus far, it has been seen that an element **Z** of $\mathbb{D}$ may be viewed in a four-dimensional vector or a 4 X 4 real matrix context. In either, the operations of the ring $\mathbb{D}$ perform actions which are different from those of the classical vector analysis. The coordinate frame of reference in $\mathbb{D}$ is set by the **1,i,j,k** basis and the declaration of the coordinates *x,y,z,t* as the vector coefficients. There is no reason why the frame of reference cannot be changed before any $\mathbb{D}$-space operations are done. In fact, the vector canonical form may be simplified from

$$\mathbf{Z} = [(x-t)+\mathbf{i}(y+z)]\,\mathbf{e}_1 + [(x+t)+\mathbf{i}(y-z)]\,\mathbf{e}_2 \tag{2.67}$$

to

$$\mathbf{Z}' = (x'+\mathbf{i}y')\,\mathbf{e}_1 + (z'+\mathbf{i}t')\,\mathbf{e}_2 \tag{2.68}$$

by means of the preliminary transformation

$$\begin{aligned} x' &= 2^{-1/2}(x + 0 + 0 - t) \\ y' &= 2^{-1/2}(0 + y + z + 0\,) \\ z' &= 2^{-1/2}(x + 0 + 0 + t) \\ t' &= 2^{-1/2}(0 + y - z + 0) \end{aligned} \tag{2.69}$$

or

$$\begin{bmatrix} x' \\ y' \\ z' \\ t' \end{bmatrix} = 2^{-1/2} \begin{bmatrix} 1 & 0 & 0 & -1 \\ 0 & 1 & 1 & 0 \\ 1 & 0 & 0 & 1 \\ 0 & 1 & -1 & 0 \end{bmatrix} \begin{bmatrix} x \\ y \\ z \\ t \end{bmatrix}, \tag{2.70}$$

which is of the classical vector analysis form $\mathbf{X}' = \mathrm{A}\,\mathbf{X}$, where $\mathbf{X}$ is a four-dimensional vector and A is an orthogonal matrix. One must be careful to not mix classical vector transformations such as this with the $\mathbb{D}$-space operations, because A is not in $\mathbb{D}$. *Orthogonal or unitary transformations may be used to set the frame of reference for the $\mathbb{D}$-space operations, then may be used to interpret the final results.* This principle will be used extensively in the applications chapters.

2.2.11 The Typical Matrix Element In $\mathbb{D}$ Can Be Diagonalized

Given four distinct eigenvalues, it follows from matrix theory that the typical element in $\mathbb{D}$ can be transformed into a diagonalized form:

$$\begin{bmatrix} (x-t)+\mathrm{i}(y+z) & 0 & 0 & 0 \\ 0 & (x+t)+\mathrm{i}(y-z) & 0 & 0 \\ 0 & 0 & (x-t)-\mathrm{i}(y+z) & 0 \\ 0 & 0 & 0 & (x+t)-\mathrm{i}(y-z) \end{bmatrix}. \tag{2.71}$$

This is of the general form

$$\begin{bmatrix} z_1 & 0 & 0 & 0 \\ 0 & z_2 & 0 & 0 \\ 0 & 0 & z_1^* & 0 \\ 0 & 0 & 0 & z_2^* \end{bmatrix}, \qquad (2.72)$$

where z_1 and z_2 are complex variables and (*) denotes the complex conjugate. Two facts may be deduced from the diagonalized form: (1) The diagonalized form of an element in $\mathbb{D}$ is not in $\mathbb{D}$ (to be in $\mathbb{D}$, all matrix principal diagonal elements must be identical); and (2) the diagonalizing matrix must be unitary (the original matrix has all real elements and the result has all complex elements).

The transformation matrix which produces this diagonalization is the same for all elements, hence the ring $\mathbb{D}$ could be represented in a diagonalized, 4 X 4, complex-valued matrix form. There may be some physics theory advantage in being able to to so, in certain situations, but there is no computational advantage. The vector canonical form allows all necessary ring operations to take place on only two eigenvalues.

2.2.12 Use Of Complex-Valued Components In Elements Of $\mathbb{D}$

Up until this point, we have been discussing hypercomplex elements (x,y,z,t) with all real components. All the operations leading up to the definition of the ring $\mathbb{D}$ can be repeated as well with components x,y,z,t that are complex (in the classical, two-dimensional sense). We have seen that the ring $\mathbb{D}$ may be viewed as a complex algebra nested within a complex algebra; from that viewpoint, allowing the x,y,z,t elements to be complex adds another level of nesting within the first two. This feature will be used in the physics application sections to help reconcile the formulas between noncommutative vector analysis and the commutative hypercomplex analysis. For example, a certain unitary transformation having complex matrix elements can change the four-dimensional Poisson equation (as formulated in the hypercomplex system) into a wave equation. In other cases, we will need to transform our $\mathbb{D}$-space results into conventional vector-analysis statements, for direct comparison purposes.

2.2.13 Are There Other, Suitable Basis Groups Of Order Eight?

From finite group theory, it is known that there are only five non-isomorphic groups of order eight. Two are non-Abelian, hence are not suitable. The remaining three are:

$$\begin{aligned} \mathbb{G}_1 &= \mathbb{C}_2 \times \mathbb{C}_4 \\ \mathbb{G}_2 &= \mathbb{C}_2 \times \mathrm{K}_4 \\ &= \mathbb{C}_2 \times (\mathbb{C}_2 \times \mathbb{C}_2) \\ \mathbb{G}_3 &= \mathbb{C}_8, \end{aligned} \tag{2.73}$$

where $\mathbb{C}_n$ is the cyclic group of order n and K_4 is the Klein four-group (which is the same as $\mathbb{C}_2 \times \mathbb{C}_2$). In developing the system of hypercomplex analysis, we started with the requirement that it must mimic and subsume the system of complex analysis. Given that it must subsume complex analysis, the underlying basis group must include an element of cyclic order four in order to reproduce the actions of the complex imaginary "i." Of the three available Abelian groups, listed above, only the first has an element of cyclic order four, and that is the group which has been used here. We conclude that there are no other suitable choices for a basis group.

2.2.14 A Group Of Orthogonal Transformations In $\mathbb{D}$

The elements of the ring $\mathbb{D}$ may be represented in a 4 X 4 real matrix form, and suitable conditions may be developed as follows on the matrix elements such that the result is orthogonal (we restrict our attention to those elements of $\mathbb{D}$ that have nonzero determinant). Let

$$\mathbf{U} = \begin{bmatrix} u & -v & -w & s \\ v & u & -s & -w \\ w & -s & u & -v \\ s & w & v & u \end{bmatrix}, \tag{2.74}$$

belong to $\mathbb{D}$; then, if $\mathbf{U}$ is to be orthogonal, it is required that the transpose of $\mathbf{U}$ be the inverse of $\mathbf{U}$, or

$$\mathbf{U}\ \mathbf{U}^{\mathrm{T}} = \begin{bmatrix} u & -v & -w & s \\ v & u & -s & -w \\ w & -s & u & -v \\ s & w & v & u \end{bmatrix} \begin{bmatrix} u & v & w & s \\ -v & u & -s & w \\ -w & -s & u & v \\ s & -w & -v & u \end{bmatrix}, \tag{2.75}$$

$$\begin{bmatrix} (u^2+v^2+w^2+s^2) & 0 & 0 & 2(us-vw) \\ 0 & (u^2+v^2+w^2+s^2) & -2(us-vw) & 0 \\ 0 & -2(us-vw) & (u^2+v^2+w^2+s^2) & 0 \\ 2(us-vw) & 0 & 0 & (u^2+v^2+w^2+s^2) \end{bmatrix} \tag{2.76}$$

$$= \begin{bmatrix} 1 & 0 & 0 & 0 \\ 0 & 1 & 0 & 0 \\ 0 & 0 & 1 & 0 \\ 0 & 0 & 0 & 1 \end{bmatrix}.$$

Evidently, one must require

$$u^2+v^2+w^2+s^2 = 1 \tag{2.77}$$

and

$$2(us-vw) = 0 \tag{2.78}$$

for orthogonality. Conditions (2.77) and (2.78) produce

$$\begin{aligned} det(\mathbf{U}) &= [(u-s)^2+(v+w)^2]\,[(u+s)^2+(v-w)^2] \\ &= [u^2+v^2+w^2+s^2]^2 - [2(us-vw)]^2 \\ &= 1, \end{aligned}$$

as required. Condition (2.77) is remarkable because it says that the Euclidean norm of **U** is unity (i.e., **U** is a *unit vector*, in the vector interpretation context).

Because the product of two orthogonal matrices is again orthogonal and because all the matrices that we are considering are in the ring $\mathbb{D}$, we have the necessary conditions for a group. We shall name it Λ_4, the *four-dimensional orthogonal transformation group in the* $\mathbb{D}$*-space*. It is a two-parameter group because the original matrix had only four parameters, and this was reduced to two by the two orthogonality conditions, (2.77) and (2.78). It is denoted as follows:

$$\Lambda_4 = \{\mathbf{U} \in \mathbb{D} \mid \mathbf{U}\mathbf{U}^T = \mathbf{1}\}. \tag{2.79}$$

2.2.15 Elements In $\mathbb{D}$ Are Invariant Under Orthogonal Transformations

The Λ_4 group has been defined by applying the orthogonality condition in a classical vector analysis sense to elements of $\mathbb{D}$. The elements of the resultant group remain elements of $\mathbb{D}$. What is the meaning of "orthogonal transformation" in the context of the $\mathbb{D}$-space? Evidently, one viewpoint to take is that $\mathbb{D}$ is a ring of matrix operators (behaves as a ring of 4 X 4 real matrices), hence the ring elements transform like operators:

$$\mathbf{Z}' = \mathbf{U}\,\mathbf{Z}\,\mathbf{U}^{-1}, \tag{2.80}$$

where $\mathbf{Z}$ and $\mathbf{Z}'$ belong to $\mathbb{D}$ and $\mathbf{U}$ belongs to Λ_4 (and $\mathbb{D}$). The ring $\mathbb{D}$ is commutative, hence

$$\mathbf{Z}' = \mathbf{Z}\,\mathbf{U}\,\mathbf{U}^{-1} = \mathbf{Z}\,\mathrm{E}_1 = \mathbf{Z}. \tag{2.81}$$

The conclusion is that Λ_4 is an *invariance group* for the ring $\mathbb{D}$, when the elements are considered as matrix operators. This property will be used in the physics applications sections. The matrix forms of the typical elements $\mathbf{Z}$ will later be interpreted also as tensors, and another viewpoint will be given regarding orthogonal transformations.

Every element $\mathbf{Z}$ has several additional invariants due to its matrix formulation. For example, the absolute magnitude $|\mathbf{Z}|^2$, the trace of the matrix form, and the determinant of $\mathbf{Z}$ in the matrix form are expected invariants. However, the fact that the determinant can be rearranged into the form

$$det(\mathbf{Z}) = |\mathbf{Z}|^4 - 4(xt - yz)^2$$

yields that the quantity $(xt-yz)^2$, also, is an invariant of $\mathbf{Z} = \mathbf{1}x+\mathbf{i}y+\mathbf{j}z+\mathbf{k}t$ under orthogonal transformations of the underlying coordinates. One might not have anticipated this result.

2.2.16 An Orthogonal Transformation Is A Rotation About The Axis Planes

Λ_4 is an orthogonal transformation group in the classical vector analysis sense, and may be applied in that way: If $\mathbf{X}$ is a four-dimensional vector and $\mathbf{U}$ belongs to Λ_4, then

$$\mathbf{X}' = \mathbf{U}\,\mathbf{X} \tag{2.82}$$

expresses an orthogonal transformation of **X**. The nature of a "rotation" in four dimensions is considerably harder to visualize than the corresponding operation in three dimensions. In four dimensions, a rotation takes place around a plane. H. P. Manning[23,24] gives several geometrical descriptions of axis planes and rotation about a plane in four dimensions.

We have seen that the eigenvectors $\mathbf{e}_1$ and $\mathbf{e}_2$ are absolute invariants under the ring multiplication operations in $\mathbb{D}$, and that they lie in the axis planes. An element **U** of Λ_4 is also an element of $\mathbb{D}$, and if it operates on (multiplies) another element **Z** of $\mathbb{D}$, we conclude that *in* $\mathbb{D}$*, an orthogonal transformation is a rotation about both axis planes, simultaneously.* The two parameters of the rotation group, Λ_4, must then be some function of the hypercomplex angles of rotation about the two axis planes.

The magnitude of both eigenvalues of elements in the rotation group Λ_4 is unity because of the orthogonality conditions, (2.77, 2.78):

$$\begin{aligned} |\xi|^2 &= (u-s)^2 + (v+w)^2 \\ &= u^2+v^2+w^2+s^2 - 2(us-vw) = 1, \end{aligned} \tag{2.83}$$

$$\begin{aligned} |\eta|^2 &= (u+s)^2 + (v-w)^2 \\ &= u^2+v^2+w^2+s^2 + 2(us-vw) = 1. \end{aligned} \tag{2.84}$$

As a consequence, another way to view a rotation in the $\mathbb{D}$-space is as follows: an element **Z** in $\mathbb{D}$ may be interpreted as a vector which is specified by two eigenvalues, each of which may be viewed as a two-dimensional complex number, or vector; then, applying a Λ_4 rotation element to an element **Z** applies the rotator eigenvalues to the corresponding vector eigenvalues. The result is that *the rotation operation rotates the individual eigenvalues of* **Z** *in their separate planes without changing their magnitudes.*

2.2.17 Extension Of The Algebra To Higher 2^n-Dimensions

In one view, the $\mathbb{D}$ algebra was obtained by starting from the two-dimensional matrix representation of a complex number and replacing the x,y elements with complex numbers z_1,z_2:

$$\begin{bmatrix} x & -y \\ y & x \end{bmatrix} \rightarrow \begin{bmatrix} z_1 & -z_2 \\ z_2 & z_1 \end{bmatrix} ; \tag{2.85}$$

the z_j complex numbers were then replaced with their two-dimensional matrix representations to get the four-dimensional system. This process may be iterated to get higher 2^n-order algebras. The next higher order is eight:

$$\begin{bmatrix} z_1 & -z_2 \\ z_2 & z_1 \end{bmatrix} \rightarrow \begin{bmatrix} \mathbf{Z}_1 & -\mathbf{Z}_2 \\ \mathbf{Z}_2 & \mathbf{Z}_1 \end{bmatrix} ; \qquad (2.86)$$

where the $\mathbf{Z}_j$ are elements of $\mathbb{D}$.

2.3 A FUNCTION THEORY AND SYSTEM OF ANALYSIS

We now come to the ultimate challenge facing William Hamilton, over 140 years ago: to define functions and analysis techniques for four-dimensional numbers that use the same axioms, concepts, and notation and behave in the same way as for the real or complex numbers. Depending on the reader's point of view, we have an advantage (disadvantage?) by having the basis algebra defined in a 4 X 4 real matrix context. But how does one define a function of a matrix, let alone make it correspond to some function in complex analysis? Further complication is caused by the basis algebra being something less than a field (a commutative ring with unity, to be exact). The elements of the ring $\mathbb{D}$, however, are not just any 4 X 4 real matrices, but have certain properties which suggest a way to define functions and analysis techniques.

2.3.1 Definition Of A Unary Operation On An Element

It was shown earlier that the ring $\mathbb{D}$ is isomorphic to the ring $\mathbb{C}^2$. As far as the ring operations are concerned, $\mathbb{C}^2$ (and $\mathbb{D}$) behave like two independent copies of the complex algebra, differing from $\mathbb{C}$ only in the existence of inverses in certain situations. We take this hint and define a unary operation Oper($\mathbf{Z}$) on an element $\mathbf{Z} = (\xi,\eta)$ in $\mathbb{D}$ as follows:

$$\text{Oper}(\mathbf{Z}) = (\text{Oper}(\xi), \text{Oper}(\eta)), \qquad (2.87)$$

with

$$\xi = (x-t) + \mathbf{i}\,(y+z)$$

$$\eta = (x+t) + \mathbf{i}\,(y-z).$$

Oper( ) can be a function, a derivative, an integral, or any other operator from complex analysis. The right-hand side of the formula behaves like two copies of the complex operation acting in concert, hence the left-hand side behaves like the same complex operation. The only complication is that for the operation on the left to even exist, both operations on the right must exist, in the complex variable sense. All of the fundamental operations for the ring $\mathbb{D}$ adhere to this definition, as we showed at the end of Section 2.2.2.

An example of the unary operation definition is the *complex conjugate*:

$$\mathbf{Z}^* = \xi^* \mathbf{e}_1 + \eta^* \mathbf{e}_2. \tag{2.88}$$

This is different from the classical vector analysis definition, where it meant "take the complex conjugate of each of the four components." It was shown in an earlier section (Eqn. 2.65) that transposing an element **Z** in the matrix representation was the same as taking the complex conjugates of the eigenvalues of **Z** in the vector canonical form, hence

$$\mathbf{Z}^* = \mathbf{Z}^{\mathrm{T}}. \tag{2.89}$$

Another operation is the *hypercomplex modulus*:

$$\mathrm{MOD}(\mathbf{Z}) = |\xi|\mathbf{e}_1 + |\eta|\mathbf{e}_2. \tag{2.90}$$

This is different from the definition of the vector magnitude (Euclidean norm) of **Z**, denoted by $|\mathbf{Z}|$, because

$$|\mathbf{Z}| = |\mathrm{MOD}(\mathbf{Z})|, \tag{2.91}$$

$$|\mathbf{Z}|^2 = [|\xi|^2 + |\eta|^2]/2,$$

and MOD(**Z**) has the following properties:

$$\mathrm{MOD}(\mathbf{Z}_1\mathbf{Z}_2) = \mathrm{MOD}(\mathbf{Z}_1)\,\mathrm{MOD}(\mathbf{Z}_2) \tag{2.92}$$

$$\mathrm{MOD}(\mathbf{Z}_1/\mathbf{Z}_2) = \mathrm{MOD}(\mathbf{Z}_1)/\mathrm{MOD}(\mathbf{Z}_2). \tag{2.93}$$

Evidently,

$$\begin{aligned} \mathbf{Z}\,\mathbf{Z}^* &= \xi\,\xi^*\,\mathbf{e}_1 + \eta\,\eta^*\,\mathbf{e}_2 \\ &= |\xi|^2\mathbf{e}_1 + |\eta|^2\mathbf{e}_2 \\ &= [\mathrm{MOD}(\mathbf{Z})]^2 \end{aligned} \tag{2.94}$$

which is still a hypercomplex number, albeit rotated into the **1**,**k** plane (Section 2.2.9). Mod(**Z**) is the hypercomplex operation in $\mathbb{D}$ that corresponds to the absolute value operation in $\mathbb{C}$, because it has all the same properties. The four-dimensional absolute value, $|\mathbf{Z}|$, does not correspond to the two-dimensional operation because, for example,

$$|\mathbf{Z}_1\ \mathbf{Z}_2| \neq |\mathbf{Z}_1|\ |\mathbf{Z}_2|, \tag{2.95}$$

except in special cases.

Another property of the MOD function is that *it forms a result that is invariant under orthogonal transformations* of the underlying coordinates, because

$$[\mathrm{MOD}(\mathbf{Z})]^2 = \mathbf{Z}\ \mathbf{Z}^* = \mathbf{Z}\mathbf{Z}^{\mathrm{T}},$$

and we showed in Section 2.2.9 that the product of a vector with its transpose is an invariant vector in the **1**,**k** plane.

2.3.2 The Function As A Particular Unary Operation

An *analytic function* of a $\mathbb{D}$-space element **Z** is a particular unary operation. We shall use the following notation:

$$\begin{aligned} \mathrm{F}(\mathbf{Z}) &= f(\xi)\mathbf{e}_1 + f(\eta)\mathbf{e}_2 \\ &\rightarrow (\ f(\xi),\ f(\eta)), \end{aligned} \tag{2.96}$$

where

$$\begin{aligned} \xi &= (x-t) + \mathbf{i}(y+z) \\ \eta &= (x+t) + \mathbf{i}(y-z), \end{aligned}$$

and $f(z)$ is an analytic function of a complex variable z.

There are several great advantages to the present definition of a function in $\mathbb{D}$. First, it is fortunate that the elements of $\mathbb{D}$ may be made to exhibit their eigenvalues explicitly, by inspection, so that the use of this definition is facilitated. Secondly, the definition rests entirely upon the classical complex variable theory, so that no new difficulties arise concerning existence, uniqueness, continuity, or other properties. Thirdly, the defined function in $\mathbb{D}$ is applied using well-understood rules from the classical complex variable theory. Fourthly, the result of applying a function to an element in $\mathbb{D}$ is also in $\mathbb{D}$, and explicitly exhibits its eigenvalues just as does any other element in $\mathbb{D}$.

Lastly, this definition reduces to a classical complex variable definition when the z and t components of $\mathbf{Z}$ are set to zero:

$$\begin{aligned} \mathrm{F}(\mathbf{Z})_{z=0,t=0} &= f((x-0)+\mathbf{i}(y+0))\ \mathbf{e}_1 + f((x+0)+\mathbf{i}(y-0))\ \mathbf{e}_2 \\ &= f(x+\mathbf{i}y)\ \mathbf{e}_1 + f(x+\mathbf{i}y)\ \mathbf{e}_2 \\ &= f(x+\mathbf{i}y)\ (\mathbf{e}_1 + \mathbf{e}_2) \\ &= f(x+\mathbf{i}y)\ (\mathbf{1}). \end{aligned} \tag{2.97}$$

In other words, *the* $\mathbb{D}$*-space function theory subsumes the classical complex function theory.*

The general formula for a function is

$$\mathrm{F}(\mathbf{Z}) = f(\xi)\ \mathbf{e}_1 + f(\eta)\ \mathbf{e}_2$$

in the vector canonical form. This is easily expanded, as follows, into the four-dimensional vector form:

$$\begin{aligned} \mathrm{F}(\mathbf{Z}) = \ & \mathbf{1}\ [Re(f(\xi)) + Re(f(\eta))]/2 \\ & +\mathbf{i}\ [Im(f(\xi)) + Im(f(\eta))]/2 \\ & +\mathbf{j}\ [Im(f(\xi)) - Im(f(\eta))]/2 \\ & +\mathbf{k}\ [-Re(f(\xi)) + Re(f(\eta))]/2. \end{aligned} \tag{2.98}$$

In subsequent discussions, the notation

$$\begin{aligned} X &= [Re(f(\xi)) + Re(f(\eta))]/2 \\ Y &= [Im(f(\xi)) + Im(f(\eta))]/2 \\ Z &= [Im(f(\xi)) - Im(f(\eta))]/2 \\ T &= [-Re(f(\xi)) + Re(f(\eta))]/2, \end{aligned} \tag{2.99}$$

will be used to write the general vector expansion of an analytic function as:

$$\mathrm{F}(\mathbf{Z}) = \mathbf{1}\ X + \mathbf{i}\ Y + \mathbf{j}\ Z + \mathbf{k}\ T, \tag{2.100}$$

which, in the canonical form, is

$$F(\mathbf{Z}) = \mathbf{e}_1\,[(X-T)+\mathbf{i}(Y+Z)] + \mathbf{e}_2\,[(X+T)+\mathbf{i}(Y-Z)].$$

Moreover, since ξ and η are analytic complex functions of x,y,z,t, it follows from complex function theory that X, Y, Z, T are analytic functions of x,y,z,t. Following general precedent in the matter, we shall call X, Y, Z, T *conjugate functions* of x,y,z,t, if F is analytic. Unless otherwise indicated, the rest of the book will be concerned with analytic functions. One other notational device will be used: a function of a hypercomplex variable will be written with all caps, and the independent variable will be written in boldface caps [e. g.: COS(**Z**)]. The complex functions which compose the higher-order function will be written in lowercase letters and will have lowercase arguments [e. g.: $cos(x+\mathbf{i}y)$].

■ *The Function Operates On The Eigenvalues*—The definition (2.96) causes a function of **Z** in $\mathbb{D}$ to operate on the eigenvalues of **Z**. This is in accord with other attempts to define functions of general matrices. The elements ξ and η in the definition are eigenvalues of the matrix form of **Z**. Bellman[25] and MacDuffee[26], among others, conclude that any consistent function definition for matrices must have the function operate on the eigenvalues of the matrix.

It is another useful fact that *the result of applying a function to an element* **Z** *in* $\mathbb{D}$ *is of the same canonical form as* **Z**, *and has the same eigenvectors.* Moreover, a hypercomplex function acts as a pair of classical complex functions applied separately to the axis (complex) planes, mapping each onto itself. Consequently, *the axis planes are invariant* under the application of a hypercomplex function.

■ *Examples Of Common Functions*—The *exponential function* is:

$$\begin{aligned}\mathrm{EXP}(\mathbf{Z}) &= exp(\xi)\,\mathbf{e}_1 + exp(\eta)\,\mathbf{e}_2 \\ &= \mathbf{1}\,[exp(x-t)cos(y+z) + exp(x+t)cos(y-z)]/2 \\ &\quad +\mathbf{i}\,[exp(x-t)sin(y+z) + exp(x+t)sin(y-z)]/2 \\ &\quad +\mathbf{j}\,[exp(x-t)sin(y+z) - exp(x+t)sin(y-z)]/2 \\ &\quad +\mathbf{k}\,[-exp(x-t)cos(y+z) + exp(x+t)cos(y-z)]/2,\end{aligned} \tag{2.101}$$

and evidently exists and has an inverse for all **Z** in $\mathbb{D}$. It has the usual property that

$$\mathrm{EXP}(\mathbf{Z}_1)\ \mathrm{EXP}(\mathbf{Z}_2) = exp(\xi_1)exp(\xi_2)\ \mathbf{e}_1 + exp(\eta_1)exp(\eta_2)\ \mathbf{e}_2 \tag{2.102}$$

$$= exp(\xi_1 + \xi_2)\ \mathbf{e}_1 + exp(\eta_1 + \eta_2)\ \mathbf{e}_2$$

$$= \mathrm{EXP}(\mathbf{Z}_1 + \mathbf{Z}_2).$$

The *square root* function is

$$\mathbf{Z}^{1/2} = \xi^{1/2}\ \mathbf{e}_1 + \eta^{1/2}\ \mathbf{e}_2 \tag{2.103}$$

$$= \mathbf{1}\{|\xi|cos[arg(\xi)/2] + |\eta|cos[arg(\eta)/2]\}/2$$
$$+\mathbf{i}\{|\xi|sin[arg(\xi)/2] + |\eta|sin[\mathrm{arg}(\eta)/2]\}/2$$
$$+\mathbf{j}\{|\xi|sin[arg(\xi)/2] - |\eta|sin[\mathrm{arg}(\eta)/2]\}/2$$
$$+\mathbf{k}\{-|\xi|cos[arg(\xi)/2] + |\eta|cos[\mathrm{arg}(\eta)/2]\}/2,$$

where, for example, the usual complex variable definitions are used:

$$arg(\xi) = arctan[Im(\xi)/Re(\xi)], \tag{2.104}$$

$$|\xi| = [(x-t)^2+(y+z)^2]^{1/2}; \tag{2.105}$$

both square root operations on the right-hand side of the square root definition, (2.103), are taken on the same sheet of the Riemann surface.

Clearly, arg(ξ), hence $\mathbf{Z}^{1/2}$, is not defined if ξ = (0,0); and similarly for η. Since ξ = (0,0) or η = (0,0) are axis plane conditions, one has an example of the general fact that *if an analytic function of a complex variable is undefined at (0,0), then its extension to* $\mathbb{D}$ *fails to be defined anywhere on the two axis planes*. Moreover, this is another example of the axis planes acting as zero elements, or zero sets.

As a direct consequence of the function operating on the eigenvalues and leaving the eigenvectors invariant, *all* of the elementary analytic functions in four dimensions have the usual complex function relationships, because one is dealing with essentially two copies of the corresponding complex functions when global manipulations are being performed. For example,

$$(\mathbf{Z}_1)^{1/2}\ (\mathbf{Z}_2)^{1/2} = (\mathbf{Z}_1\mathbf{Z}_2)^{1/2},$$

$$\mathrm{COS}^2(\mathbf{Z}) + \mathrm{SIN}^2(\mathbf{Z}) = \mathbf{1}, \tag{2.106}$$

$$\mathrm{COSH}^2(\mathbf{Z}) - \mathrm{SINH}^2(\mathbf{Z}) = \mathbf{1},$$

$$\mathrm{EXP}[\mathrm{LOG}(\mathbf{Z})] = \mathbf{Z}.$$

One should not be lulled to sleep by the simplicity, even triviality, of these function constructions. Recall that the functions are operating on the eigenvalues of the independent hypercomplex variable **Z**, by definition, and that each eigenvalue is a function of all four of the independent variables x,y,z,t. Later sections will investigate the extensive consequences of this simple fact.

■ *DeMoivre's Theorem In Four Dimensions*—The following theorem will be proved as an example of how to carry forward certain complex-function concepts into the four-dimensional $\mathbb{D}$-space:

Theorem: If n is a positive integer and $\mathbf{Z} \in \mathbb{D}$, then

$$[\mathrm{COS}(\mathbf{Z}) + \mathbf{i}\,\mathrm{SIN}(\mathbf{Z})]^n = [\mathrm{EXP}(\mathbf{iZ})]^n$$
$$= \mathrm{COS}(n\mathbf{Z}) + \mathbf{i}\,\mathrm{SIN}(n\mathbf{Z}), \qquad (2.107)$$

where **i** is a hypercomplex basis vector.

Proof: As a consequence of the fact that $\mathbf{1}^2 = \mathbf{1}$ and $\mathbf{i}^2 = -\mathbf{1}$, the set of all numbers of the form $\mathbf{1}x+\mathbf{i}y$ make up a field of numbers that is isomorphic to the field of complex numbers. Moreover, the entire system of analysis of one complex variable is brought over because of the isomorphism. One may assert that

$$[exp(\mathbf{i}\xi) + exp(-\mathbf{i}\xi)]/2 = cos(\xi) \qquad (2.108)$$

$$[exp(\mathbf{i}\xi) - exp(-\mathbf{i}\xi)]/2 = sin(\xi), \qquad (2.109)$$

and

$$exp(\mathbf{i}\xi) = cos(\xi) + \mathbf{i}sin(\xi), \qquad (2.110)$$

with

$$\xi = (x-t) + \mathbf{i}(y+z)$$

$$\eta = (x+t) + \mathbf{i}(y-z).$$

Having these "complex" functions of eigenvalues, one may now apply the analytic function definition (2.96) to write

$$\begin{aligned}\mathrm{EXP}(\mathbf{iZ}) &= \mathbf{e}_1\, exp(\mathbf{i}\xi) + \mathbf{e}_2\, exp(\mathbf{i}\eta)\\ &= \mathbf{e}_1\,[cos(\xi) + \mathbf{i}\, sin(\xi)] + \mathbf{e}_2\,[cos(\eta) + \mathbf{i}\, sin(\eta)]\\ &= [\mathbf{e}_1\, cos(\xi) + \mathbf{e}_2\, cos(\eta)] + \mathbf{i}\,[\mathbf{e}_1\, sin(\xi) + \mathbf{e}_2\, sin(\eta)]\\ &= \mathrm{COS}(\mathbf{Z}) + \mathbf{i}\,\mathrm{SIN}(\mathbf{Z}).\end{aligned} \tag{2.111}$$

One may show that

$$[\mathrm{EXP}(\mathbf{iZ})]^n = \mathrm{EXP}(\mathbf{i}n\mathbf{Z}) \tag{2.112}$$

by induction, as follows. Certainly, it is true for $n = 1$. Suppose that it is also true for some fixed positive integer n; then one may multiply both sides of the relation by the quantity EXP(**iZ**),

$$[\mathrm{EXP}(\mathbf{iZ})]^n\, \mathrm{EXP}(\mathbf{iZ}) = \mathrm{EXP}(\mathbf{i}n\mathbf{Z})\, \mathrm{EXP}(\mathbf{iZ}), \tag{2.113}$$

and, as a consequence of the properties of the complex exponential function (e.g., (2.102)),

$$[\mathrm{EXP}(\mathbf{iZ})]^{n+1} = \mathrm{EXP}(\mathbf{i}n\mathbf{Z} + \mathbf{iZ}) = \mathrm{EXP}[\mathbf{i}(n+1)\mathbf{Z}], \tag{2.114}$$

hence (2.112) is also true for $n+1$ when it is true for n, then by induction is true for all n.

As a special case of (2.111),

$$\mathrm{EXP}(\mathbf{i}n\mathbf{Z}) = \mathrm{COS}(n\mathbf{Z}) + \mathbf{i}\,\mathrm{SIN}(n\mathbf{Z}), \tag{2.115}$$

and the proof is concluded.

■ *DeMoivre's Theorem For Hyperbolic Functions*

Theorem: If t is real, if n is a positive integer, and if **k** is the $\mathbb{D}$-Space basis element such that $\mathbf{k}^2 = \mathbf{1}$, then

$$\begin{aligned}[\mathbf{1}\, cosh(t) + \mathbf{k}\, sinh(t)]^n &= [\mathrm{EXP}(\mathbf{k}t)]^n\\ &= \mathbf{1}\, cosh(nt) + \mathbf{k}\, sinh(nt).\end{aligned} \tag{2.116}$$

Proof: As a special case of the exponential function, (2.101), with $x = y = z = 0$, we have

$$\begin{aligned}\mathrm{EXP}(\mathbf{k}t) &= exp(-t)\,\mathbf{e}_1 + exp(t)\,\mathbf{e}_2 \\ &= exp(-t)\,(\mathbf{1}-\mathbf{k})/2 + exp(t)\,(\mathbf{1}+\mathbf{k})/2 \\ &= \mathbf{1}\,[exp(t)+exp(-t)]/2 + \mathbf{k}\,[exp(t)-exp(-t)]/2 \\ &= \mathbf{1}\,cosh(t) + \mathbf{k}\,sinh(t).\end{aligned} \tag{2.117}$$

We notice that

$$[\mathrm{EXP}(\mathbf{k}t)]^n = \mathrm{EXP}(\mathbf{k}nt) \tag{2.118}$$

is a special case of (2.112), with $\mathbf{iZ} = \mathbf{k}t$. Lastly, as a special case of (2.117),

$$\mathrm{EXP}(\mathbf{k}nt) = \mathbf{1}cosh(nt) + \mathbf{k}sinh(nt), \tag{2.119}$$

and the proof is concluded.

■ *Argand's Representation In Four Dimensions*—In the classical complex variables, any nonzero number $z = x+\mathrm{i}y$ may be represented in the form

$$z = r\,exp(\mathrm{i}\theta), \quad \text{(Argand's representation)}$$

where

$$r^2 = x^2 + y^2$$

and

$$\theta = arctan(y/x).$$

It is possible to extend this concept to four dimensions, as follows: First, we already have a modulus function, (2.90), which corresponds to "r" and has the right properties. A *hypercomplex argument* function is also easy to define:

$$\begin{aligned}\mathrm{ARG}(\mathbf{Z}) &= \mathbf{e}_1 arg(\xi) + \mathbf{e}_2 arg(\eta) \\ &= \mathbf{e}_1 arctan[Im(\xi)/Re(\xi)] + \mathbf{e}_2 arctan[Im(\eta)/Re(\eta)],\end{aligned} \tag{2.120}$$

with

$$\xi = (x-t) + \mathbf{i}(y+z)$$

$$\eta = (x+t) + \mathbf{i}(y-z).$$

This has the necessary property [using (2.101)] that

$$|\mathrm{EXP}[\mathbf{i}\ \mathrm{ARG}(\mathbf{Z})]|^2 = |exp[\mathbf{i}\ arg(\xi)]|^2/2 + |exp[\mathbf{i}\ arg(\eta)]|^2/2 = 1/2 + 1/2 = 1. \tag{2.121}$$

Evidently, (2.90), (2.101), and (2.120) are defined everywhere except when $det(\mathbf{Z}) = 0$; combining these, one has

$$\mathbf{Z} = \mathrm{MOD}(\mathbf{Z})\ \mathrm{EXP}[\mathbf{i}\ \mathrm{ARG}(\mathbf{Z})] = \mathbf{e}_1|\xi|\ exp[\mathbf{i} arg(\xi)] + \mathbf{e}_2|\eta|\ exp[\mathbf{i}\ arg(\eta)], \tag{2.122}$$

which is *Argand's representation in four dimensions*. This represents a broadening of Argand's original concept, because MOD($\mathbf{Z}$) is not the Euclidean norm of $\mathbf{Z}$, the latter not having suitable properties under multiplication for this application. In fact, (2.122) is just Argand's representation applied to each eigenvalue of $\mathbf{Z}$, as in any standard hypercomplex function definition.

One interpretation of (2.122) is that the vector $\mathbf{Z}$ is rotated into the **1**,**k**-plane (because $|\mathbf{Z}| = |\mathrm{MOD}(\mathbf{Z})|$; i.e., the vector magnitude is carried into the **1**,**k**-plane), and the EXP(**i**ARG($\mathbf{Z}$) function specifies the angle between the original and rotated positions. Because of the absolute value signs, the rotated vector will not go to a unique position in the **1**,**k**-plane, but the argument function will specify a unique angle of rotation. Moreover, we showed in Section 2.3.1 that $[\mathrm{MOD}(\mathbf{Z})]^2$ is an invariant vector under orthogonal transformations, and it follows from its form that MOD($\mathbf{Z}$), also, is invariant; hence Argand's representation is a product of an invariant, magnitude-embodying vector and a unit directional vector.

2.3.3 The Limit, Derivative, And Integral Operations

All of the concepts and operations that will be defined in this section follow naturally from the observation that the function space which has been constructed over $\mathbb{D}$ behaves as two copies of the complex function space. Any question about existence, uniqueness, etc. is thereby resolved into the more familiar question in the complex plane, except that *two* cases must be resolved, simultaneously. The following subsections will all make implicit use of the unary operation (2.87) and function (2.96) definitions.

■ *Definition Of The Limit Operation*—The *limit operation* for analytic functions, F, is as follows:

$$\underset{\mathbf{Z}\to\mathbf{Z}_o}{\mathrm{LIM}}\ \mathrm{F}(\mathbf{Z}) = \mathbf{e}_1 \underset{\xi\to\xi_o}{lim} f(\xi) + \mathbf{e}_2 \underset{\eta\to\eta_o}{lim} f(\eta), \tag{2.123}$$

with

$$\xi = (x-t) + \mathbf{i}(y+z)$$

$$\eta = (x+t) + \mathbf{i}(y-z).$$

Definition (2.123) has the usual interpretation, as follows: suppose

$$\underset{\xi\to\xi_o}{lim} f(\xi) \ \text{ and } \ \underset{\eta\to\eta_o}{lim} f(\eta) \tag{2.124}$$

both exist; then for every $\varepsilon > 0$ there exists δ_1 and δ_2 such that

$$| f(\xi)-f(\xi_o) | < \varepsilon \quad \text{whenever} \quad | \xi-\xi_o | < \delta_1, \tag{2.125}$$

$$| f(\eta)-f(\eta_o) | < \varepsilon \quad \text{whenever} \quad | \eta-\eta_o | < \delta_2.$$

As a result, if one chooses $\delta = min(\delta_1,\delta_2)$, then

$$| \mathrm{F}(\mathbf{Z})-\mathrm{F}(\mathbf{Z}_o)|^2 = |f(\xi)-f(\xi_o)|^2/2 + |f(\eta)-f(\eta_o)|^2/2$$
$$< \varepsilon^2/2 + \varepsilon^2/2 = \varepsilon^2, \tag{2.126}$$

and

$$| \mathbf{Z}-\mathbf{Z}_o |^2 = | \xi-\xi_o |^2/2 + | \eta-\eta_o|^2/2$$
$$< \delta^2/2 + \delta^2/2 = \delta^2. \tag{2.127}$$

By (2.126) and (2.127) if one is given an $\varepsilon > 0$ one can find a $\delta > 0$ such that

$$| \mathrm{F}(\mathbf{Z})-\mathrm{F}(\mathbf{Z}_o) | < \varepsilon \quad \text{whenever} \ | \mathbf{Z}-\mathbf{Z}_o | < \delta. \tag{2.128}$$

■ *The Derivative Of A Hypercomplex Function*—In the following, primes (′) will denote differentiation. The *derivative* operation is defined as follows:

$$
\begin{aligned}
\mathrm{F}'(\mathbf{Z})|_{Z_o} &= \lim_{\mathbf{Z}\to\mathbf{Z}_o} \{[\mathrm{F}(\mathbf{Z})-\mathrm{F}(\mathbf{Z}_o)] \,/\, [\mathbf{Z}-\mathbf{Z}_o]\} \\
&= \mathbf{e}_1 \lim_{\xi\to\xi_o} \{[f(\xi)-f(\xi_o)]/[\xi-\xi_o]\} \\
&\quad + \mathbf{e}_2 \lim_{\eta\to\eta_o} \{[f(\eta)-f(\eta_o)] \,/\, [\eta-\eta_o]\} \\
&= \mathbf{e}_1 f'(\xi_o) + \mathbf{e}_2 f'(\eta_o).
\end{aligned}
\tag{2.129}
$$

The derivative operation has the usual properties; for example,

$$
\frac{d}{d\mathbf{Z}} \mathrm{LOG}(\mathbf{Z}) = \mathbf{e}_1 \frac{d}{d\xi} \log(\xi) + \mathbf{e}_2 \frac{d}{d\eta} \log(\eta) \tag{2.130}
$$

$$
= \mathbf{e}_1(1/\xi) + \mathbf{e}_2(1/\eta) = 1/\mathbf{Z}.
$$

$$
\frac{d}{d\mathbf{Z}} \mathrm{SIN}(\mathbf{Z}) = \mathbf{e}_1 \frac{d}{d\xi} \sin(\xi) + \mathbf{e}_2 \frac{d}{d\eta} \sin(\eta)
$$

$$
= \mathbf{e}_1 \cos(\xi) + \mathbf{e}_2 \cos(\eta) \tag{2.131}
$$

$$
= \mathrm{COS}(\mathbf{Z}).
$$

■ *The Integral Of A Hypercomplex Function*—The *indefinite integral* is defined as follows:

$$
\int \mathrm{F}(\mathbf{Z})\, d\mathbf{Z} = \mathbf{e}_1 \int f(\xi)d\xi + \mathbf{e}_2 \int f(\eta)d\eta, \tag{2.132}
$$

where

$$\xi = (x-t) + \mathbf{i}(y+z)$$

$$\eta = (x+t) + \mathbf{i}(y-z).$$

For example,

$$\int \frac{d\mathbf{Z}}{1+\mathbf{Z}^2} = \mathbf{e}_1 \int \frac{d\xi}{1+\xi^2} + \mathbf{e}_2 \int \frac{d\eta}{1+\eta^2} \tag{2.133}$$

$$= \mathbf{e}_1\, arctan(\xi) + \mathbf{e}_2\, arctan(\eta) = \mathrm{ARCTAN}(\mathbf{Z}).$$

Functions such as this, which have *branch cuts* in their Riemann surfaces, must be applied with due consideration to Riemann surface effects. It follows from classical complex variable theory that if the function values in the canonical vector form are both taken on the same branch of the Riemann surface, and if the branch cuts in both are placed in the same way, then the hypercomplex result will be well-defined. Other cases, such as with differing placements of the branch cuts or using differing branches of the Riemann surface, could be the basis of a separate investigation.

2.3.4 The Axis Planes As Function Space Invariants

The canonical vector formulation of the ring $\mathbb{D}$ emphasizes that the fundamental ring operations take place in the axis planes (Eqns. 2.34–2.37), and that the eigenvectors $\mathbf{e}_1$ and $\mathbf{e}_2$ are absolute invariants. As a result, an algebraic operation may map the axis planes into themselves, but will leave the planes in their previous orientation relative to the underlying coordinate frame. The unary operation, (2.87), which includes functions, derivatives, integrals, and other analysis operations, likewise acts within the axis planes and leaves their overall orientation unchanged. One may conclude that the axis planes are function space invariants.

The notion that some feature, any feature, of the underlying space remains unchanged by any and all allowed operations makes the $\mathbb{D}$-space different in concept from an ordinary real four-space or a four-dimensional vector space. The nearest existing concept is the light cone of relativity physics that divides the real four-space into the reachable and unreachable regions of the universe. The connection between the axis planes of the $\mathbb{D}$-space and the light cone of relativity will be investigated in the relativity applications sections.

2.3.5 The Cauchy-Riemann Conditions In Four Dimensions

In the classical complex variable theory, if one has a complex variable $z = x + \mathrm{i}y$ and a function $f(z) = u(x,y) + \mathrm{i}v(x,y)$, then the *Cauchy-Riemann conditions* are:

$$\frac{\partial u}{\partial x} = \frac{\partial v}{\partial y} \qquad (2.134)$$

$$\frac{\partial u}{\partial y} = -\frac{\partial v}{\partial x}$$

The two-dimensional case, (2.134), may be generalized as follows. It was shown earlier, (2.100), that the general analytic function in four dimensions could always be represented in the form

$$\mathrm{F}(\mathbf{Z}) = \mathbf{1}X + \mathbf{i}Y + \mathbf{j}Z + \mathbf{k}T, \qquad (2.135)$$

where X, Y, Z, T are analytic functions of the independent variables x,y,z,t. Putting this into the canonical form, one obtains

$$\mathrm{F}(\mathbf{Z}) = [(X-T) + \mathbf{i}(Y+Z)]\,\mathbf{e}_1 + [(X+T) + \mathbf{i}(Y-Z)]\,\mathbf{e}_2. \qquad (2.136)$$

By a more fundamental definition, (2.96), the general analytic function is of the form

$$\mathrm{F}(\mathbf{Z}) = \mathbf{e}_1 f(\xi) + \mathbf{e}_2 f(\eta), \qquad (2.137)$$

with

$$\xi = (x-t) + \mathbf{i}(y+z) \qquad (2.138)$$

$$\eta = (x+t) + \mathbf{i}(y-z),$$

and $f(\xi), f(\eta)$ analytic functions of the complex variables ξ,η. Comparing forms (2.136) and (2.137), one observes that

$$f(\xi) = (X-T) + \mathbf{i}(Y+Z) \qquad (2.139)$$

$$f(\eta) = (X+T) + \mathbf{i}(Y-Z).$$

Forms (2.138) and (2.139) yield two sets of the classical Cauchy-Riemann conditions in two dimensions, or the *Cauchy-Riemann conditions in four dimensions*:

$$\frac{\partial(X-T)}{\partial(x-t)} = \frac{\partial(Y+Z)}{\partial(y+z)} \tag{2.140}$$

$$\frac{\partial(X-T)}{\partial(y+z)} = -\frac{\partial(Y+Z)}{\partial(x-t)} \tag{2.141}$$

$$\frac{\partial(X+T)}{\partial(x+t)} = \frac{\partial(Y-Z)}{\partial(y-z)} \tag{2.142}$$

$$\frac{\partial(X+T)}{\partial(y-z)} = -\frac{\partial(Y-Z)}{\partial(x+t)}. \tag{2.143}$$

The functions X, Y, Z, T of the independent variables x,y,z,t were derived from the analytic functions $f(\xi), f(\eta)$, where ξ,η are themselves analytic functions of x,y,z,t [see (2.99)], hence are analytic in the independent variables x,y,z,t. One may apply the chain rule for partial derivatives to write (2.140) through (2.143) in the form

$$\left(\frac{\partial}{\partial x} - \frac{\partial}{\partial t}\right)(X-T) = \left(\frac{\partial}{\partial y} + \frac{\partial}{\partial z}\right)(Y+Z) \tag{2.144}$$

$$\left(\frac{\partial}{\partial y} + \frac{\partial}{\partial z}\right)(X-T) = -\left(\frac{\partial}{\partial x} - \frac{\partial}{\partial t}\right)(Y+Z) \tag{2.145}$$

$$\left(\frac{\partial}{\partial x} + \frac{\partial}{\partial t}\right)(X+T) = \left(\frac{\partial}{\partial y} - \frac{\partial}{\partial z}\right)(Y-Z) \tag{2.146}$$

$$\left(\frac{\partial}{\partial y} - \frac{\partial}{\partial z}\right)(X+T) = -\left(\frac{\partial}{\partial x} + \frac{\partial}{\partial t}\right)(Y-Z) \tag{2.147}$$

A more conventional-looking representation may be derived from (2.140) through (2.147) as follows. (Underlying the derivation will be the implicit requirement that the derivative or partial derivative at a point be independent of the direction of approach to the point, which amounts to requiring that the function be analytic at the point under discussion.) In (2.144), if the partial derivative is taken in a plane in which z and t are constant, one obtains

$$\frac{\partial}{\partial x}(X-T) = \frac{\partial}{\partial y}(Y+Z).$$

Similarly, in a plane in which y and t are constant, one obtains

$$\frac{\partial}{\partial x}(X-T) = \frac{\partial}{\partial z}(Y+Z);$$

hence it is a consequence of (2.144) that

$$\frac{\partial X}{\partial x} - \frac{\partial T}{\partial x} = \frac{\partial Y}{\partial y} + \frac{\partial Z}{\partial y} = \frac{\partial Y}{\partial z} + \frac{\partial Z}{\partial z}. \tag{2.148}$$

From similar manipulations on (2.144) in planes in which either (x and y are constant) or (x and z are constant), we find

$$-\frac{\partial X}{\partial t} + \frac{\partial T}{\partial t} = \frac{\partial Y}{\partial y} + \frac{\partial Z}{\partial y} = \frac{\partial Y}{\partial z} + \frac{\partial Z}{\partial z}, \tag{2.149}$$

The above operations may be repeated with (2.145), (2.146), and (2.147), with the results

$$\frac{\partial X}{\partial y} - \frac{\partial T}{\partial y} = -\frac{\partial Y}{\partial x} - \frac{\partial Z}{\partial x} = \frac{\partial Y}{\partial t} + \frac{\partial Z}{\partial t}, \tag{2.150}$$

$$\frac{\partial X}{\partial z} - \frac{\partial T}{\partial z} = -\frac{\partial Y}{\partial x} - \frac{\partial Z}{\partial x} = \frac{\partial Y}{\partial t} + \frac{\partial Z}{\partial t}, \tag{2.151}$$

$$\frac{\partial X}{\partial x} + \frac{\partial T}{\partial x} = \frac{\partial Y}{\partial y} - \frac{\partial Z}{\partial y} = -\frac{\partial Y}{\partial z} + \frac{\partial Z}{\partial z}, \tag{2.152}$$

$$\frac{\partial X}{\partial t} + \frac{\partial T}{\partial t} = \frac{\partial Y}{\partial y} - \frac{\partial Z}{\partial y} = -\frac{\partial Y}{\partial z} + \frac{\partial Z}{\partial z}, \tag{2.153}$$

$$\frac{\partial X}{\partial y} + \frac{\partial T}{\partial y} = -\frac{\partial Y}{\partial x} + \frac{\partial Z}{\partial x} = -\frac{\partial Y}{\partial t} + \frac{\partial Z}{\partial t}, \tag{2.154}$$

$$-\frac{\partial X}{\partial z} - \frac{\partial T}{\partial z} = -\frac{\partial Y}{\partial x} + \frac{\partial Z}{\partial x} = -\frac{\partial Y}{\partial t} + \frac{\partial Z}{\partial t}. \tag{2.155}$$

By addition of (2.148) and (2.152), one obtains

$$\frac{\partial X}{\partial x} = \frac{\partial Y}{\partial y} = \frac{\partial Z}{\partial z}.$$

By similar additions and subtractions of appropriate pairs of equations (2.148) through (2.155), one obtains a conventional-looking extension of the Cauchy-Riemann conditions to spaces of four dimensions:

$$\begin{array}{|cccc|} \hline \dfrac{\partial X}{\partial x} = & \dfrac{\partial Y}{\partial y} = & \dfrac{\partial Z}{\partial z} = & \dfrac{\partial T}{\partial t} \\ \dfrac{\partial X}{\partial y} = & -\dfrac{\partial Y}{\partial x} = & \dfrac{\partial Z}{\partial t} = & -\dfrac{\partial T}{\partial z} \\ \dfrac{\partial X}{\partial z} = & \dfrac{\partial Y}{\partial t} = & -\dfrac{\partial Z}{\partial x} = & -\dfrac{\partial T}{\partial y} \\ \dfrac{\partial X}{\partial t} = & -\dfrac{\partial Y}{\partial z} = & -\dfrac{\partial Z}{\partial y} = & \dfrac{\partial T}{\partial x} \\ \hline \end{array} \qquad (2.156)$$

Notation: $\mathbf{Z} = \mathbf{1}x + \mathbf{i}y + \mathbf{j}z + \mathbf{k}t$, $\mathrm{F}(\mathbf{Z}) = \mathbf{1}X + \mathbf{i}Y + \mathbf{j}Z + \mathbf{k}T$.

The original two Cauchy-Riemann conditions (2.134) are included here, in the upper left corner. Just as the two-dimensional conditions produced far-reaching consequences, we shall see that the four-dimensional conditions have extensive consequences of importance to, for example, the physics of conservative force fields and the mathematics of the wave equation and related partial differential equations. Extensive use will be made of the Cauchy-Riemann (C-R) conditions in developing the $\mathbb{D}$-space version of vector analysis.

2.3.6 A Vector-Matrix Notation For The Algebraic Operations In $\mathbb{D}$

In Section 2.1.4, it was shown that all the fundamental operations for the ring $\mathbb{D}$ can be stated completely in 4 X 4 real matrix notation. This can be abbreviated to a vector-matrix notation, as follows, yielding a notational form which will allow insights about the relationship of the $\mathbb{D}$-space operations to classical vector analysis and will be useful in later sections. Consider the typical element in $\mathbb{D}$ in matrix form:

$$\mathbf{Z} = \begin{bmatrix} x & -y & -z & t \\ y & x & -t & -z \\ z & -t & x & -y \\ t & z & y & x \end{bmatrix}.$$

The first column contains sufficient information to define the rest of the matrix, given the particular sign pattern which must be observed. One could just as well write

$$\mathbf{Z} = \begin{bmatrix} x \\ y \\ z \\ t \end{bmatrix}, \tag{2.157}$$

leaving the rest of the structure implicit; then, by suitable definitions, all of the ring operations can be stated in this notation. For examples, one may define

$$\mathbf{Z}_1 + \mathbf{Z}_2 = \begin{bmatrix} x_1 \\ y_1 \\ z_1 \\ t_1 \end{bmatrix} + \begin{bmatrix} x_2 \\ y_2 \\ z_2 \\ t_2 \end{bmatrix} = \begin{bmatrix} x_1 + x_2 \\ y_1 + y_2 \\ z_1 + z_2 \\ t_1 + t_2 \end{bmatrix} \tag{2.158}$$

and

$$\mathbf{Z}^{-1} = \begin{bmatrix} x \\ y \\ z \\ t \end{bmatrix}^{-1} \tag{2.159}$$

$$= \text{Column (1) of} \begin{bmatrix} x & -y & -z & t \\ y & x & -t & -z \\ z & -t & x & -y \\ t & z & y & x \end{bmatrix}^{-1}.$$

This is not of much interest or consequence until one considers the multiplication operation. In full matrix form, it can be represented by

$$\mathbf{Z}_1\mathbf{Z}_2 = \begin{bmatrix} x_1 & -y_1 & -z_1 & t_1 \\ y_1 & x_1 & -t_1 & -z_1 \\ z_1 & -t_1 & x_1 & -y_1 \\ t_1 & z_1 & y_1 & x_1 \end{bmatrix} \begin{bmatrix} x_2 & -y_2 & -z_2 & t_2 \\ y_2 & x_2 & -t_2 & -z_2 \\ z_2 & -t_2 & x_2 & -y_2 \\ t_2 & z_2 & y_2 & x_2 \end{bmatrix} \qquad (2.160)$$

$$= \begin{bmatrix} x_2 & -y_2 & -z_2 & t_2 \\ y_2 & x_2 & -t_2 & -z_2 \\ z_2 & -t_2 & x_2 & -y_2 \\ t_2 & z_2 & y_2 & x_2 \end{bmatrix} \begin{bmatrix} x_1 & -y_1 & -z_1 & t_1 \\ y_1 & x_1 & -t_1 & -z_1 \\ z_1 & -t_1 & x_1 & -y_1 \\ t_1 & z_1 & y_1 & x_1 \end{bmatrix} \qquad \text{(Commutativity)}$$

Now it is a remarkable circumstance that the general multiplication formula in 4 X 4 matrix notation, (2.160), can be shortened to the following and still be mathematically correct:

$$\mathbf{Z}_1\mathbf{Z}_2 = \begin{bmatrix} x_1 & -y_1 & -z_1 & t_1 \\ y_1 & x_1 & -t_1 & -z_1 \\ z_1 & -t_1 & x_1 & -y_1 \\ t_1 & z_1 & y_1 & x_1 \end{bmatrix} \begin{bmatrix} x_2 \\ y_2 \\ z_2 \\ t_2 \end{bmatrix} \qquad (2.161)$$

$$= \begin{bmatrix} x_2 & -y_2 & -z_2 & t_2 \\ y_2 & x_2 & -t_2 & -z_2 \\ z_2 & -t_2 & x_2 & -y_2 \\ t_2 & z_2 & y_2 & x_2 \end{bmatrix} \begin{bmatrix} x_1 \\ y_1 \\ z_1 \\ t_1 \end{bmatrix} \qquad \text{(Commutativity)}$$

Equation (2.161) is the result we were seeking in this Section. There are several important observations to make: (1) Multiplication may be viewed as having the same form as a coordinate transformation X′ = AX in the classical vector analysis; (2) Either variable may be considered as a matrix operator applied to a vector (the operation is symmetric); (3) The transformation in the general case is not orthogonal because

$$det(\mathbf{Z}) = \{[(x-t)^2+(y+z)^2]\ [(x+t)^2+(y-z)^2]\},$$

which is not always of magnitude one; and (4), Eqn. (2.161) provides a way to relate certain classical analytical geometry formulas to corresponding operations in the $\mathbb{D}$-space. Section 2.3.8 will illustrate the use of observation (4).

2.3.7 The Basis Vectors Are Rotation Operators

One may use the vector-matrix formulation from Section 2.3.6 to interpret the basis vectors as rotation operators. Let the "vector" part of the formula (2.161) be the general element

$$\mathbf{Z} = \mathbf{1}x + \mathbf{i}\,y + \mathbf{j}z + \mathbf{k}t$$

in $\mathbb{D}$ and let any of the basis vectors be multipliers of $\mathbf{Z}$ (e.g., $\mathbf{iZ}$). Recall that the basis vectors have a 4 X 4 real, orthogonal matrix representation, (2.2), hence could be interpreted as pure rotation operators in four dimensions. The question arises: do they rotate a vector to an orthogonal direction with respect to the original vector? One may test this hypothesis directly, by use of a vector dot product (defined in the usual way):

$$\mathbf{Z} \bullet (\mathbf{1Z}) = \mathbf{Z} \bullet \mathbf{Z} = x^2 + y^2 + z^2 + t^2\,; \tag{2.162}$$

$$\begin{aligned}\mathbf{Z} \bullet (\mathbf{iZ}) &= (\mathbf{1}x + \mathbf{i}y + \mathbf{j}z + \mathbf{k}t) \bullet (-\mathbf{1}y + \mathbf{i}x - \mathbf{j}t + \mathbf{k}z)\\ &= -xy + yx - zt + zt = 0;\end{aligned} \tag{2.163}$$

$$\begin{aligned}\mathbf{Z} \bullet (\mathbf{jZ}) &= (\mathbf{1}x + \mathbf{i}y + \mathbf{j}z + \mathbf{k}t) \bullet (-\mathbf{1}z - \mathbf{i}t + \mathbf{j}x + \mathbf{k}y)\\ &= -xz - yt + zx + ty = 0;\end{aligned} \tag{2.164}$$

$$\begin{aligned}\mathbf{Z} \bullet (\mathbf{kZ}) &= (\mathbf{1}x + \mathbf{i}y + \mathbf{j}z + \mathbf{k}t) \bullet (\mathbf{1}t - \mathbf{i}z - \mathbf{j}y + \mathbf{k}x)\\ &= xt - yz - zy + tx = 2(xt - yz).\end{aligned} \tag{2.165}$$

Evidently $\mathbf{1}$ is a "zero angle" operator in this interpretation, both $\mathbf{i}$ and $\mathbf{j}$ are "90-degree" operators, and $\mathbf{k}$ is a "180-degree" operator (recall that $\mathbf{k}^2 = \mathbf{1}$). This is an unusual aspect of rotation in four dimensions in that the hypercomplex equivalent of a 180-degree rotation does not produce merely the negative of a vector or its reflection through its point of origin, but something else which depends upon position in the four-space. In some cases, for those vectors for which $xt-yz = 0$, the rotation produced by **k** does reduce to the hypercomplex equivalent of 90 degrees.

2.3.8 The Derivative Is Taken Along A Line Of Arbitrary Orientation

As developed in Sec. 2.3.3, the derivative F′(**Z**) of a function F of a single hypercomplex variable **Z** is

$$\mathrm{F}'(\mathbf{Z}) = f'(\xi)\,\mathbf{e}_1 + f'(\eta)\,\mathbf{e}_2,$$

which, by use of (2.99) and (2.100), can be expanded as follows:

$$\mathrm{F}'(\mathbf{Z}) = \mathbf{e}_1\left(\frac{d}{d[(x-t)+\mathbf{i}(y+z)]}\right)[(X-T)+\mathbf{i}(Y+Z)]$$

$$+\,\mathbf{e}_2\left(\frac{d}{d[(x+t)+\mathbf{i}(y-z)]}\right)[(X+T)+\mathbf{i}(Y-Z)]\ . \qquad (2.166)$$

Now the terms involving X, Y, Z, T and x, y, z, t all have the properties of the classical complex variables. One may use the classical complex variable result that, if $f(z) = u + \mathrm{i}v$, then

$$\frac{df}{dz} = \frac{\partial u}{\partial x} + \mathrm{i}\,\frac{\partial v}{\partial x}$$

to further expand (2.166):

$$\mathrm{F}'(\mathbf{Z}) = \mathbf{e}_1\left[\frac{\partial}{\partial(x-t)}(X-T) + \mathbf{i}\frac{\partial}{\partial(x-t)}(Y+Z)\right]$$

$$+\,\mathbf{e}_2\left[\frac{\partial}{\partial(x+t)}(X+T) + \mathbf{i}\frac{\partial}{\partial(x+t)}(Y-Z)\right]$$

$$= \mathbf{e}_1\left\{\left[\frac{\partial}{\partial x}(X-T) - \frac{\partial}{\partial t}(X-T)\right]/2 + \mathbf{i}\left[\frac{\partial}{\partial x}(Y+Z) - \frac{\partial}{\partial t}(Y+Z)\right]/2\right\}$$

$$+\,\mathbf{e}_2\left\{\left[\frac{\partial}{\partial x}(X+T) + \frac{\partial}{\partial t}(X+T)\right]/2 + \mathbf{i}\left[\frac{\partial}{\partial x}(Y-Z) + \frac{\partial}{\partial t}(Y-Z)\right]/2\right\}$$

$$= \mathbf{e}_1 \left\{ \left[\frac{\partial X}{\partial x} - \frac{\partial T}{\partial x} - \frac{\partial X}{\partial t} + \frac{\partial T}{\partial t} \right] /2 + \mathbf{i} \left[\frac{\partial Y}{\partial x} + \frac{\partial Z}{\partial x} - \frac{\partial Y}{\partial t} - \frac{\partial Z}{\partial t} \right] /2 \right\}$$
$$+ \mathbf{e}_2 \left\{ \left[\frac{\partial X}{\partial x} + \frac{\partial T}{\partial x} + \frac{\partial X}{\partial t} + \frac{\partial T}{\partial t} \right] /2 + \mathbf{i} \left[\frac{\partial Y}{\partial x} - \frac{\partial Z}{\partial x} + \frac{\partial Y}{\partial t} - \frac{\partial Z}{\partial t} \right] /2 \right\}. \tag{2.167}$$

One may now substitute freely from the four-dimensional Cauchy-Riemann conditions (2.156) to obtain

$$\mathrm{F}'(\mathbf{Z}) = \mathbf{e}_1 \left\{ \left[\frac{\partial X}{\partial x} - \frac{\partial T}{\partial x} - \frac{\partial T}{\partial x} + \frac{\partial X}{\partial x} \right] /2 + \mathbf{i} \left[\frac{\partial Y}{\partial x} + \frac{\partial Z}{\partial x} + \frac{\partial Z}{\partial x} + \frac{\partial Y}{\partial x} \right] /2 \right\}$$
$$+ \mathbf{e}_2 \left\{ \left[\frac{\partial X}{\partial x} + \frac{\partial T}{\partial x} + \frac{\partial T}{\partial x} + \frac{\partial X}{\partial x} \right] /2 + \mathbf{i} \left[\frac{\partial Y}{\partial x} - \frac{\partial Z}{\partial x} - \frac{\partial Z}{\partial x} + \frac{\partial Y}{\partial x} \right] /2 \right\}$$

$$= \mathbf{e}_1 \left\{ \left[\frac{\partial X}{\partial x} - \frac{\partial T}{\partial x} \right] + \mathbf{i} \left[\frac{\partial Y}{\partial x} + \frac{\partial Z}{\partial x} \right] \right\}$$
$$+ \mathbf{e}_2 \left\{ \left[\frac{\partial X}{\partial x} + \frac{\partial T}{\partial x} \right] + \mathbf{i} \left[\frac{\partial Y}{\partial x} - \frac{\partial Z}{\partial x} \right] \right\},$$

which reduces to the vector form

$$\frac{d\mathrm{F}}{d\mathbf{Z}} = 1 \frac{\partial X}{\partial x} + \mathbf{i} \frac{\partial Y}{\partial x} + \mathbf{j} \frac{\partial Z}{\partial x} + \mathbf{k} \frac{\partial T}{\partial x} = \frac{\partial \mathrm{F}}{\partial \mathrm{x}} . \tag{2.168}$$

Eqn. (2.168) asserts that the four-dimensional derivative may be determined by considering only the variation along the x-axis (i.e., along a line). We may capitalize on this notion by considering variation along the other axes to obtain

$$\frac{d\mathrm{F}}{d\mathbf{Z}} = \frac{\partial \mathrm{F}}{\partial x} = -\mathbf{i} \frac{\partial \mathrm{F}}{\partial y} = -\mathbf{j} \frac{\partial \mathrm{F}}{\partial z} = \mathbf{k} \frac{\partial \mathrm{F}}{\partial t} . \tag{2.169}$$

This result is merely a logical extension of a corresponding result from the classical complex analysis, from which we have the first two equalities on the left.

The relations (2.169) are important for understanding the meaning of "derivative" in the context of physics applications. There is nothing sacrosanct about the four coordinate axis directions. It should be equally valid to take the derivative along any line whatsoever in the four-space; then *the "derivative" of a function at a point is the variation along any line through the point.* This is easier to understand if one realizes that the underlying coordinate frame can be rotated to bring any axis into alignment with any given line in the four-space.

The result of the derivative operation is another vector function whose components are the variations of the corresponding original components along a given line, hence will have a vector direction different from the original function and not, in general, the same direction as the line along which the variation is computed.

2.3.9 A Chain Rule For Derivatives

This section will develop a chain rule for derivatives in one particular way, possibly not the most direct way but one which will illustrate the consequences of the C-R conditions and the utility of the vector-matrix notation. Let

$$\mathbf{Z} = \mathbf{1}x + \mathbf{i}y + \mathbf{j}z + \mathbf{k}t$$

be the independent variable, and let

$$\mathrm{G}(\mathbf{Z}) = \mathbf{1}u + \mathbf{i}v + \mathbf{j}w + \mathbf{k}s, \tag{2.170}$$

and

$$\mathrm{F}(\mathrm{G}) = \mathbf{1}U + \mathbf{i}V + \mathbf{j}W + \mathbf{k}S; \tag{2.171}$$

be analytic; then we want to show that

$$\frac{d\mathrm{F}}{d\mathbf{Z}} = \frac{d\mathrm{F}}{d\mathrm{G}} \frac{d\mathrm{G}}{d\mathbf{Z}} . \tag{2.172}$$

We start by noting that the conjugate functions of F are real, analytic and of the form *U(u,v,w,s)*, *V(u,v,w,s)*, etc. One may apply the usual chain rule for real functions to each of the conjugate functions *U, V, W, S* to get

$$\begin{aligned}
\frac{\partial U}{\partial x} &= \frac{\partial U}{\partial u}\frac{\partial u}{\partial x} + \frac{\partial U}{\partial v}\frac{\partial v}{\partial x} + \frac{\partial U}{\partial w}\frac{\partial w}{\partial x} + \frac{\partial U}{\partial s}\frac{\partial s}{\partial x} \\
\frac{\partial V}{\partial x} &= \frac{\partial V}{\partial u}\frac{\partial u}{\partial x} + \frac{\partial V}{\partial v}\frac{\partial v}{\partial x} + \frac{\partial V}{\partial w}\frac{\partial w}{\partial x} + \frac{\partial V}{\partial s}\frac{\partial s}{\partial x} \\
\frac{\partial W}{\partial x} &= \frac{\partial W}{\partial u}\frac{\partial u}{\partial x} + \frac{\partial W}{\partial v}\frac{\partial v}{\partial x} + \frac{\partial W}{\partial w}\frac{\partial w}{\partial x} + \frac{\partial W}{\partial s}\frac{\partial s}{\partial x} \\
\frac{\partial S}{\partial x} &= \frac{\partial S}{\partial u}\frac{\partial u}{\partial x} + \frac{\partial S}{\partial v}\frac{\partial v}{\partial x} + \frac{\partial S}{\partial w}\frac{\partial w}{\partial x} + \frac{\partial S}{\partial s}\frac{\partial s}{\partial x}
\end{aligned} \tag{2.173}$$

This can be written in matrix form as

$$\begin{bmatrix} \frac{\partial U}{\partial x} \\ \frac{\partial V}{\partial x} \\ \frac{\partial W}{\partial x} \\ \frac{\partial S}{\partial x} \end{bmatrix} = \begin{bmatrix} \frac{\partial U}{\partial u} & \frac{\partial U}{\partial v} & \frac{\partial U}{\partial w} & \frac{\partial U}{\partial s} \\ \frac{\partial V}{\partial u} & \frac{\partial V}{\partial v} & \frac{\partial V}{\partial w} & \frac{\partial V}{\partial s} \\ \frac{\partial W}{\partial u} & \frac{\partial W}{\partial v} & \frac{\partial W}{\partial w} & \frac{\partial W}{\partial s} \\ \frac{\partial S}{\partial u} & \frac{\partial S}{\partial v} & \frac{\partial S}{\partial w} & \frac{\partial S}{\partial s} \end{bmatrix} \begin{bmatrix} \frac{\partial u}{\partial x} \\ \frac{\partial v}{\partial x} \\ \frac{\partial w}{\partial x} \\ \frac{\partial s}{\partial x} \end{bmatrix} \tag{2.174}$$

Since F is analytic in G, one may apply the C-R conditions to the partial derivatives in the matrix in (2.174) to get

$$\begin{bmatrix} \frac{\partial U}{\partial x} \\ \frac{\partial V}{\partial x} \\ \frac{\partial W}{\partial x} \\ \frac{\partial S}{\partial x} \end{bmatrix} = \begin{bmatrix} \frac{\partial U}{\partial u} & -\frac{\partial V}{\partial u} & -\frac{\partial W}{\partial u} & \frac{\partial S}{\partial u} \\ \frac{\partial V}{\partial u} & \frac{\partial U}{\partial u} & -\frac{\partial S}{\partial u} & -\frac{\partial W}{\partial u} \\ \frac{\partial W}{\partial u} & -\frac{\partial S}{\partial u} & \frac{\partial U}{\partial u} & -\frac{\partial V}{\partial u} \\ \frac{\partial S}{\partial u} & \frac{\partial W}{\partial u} & \frac{\partial V}{\partial u} & \frac{\partial U}{\partial u} \end{bmatrix} \begin{bmatrix} \frac{\partial u}{\partial x} \\ \frac{\partial v}{\partial x} \\ \frac{\partial w}{\partial x} \\ \frac{\partial s}{\partial x} \end{bmatrix} \qquad (2.175)$$

The matrix in (2.175) has been transformed into an element of $\mathbb{D}$. We next recognize by the arguments leading up to the vector-matrix notation in (2.161) that (2.175) is equivalent to

$$\frac{\partial \mathrm{F}}{\partial x} = \frac{\partial \mathrm{F}}{\partial u}\frac{\partial \mathrm{G}}{\partial x}\,, \qquad (2.176)$$

then we apply the appropriate notational variations of (2.169) to get

$$\frac{\partial \mathrm{F}}{\partial x} = \frac{d\mathrm{F}}{d\mathbf{Z}} \qquad \frac{\partial \mathrm{F}}{\partial u} = \frac{d\mathrm{F}}{d\mathrm{G}} \qquad \frac{\partial \mathrm{G}}{\partial x} = \frac{d\mathrm{G}}{d\mathbf{Z}}\ ; \qquad (2.177)$$

hence (2.175) is converted to the usual *chain rule for derivatives*:

$$\frac{\mathrm{dF}}{\mathrm{d}\mathbf{Z}} = \frac{\mathrm{dF}}{\mathrm{dG}}\frac{\mathrm{dG}}{\mathrm{d}\mathbf{Z}}\,. \qquad (2.178)$$

2.3.10 A Lie Algebra Over The $\mathbb{D}$ Space

For the physicists among us, a Lie algebra can be constructed over ordered n-tuples of complex numbers, including the case of pairs of complex numbers that we have here. Hermann[48], for example, gives the details, which are beyond the scope of this work.

The $\mathbb{D}$-space Lie algebra is attractive for physics applications for several reasons. It can be represented in vector notation, all-matrix notation (either 4 X 4 real or 2 X 2 complex), or as ordered pairs of complex numbers. We have an explicit function theory, with corresponding definitions for any classical function of a complex variable. Moreover, we have a complete and rich system of analysis, beginning with classically-behaving derivative and integral operations, in which we may apply the four-dimensional analogue of any classical complex variable operation. Even more importantly, we shall see in the last chapter that much of special relativity is implicit in the $\mathbb{D}$-space algebra, and that a relativity transform group corresponding to the Lorentz group fits quite naturally into the $\mathbb{D}$-space mathematics.

III. 𝔻-SPACE OPERATIONS RELATED TO CLASSICAL VECTOR ANALYSIS

3.1 Classical Vector Operator Analogues In 𝔻

This chapter will develop the 𝔻-space analogues or equivalents of the main classical vector analysis operations, in order to facilitate a comparison and reconciliation of results between the two systems. As a side benefit, we shall see the vectorial aspects of the 𝔻-space and a formulation of the more useful vectorial operations. The 𝔻-space formulations will be constructed such that the classical vector analysis results may be easily deduced from them, because in this way we shall have a correctness check. We emphasize that we are not claiming that the 𝔻-space mathematics are somehow "more correct," but we are claiming that the new system as a whole is a more efficient, concise, and illuminating means for doing an important body of science and engineering calculations.

As an explicit test of the newly-constructed 𝔻-space operators, Maxwell's equations will be stated in the 𝔻-space and then will be manipulated to obtain the classical vector analysis results. It will be shown that the electromagnetic field, indeed any conservative force field as defined by physics theory, can be treated as a four-dimensional analytic function, and that several important field theory results follow naturally from function theory, alone. The largest gain, however, will be computational simplicity and power arising from commutativity and complex analysis techniques.

It will be shown that the form and results of the classical vector analysis, especially as regards the sign combinations, are determined by the underlying algebra (the quaternion algebra). The $\mathbb{D}$-space algebra produces similar forms and results, up to only a differing sign pattern, and the results produced by the two will be reconciled by means of unitary transformations or other mappings as a last step in the calculation. It will be demonstrated in several places that the $\mathbb{D}$-space formulation of a theorem or operation is far more concise and illuminating than the corresponding classical vector analysis formulation, and that subsequent results follow far more easily. The largest part of the material in this chapter will be stated in terms of matrices and classical vector forms, expressly for the purpose of comparison with the classical work.

The program for the following sections will be to first present the classical vector analysis operator/operation, then develop the corresponding $\mathbb{D}$-space form. **Note**: for the rest of the book, "ct" will be used in place of the "t" which has been used to develop the hypercomplex algebra and function theory. In this way, the coordinates x,y,z,ct can represent points in the real universe of physics.

3.1.1 Elementary Multiplication

A large part of the differences in form between classical vector analysis forms and operations and the corresponding $\mathbb{D}$-space forms is due to a sign pattern difference resulting from the basis group multiplication rules. In the following, the multiplication rules for the two systems will be compared. For later purposes, we will also show how the vector dot and cross products relate to quaternion multiplication.

■ *Quaternion Multiplication Rules*

$$\begin{array}{llll} \mathbf{ij} = \mathbf{k} & \mathbf{jk} = \mathbf{i} & \mathbf{ki} = \mathbf{j} & \\ \mathbf{ji} = -\mathbf{k} & \mathbf{kj} = -\mathbf{i} & \mathbf{ik} = -\mathbf{j} & \text{(Anticommutative)} \qquad (3.1) \\ \mathbf{ii} = \mathbf{jj} = \mathbf{kk} = -\mathbf{1} & \mathbf{ijk} = -\mathbf{1} & & \end{array}$$

$$\begin{aligned} \mathbf{Z}_1\mathbf{Z}_2 = {} & \mathbf{1}\,(x_1x_2 - y_1y_2 - z_1z_2 - ct_1ct_2) \\ & + \mathbf{i}\,(y_1x_2 + x_1y_2 + ct_1z_2 - z_1ct_2) \\ & + \mathbf{j}\,(z_1x_2 - ct_1y_2 + x_1z_2 + y_1ct_2) \\ & + \mathbf{k}\,(ct_1x_2 + z_1y_2 - y_1z_2 + x_1ct_2) \neq \mathbf{Z}_2\mathbf{Z}_1\,. \end{aligned} \qquad (3.2)$$

■ $\mathbb{D}$-*Space Multiplication Rules*

$$\begin{array}{lll} \mathbf{ij} = \mathbf{k} & \mathbf{jk} = -\mathbf{i} & \mathbf{ki} = -\mathbf{j} \\ \mathbf{ji} = \mathbf{k} & \mathbf{kj} = -\mathbf{i} & \mathbf{ik} = -\mathbf{j} \\ \mathbf{ii} = \mathbf{jj} = -\mathbf{kk} = -1 & & \mathbf{ijk} = 1 \end{array} \qquad \text{(Commutative)} \qquad (3.3)$$

$$\begin{aligned} \mathbf{Z}_1\mathbf{Z}_2 = \mathbf{1}\,(& x_1x_2 - y_1y_2 - z_1z_2 + ct_1ct_2) \\ + \mathbf{i}\,(& y_1x_2 + x_1y_2 - ct_1z_2 - z_1ct_2) \\ + \mathbf{j}\,(& z_1x_2 - ct_1y_2 + x_1z_2 - y_1ct_2) \\ + \mathbf{k}\,(& ct_1x_2 + z_1y_2 + y_1z_2 + x_1ct_2) = \mathbf{Z}_2\mathbf{Z}_1\,. \end{aligned} \qquad (3.4)$$

It is clear that multiplication is the same in principle except for sign pattern differences and commutativity. This same sign pattern difference will appear throughout all the forms comparisons which will be made below, and it will be helpful to remember that it arises solely from the underlying algebra. Our examples below will illustrate that all the classical vector analysis forms have counterparts in the $\mathbb{D}$-space which have all the same terms, but with a different sign pattern.

■ *The 3-D Vector Cross Product (Outer Product)*

The cross products among the basis elements obey the following rules:

$$\begin{array}{lll} \mathbf{i}\mathsf{X}\mathbf{j} = \mathbf{k} & \mathbf{j}\mathsf{X}\mathbf{k} = \mathbf{i} & \mathbf{k}\mathsf{X}\mathbf{i} = \mathbf{j} \\ \mathbf{j}\mathsf{X}\mathbf{i} = -\mathbf{k} & \mathbf{k}\mathsf{X}\mathbf{j} = -\mathbf{i} & \mathbf{i}\mathsf{X}\mathbf{k} = -\mathbf{j} \\ \mathbf{i}\mathsf{X}\mathbf{i} = \mathbf{j}\mathsf{X}\mathbf{j} = \mathbf{k}\mathsf{X}\mathbf{k} = 0 & & \mathbf{i}\mathsf{X}\mathbf{j}\mathsf{X}\mathbf{k} = 0\,. \end{array} \qquad (3.5)$$

As a consequence, the cross product between two three-dimensional vectors is as follows: let

$$\begin{aligned} \mathbf{A} &= A_1\mathbf{i} + A_2\mathbf{j} + A_3\mathbf{k} \\ \mathbf{B} &= B_1\mathbf{i} + B_2\mathbf{j} + B_3\mathbf{k}\,; \end{aligned} \qquad (3.6)$$

then

$$
\begin{aligned}
\mathbf{AXB} &= (A_1\mathbf{i} + A_2\mathbf{j} + A_3\mathbf{k}) \times (B_1\mathbf{i} + B_2\mathbf{j} + B_3\mathbf{k}) \\
&= A_1B_1\, \mathbf{iXi} + A_1B_2\, \mathbf{iXj} + A_1B_3\, \mathbf{iXk} \\
&\quad + A_2B_1\, \mathbf{jXi} + A_2B_2\, \mathbf{jXj} + A_2B_3\, \mathbf{jXk} \\
&\quad + A_3B_1\, \mathbf{kXi} + A_3B_2\, \mathbf{kXj} + A_3B_3\, \mathbf{kXk} \\
&= A_1B_1(0) + A_1B_2\,\mathbf{k} - A_1B_3\,\mathbf{j} \\
&\quad - A_2B_1\,\mathbf{k} + A_2B_2(0) + A_2B_3\,\mathbf{i} \\
&\quad + A_3B_1\,\mathbf{j} - A_3B_2\,\mathbf{i} + A_3B_3(0) \\
&= \mathbf{i}(A_2B_3 - A_3B_2) + \mathbf{j}(A_3B_1 - A_1B_3) + \mathbf{k}(A_1B_2 - A_2B_1).
\end{aligned}
\tag{3.7}
$$

Comparing the quaternion multiplication rules (3.1) and the cross product rules (3.5), one can see that they are the same except for those products of a unit vector with itself; e.g., **ii**=−**1**, but **iXi** =0. Why was the cross product defined in this way? In the author's opinion, so that the cross product of two vectors with **i**,**j**,**k** terms will be another vector with only **i**,**j**,**k** terms (i.e. closure under the cross product operation with three-dimensional vectors). In effect, Gibbs and Heaviside took part of the quaternion product, gave it its own notation, and called it the cross product (or outer product). One might suspect that the remaining part of the quaternion product was given some meaning, and it was, as follows.

■ *The 3-D Vector Dot Product (Inner Product)*

Defining **A** and **B** as in (3.6), one has

$$\mathbf{A} \bullet \mathbf{B} = A_1B_1 + A_2B_2 + A_3B_3. \tag{3.8}$$

The dot product is the "missing part" of the quaternion product when only the cross product is performed, because the full quaternion product of two **i**,**j**,**k** vectors is

$$\mathbf{AB} = -\mathbf{A} \bullet \mathbf{B} + \mathbf{AXB} \qquad (\mathbf{A},\mathbf{B} \text{ three-dimensional}). \tag{3.9}$$

By these devices, Gibbs and Heaviside constrained their notation so that only three-dimensional vectors would ever appear. Additionally, they were able to use the quantities **A • B** and **A X B** in a natural way to describe two distinct aspects of conservative force fields in physics. Nevertheless, the quaternion notation is implicit in the vector notation. In the present view, vector analysis is quaternion analysis constrained to three dimensions.

Vector Operations In D-Space Notation

We have seen that the vector dot product and the vector cross product are merely two terms in the quaternion product of two three-dimensional vector entities and that the quaternion and D-space hypercomplex products have closely similar forms, up to sign pattern. For later use, we generate the following correspondences, using vectors of the form

$$\begin{aligned} \mathbf{A} &= A_1\mathbf{i} + A_2\mathbf{j} + A_3\mathbf{k} \\ \mathbf{B} &= B_1\mathbf{i} + B_2\mathbf{j} + B_3\mathbf{k}. \end{aligned} \qquad (3.10)$$

Vector Dot Product:

$$\begin{aligned} \mathbf{A} \cdot \mathbf{B} &= A_1B_1 + A_2B_2 + A_3B_3 && \text{(Classical)} \\ &\rightarrow A_1B_1 + A_2B_2 - A_3\,B_3\,. && \text{(D-space)} \end{aligned} \qquad (3.11)$$

Vector Cross Product:

$$\begin{aligned} \mathbf{A}\times\mathbf{B} &= \mathbf{i}(A_2B_3 - A_3B_2) + \mathbf{j}(A_3B_1 - A_1B_3) + \mathbf{k}(A_1B_2 - A_2B_1) && \text{(Classical)} \\ &\rightarrow -\mathbf{i}(A_2B_3 + A_3B_2) + -\mathbf{j}(A_3B_1 + A_1B_3) + -\mathbf{k}(A_1B_2 + A_2B_1) && \text{(D-space)} \end{aligned} \qquad (3.12)$$

The important thing to observe is that *the corresponding terms are the same except for sign, and the sign patterns are fixed and are due to the properties of the underlying algebras.* If one is given a hypercomplex vector result in the D-space, the corresponding classical vector result may be stated by inspection, and vice-versa. One may carry out any desired calculation in the D-space, taking advantage of commutativity and the wide range of complex analysis techniques, and then may state the final results in classical vector analysis terms. We emphasize that the two systems cannot be mixed at any intermediate step.

Another way to state the conversion of results between the quaternion algebra and the D-space algebra is as follows. There is a one-to-one mapping of elements between the two systems, up to sign, indicated by

$$\mathrm{Q}(x,y,z,ct) \rightarrow \mathbb{D}(x,y,z,ct)$$

$$\begin{bmatrix} x & y & z & ct \\ -y & x & -ct & z \\ -z & ct & x & -y \\ -ct & -z & y & x \end{bmatrix} \rightarrow \begin{bmatrix} x & -y & -z & ct \\ y & x & -ct & -z \\ z & -ct & x & -y \\ ct & z & y & x \end{bmatrix} . \quad (3.13)$$

The components x,y,z,ct may be the fundamental coordinates in either system or may themselves be functions of the underlying coordinates. In particular when the final result is a product, as in this section, then the present approach is especially applicable. The story of applied vector analysis is largely written in terms of gradient, divergence, and curl, all of which are product operations obeying quaternion rules.

It is important to note that one cannot construct a similarity transformation between the two matrices in (3.13), because they implicitly carry the commutativity characteristics of two different rings, one commutative and one not.

3.1.2 The Inner Product And Four-Dimensional Length

The length of a real, Cartesian vector (x,y,z) is its inner product with itself:

$$|\mathbf{X}|^2 = \mathbf{X} \cdot \mathbf{X} = x^2 + y^2 + z^2. \quad (3.14)$$

For the corresponding $\mathbb{D}$-space element/vector (x,y,z,ct), the formulation is the same:

$$|\mathbf{Z}|^2 = \mathbf{Z} \cdot \mathbf{Z} = x^2 + y^2 + z^2 + c^2t^2. \quad (3.15)$$

In theoretical physics and other science and engineering calculations, it is common to encounter vectors whose components are complex variables or constants. As discussed in Section 2.2.12, one could construct a "complex $\mathbb{D}$-space" whose elements have classical complex variables as components. In such a case, the length of a vector would be found by taking the dot product of the vector with a component-wise complex conjugate of itself, which is the classical method.

3.1.3 The Transpose Of A Hypercomplex Element

This operation must be done in the matrix formulation, and is not a common classical vector analysis operation. We will instead compare with the classical complex variable form. The ordinary complex variable can be represented by

$$z = \begin{bmatrix} x & -y \\ y & x \end{bmatrix} \quad ; \tag{3.16}$$

then the *transpose* is

$$z^{\mathrm{T}} = \begin{bmatrix} x & y \\ -y & x \end{bmatrix} \quad ; \tag{3.17}$$

This is the same as

$$z^{\mathrm{T}} = z^{*}. \tag{3.18}$$

The corresponding hypercomplex variable is

$$\mathbf{Z} = \begin{bmatrix} x & -y & -z & ct \\ y & x & -ct & -z \\ z & -ct & x & -y \\ ct & z & y & x \end{bmatrix} , \tag{3.19}$$

with transpose

$$\mathbf{Z}^{\mathrm{T}} = \begin{bmatrix} x & y & z & ct \\ -y & x & -ct & z \\ -z & -ct & x & y \\ ct & -z & -y & x \end{bmatrix} , \tag{3.20}$$

As shown in Sec. (2.2.9), in the vector canonical form this is the same as

$$\mathbf{Z}^{\mathrm{T}} = \xi^* \mathbf{e}_1 + \eta^* \mathbf{e}_2 = \mathbf{Z}^*, \tag{3.21}$$

where

$$\xi = (x-ct) + \mathbf{i}(y+z) \tag{3.22}$$

$$\eta = (x+ct) + \mathbf{i}(y-z).$$

The complex variable quantity

$$zz^{\mathrm{T}} = zz^*$$

is the real scalar length of z. The corresponding hypercomplex quantity

$$\mathbf{ZZ}^{\mathrm{T}} = \mathbf{ZZ}^*$$

has all the same properties (Section 2.3.1), except is still a hypercomplex quantity lying in the **1**,**k**-plane (see 2.66). The real scalar length of $\mathbf{Z}$ in terms of the hypercomplex transpose (conjugate) is

$$|\mathbf{Z}| = |\mathbf{ZZ}^*|^{1/2} = \{[|\xi|^2 + |\eta|^2]/2\}^{1/2}$$
$$= [x^2 + y^2 + z^2 + c^2t^2]^{1/2}, \tag{3.23}$$

when x,y,z,ct are all real. In two dimensions (complex variables), (3.23) is

$$|z| = (zz^*)^{1/2}, \tag{3.24}$$

thus, because of the way the $\mathbb{D}$-space hypercomplex conjugate is defined, (2.88), we have had to apply the absolute value operation one extra time to get the real scalar four-dimensional length.

3.1.4 The Gradient Operator

The typical three-dimensional position vector is

$$\mathbf{X} = \mathbf{i}x + \mathbf{j}y + \mathbf{k}z, \tag{3.25}$$

and the *gradient operator* is

$$\nabla = \mathbf{i}\frac{\partial}{\partial x} + \mathbf{j}\frac{\partial}{\partial y} + \mathbf{k}\frac{\partial}{\partial z} \quad . \tag{3.26}$$

The corresponding $\mathbb{D}$-space element is

$$\mathbf{Z} = \mathbf{1}x + \mathbf{i}y + \mathbf{j}z + \mathbf{k}ct, \tag{3.27}$$

with a gradient operator

$$\Box = \mathbf{1}\frac{\partial}{\partial x} + \mathbf{i}\frac{\partial}{\partial y} + \mathbf{j}\frac{\partial}{\partial z} + \mathbf{k}\frac{\partial}{\partial ct} \quad . \tag{3.28}$$

Comparing (3.25) and (3.27), one observes that the vector coordinates x,y,z are associated with different basis vectors **i**,**j**,**k** in the two different systems. The former arose quite naturally from the idea of Cartesian coordinates in three dimensions, and the latter was adopted in the present work because it is a natural extension of the classical complex variable notation (i.e., $x+iy$). We shall use the two notational systems as stated; but one could, for display purposes only, convert from the $\mathbb{D}$-space form (3.27) to the classical vector form (3.25) by rotating the coordinates to the right: $x\rightarrow y$, $y\rightarrow z$, $z\rightarrow ct$, $ct\rightarrow x$, to obtain the typical element

$$\mathbf{Z}' = \mathbf{1}ct + \mathbf{i}x + \mathbf{j}y + \mathbf{k}z, \tag{3.29}$$

with the transformed gradient operator

$$\Box' = \mathbf{1}\frac{\partial}{\partial ct} + \mathbf{i}\frac{\partial}{\partial x} + \mathbf{j}\frac{\partial}{\partial y} + \mathbf{k}\frac{\partial}{\partial z} \quad . \tag{3.30}$$

The orthogonal transformation

$$\begin{bmatrix} x' \\ y' \\ z' \\ ct' \end{bmatrix} = \begin{bmatrix} 0 & 0 & 0 & 1 \\ 1 & 0 & 0 & 0 \\ 0 & 1 & 0 & 0 \\ 0 & 0 & 1 & 0 \end{bmatrix} \begin{bmatrix} x \\ y \\ z \\ ct \end{bmatrix} \tag{3.31}$$

produces the transformation (3.29) of the coordinates. Note that the transformation matrix in (3.31) is not an element of $\mathbb{D}$, hence should not be intermixed with calculations in the $\mathbb{D}$-space; but (3.31) is an example of how one may transform the final results of a $\mathbb{D}$-space operation by means of orthogonal or unitary transformations to allow comparison with established forms or results from classical vector analysis. We again emphasize that (3.30) will not produce classical vector results, at least not directly, because of the differing basis groups. More discussion on this aspect will be given below.

■ *Gradient Of A Hypercomplex Function*—As a first application of the hypercomplex gradient operator (3.28), one may calculate the four-dimensional gradient of a hypercomplex, analytic function

$$F(\mathbf{Z}) = \mathbf{1}X + \mathbf{i}Y + \mathbf{j}Z + \mathbf{k}T: \tag{3.32}$$

$$\begin{aligned}\Box\, F(\mathbf{Z}) = {} & \mathbf{1}\left(\frac{\partial X}{\partial x} - \frac{\partial Y}{\partial y} - \frac{\partial Z}{\partial z} + \frac{\partial T}{\partial ct}\right) \\ & + \mathbf{i}\left(\frac{\partial X}{\partial y} + \frac{\partial Y}{\partial x} - \frac{\partial Z}{\partial ct} - \frac{\partial T}{\partial z}\right) \\ & + \mathbf{j}\left(\frac{\partial X}{\partial z} - \frac{\partial Y}{\partial ct} + \frac{\partial Z}{\partial x} - \frac{\partial T}{\partial y}\right) \\ & + \mathbf{k}\left(\frac{\partial X}{\partial ct} + \frac{\partial Y}{\partial z} + \frac{\partial Z}{\partial y} + \frac{\partial T}{\partial x}\right)\end{aligned} \tag{3.33}$$

By "gradient," in the rest of the book we shall mean the hypercomplex gradient as defined (3.33), unless otherwise indicated. In classical vector analysis the term usually means the gradient operator applied to a scalar function as illustrated in the next section.

■ *The Gradient Of A Real Analytic Function*—Suppose one has a scalar analytic function $\Psi(x, y, z, ct)$ of four real variables; then the hypercomplex gradient is

$$\Box\, \Psi = \mathbf{1}\frac{\partial \Psi}{\partial x} + \mathbf{i}\frac{\partial \Psi}{\partial y} + \mathbf{j}\frac{\partial \Psi}{\partial z} + \mathbf{k}\frac{\partial \Psi}{\partial ct}\,. \tag{3.34}$$

The classical vector gradient is similar except it has only three dimensions:

$$\nabla\ \Psi = \mathbf{i}\frac{\partial \Psi}{\partial x} + \mathbf{j}\ \frac{\partial \Psi}{\partial y} + \mathbf{k}\ \frac{\partial \Psi}{\partial z}\ . \tag{3.35}$$

3.1.5 Relationship Of Gradient To Vector Divergence And Curl

The hypercomplex gradient is a $\mathbb{D}$-space product corresponding to the quaternion product (3.9) of the ∇ operator with a three-dimensional vector function. The quaternion product is a sum of the vector divergence and the curl of a three-dimensional vector function. Suppose one has a vector function

$$\mathbf{F} = \mathbf{i}X + \mathbf{j}Y + \mathbf{k}Z \tag{3.36}$$

and a gradient operator

$$\nabla\ = \mathbf{i}\frac{\partial}{\partial x} + \mathbf{j}\ \frac{\partial}{\partial y} + \mathbf{k}\ \frac{\partial}{\partial z}\ . \tag{3.37}$$

involving the three coordinates x, y, z; then, from (3.9), their quaternion product has the form

$$\begin{aligned} \nabla\ \mathbf{F} = & -\mathbf{1}\left(\frac{\partial X}{\partial x} + \frac{\partial Y}{\partial y} + \frac{\partial Z}{\partial z}\right) \\ & + \mathbf{i}\left(\frac{\partial Z}{\partial y} - \frac{\partial Y}{\partial z}\right) \\ & + \mathbf{j}\left(\frac{\partial X}{\partial z} - \frac{\partial Z}{\partial x}\right) \\ & + \mathbf{k}\left(\frac{\partial Y}{\partial x} - \frac{\partial X}{\partial y}\right) \\ = & -\nabla \bullet \mathbf{F} + \nabla\ \mathrm{X}\ \mathbf{F} \qquad (\mathbf{F}\text{ is three-dimensional}). \end{aligned} \tag{3.38}$$

To enable a comparison, we reduce the $\mathbb{D}$-space form, (3.33), to something involving only three coordinates by eliminating all terms involving T or ct:

$$\begin{aligned}\square\, \mathrm{F(Z)} \rightarrow \mathbf{1}&\left(\frac{\partial X}{\partial x} - \frac{\partial Y}{\partial y} - \frac{\partial Z}{\partial z}\right)\\ + \mathbf{i}&\left(\frac{\partial X}{\partial y} + \frac{\partial Y}{\partial x}\right)\\ + \mathbf{j}&\left(\frac{\partial X}{\partial z} + \frac{\partial Z}{\partial x}\right)\\ + \mathbf{k}&\left(\frac{\partial Y}{\partial z} + \frac{\partial Z}{\partial y}\right)\end{aligned} \tag{3.39}$$

Comparing (3.38) and (3.39), one observes that all the same terms are present but have differing signs in some cases and are associated with different basis vectors in others. The basis vector differences arise because of the way in which the position vector and function notations are defined in the two systems [compare (3.25) with (3.27) and (3.32) with (3.33)]. For several reasons which are clear only in the overall context, we intend to retain the $\mathbb{D}$-space notation. We must, therefore, find another way to reconcile the $\mathbb{D}$-space result (3.39) with the classical vector result (3.38). The form (3.39) may be treated as a vector expression, hence may be transformed as follows: let

$$A = \begin{bmatrix} 1 & 0 & 0 & 0 \\ 0 & 0 & 0 & 1 \\ 0 & 0 & 1 & 0 \\ 0 & 1 & 0 & 0 \end{bmatrix} \tag{3.40}$$

and $\mathbf{W} = \square\ \mathrm{F}(\mathbf{Z});$

then $\mathbf{W}' = \mathrm{A}\,\mathbf{W}$

$$= \mathbf{1}\left(\frac{\partial X}{\partial x} - \frac{\partial Y}{\partial y} - \frac{\partial Z}{\partial z}\right) + \mathbf{i}\left(\frac{\partial Y}{\partial z} + \frac{\partial Z}{\partial y}\right) + \mathbf{j}\left(\frac{\partial X}{\partial z} + \frac{\partial Z}{\partial x}\right) + \mathbf{k}\left(\frac{\partial X}{\partial y} + \frac{\partial Y}{\partial x}\right)$$

$$= \mathbf{1}\left(\frac{\partial X}{\partial x} - \frac{\partial Y}{\partial y} - \frac{\partial Z}{\partial z}\right) + \mathbf{i}\left(\frac{\partial Z}{\partial y} + \frac{\partial Y}{\partial z}\right) + \mathbf{j}\left(\frac{\partial X}{\partial z} + \frac{\partial Z}{\partial x}\right) + \mathbf{k}\left(\frac{\partial Y}{\partial x} + \frac{\partial X}{\partial y}\right) \qquad (3.41)$$

Now all the same terms are present, but have a different sign pattern. The sign pattern is fixed and is due to the underlying algebra, hence if we have a $\mathbb{D}$-space expression like (3.33) we can immediately write the corresponding classical vector expression (3.38).

3.1.6 Relationship Of Gradient To The Hypercomplex Derivative

The derivative, (2.168), and the hypercomplex gradient, (3.33), both involve only first partial derivatives with respect to the coordinates x,y,z,ct, hence both, in some sense, measure the space variation of the function at a point. One might suspect that they are related in some way, and they are. Suppose one has a hypercomplex function

$$\mathrm{F}(\mathbf{Z}) = \mathbf{1}X + \mathbf{i}Y + \mathbf{j}Z + \mathbf{k}T; \qquad (3.42)$$

then

$$\square^{\mathrm{T}}\mathrm{F}(\mathbf{Z}) = \mathbf{1}\Big(\frac{\partial X}{\partial x} + \frac{\partial Y}{\partial y} + \frac{\partial Z}{\partial z} + \frac{\partial T}{\partial ct}\Big)$$
$$+\ \mathbf{i}\Big(-\frac{\partial X}{\partial y} + \frac{\partial Y}{\partial x} - \frac{\partial Z}{\partial ct} + \frac{\partial T}{\partial z}\Big)$$
$$+\ \mathbf{j}\Big(-\frac{\partial X}{\partial z} - \frac{\partial Y}{\partial ct} + \frac{\partial Z}{\partial x} + \frac{\partial T}{\partial y}\Big) \tag{3.43}$$
$$+\ \mathbf{k}\Big(\frac{\partial X}{\partial ct} - \frac{\partial Y}{\partial z} - \frac{\partial Z}{\partial y} + \frac{\partial T}{\partial x}\Big) .$$

One may apply the C-R conditions, (2.156), to (3.43) to obtain

$$\square^{\mathrm{T}}\mathrm{F}(\mathbf{Z}) = \mathbf{1}\Big(\frac{\partial X}{\partial x} + \frac{\partial X}{\partial x} + \frac{\partial X}{\partial x} + \frac{\partial X}{\partial x}\Big)$$
$$+\ \mathbf{i}\Big(\frac{\partial Y}{\partial x} + \frac{\partial Y}{\partial x} + \frac{\partial Y}{\partial x} + \frac{\partial Y}{\partial x}\Big)$$
$$+\ \mathbf{j}\Big(\frac{\partial Z}{\partial x} + \frac{\partial Z}{\partial x} + \frac{\partial Z}{\partial x} + \frac{\partial Z}{\partial x}\Big) \tag{3.44}$$
$$+\ \mathbf{k}\Big(\frac{\partial T}{\partial x} + \frac{\partial T}{\partial x} + \frac{\partial T}{\partial x} + \frac{\partial T}{\partial x}\Big)$$
$$= \mathbf{1}\, 4\frac{\partial \boldsymbol{X}}{\partial x} + \mathbf{i}\, 4\frac{\partial \boldsymbol{Y}}{\partial x} + \mathbf{j}\, 4\frac{\partial \boldsymbol{Z}}{\partial x} + \mathbf{k}\, 4\frac{\partial \boldsymbol{T}}{\partial x}$$
$$= 4\,\frac{\partial \mathrm{F}}{\partial x} .$$

Now, using (2.168), one may write

$$\square^{\mathrm{T}}\mathrm{F} = 4\,\frac{d\mathrm{F}}{d\mathbf{Z}} . \tag{3.45}$$

3.1.7 The D'Alembertian Operator

We shall define the $\mathbb{D}$-space D'Alembertian operator as follows:

$$\Box^2 = \Box \cdot \Box$$

$$= \frac{\partial^2}{\partial x^2} + \frac{\partial^2}{\partial y^2} + \frac{\partial^2}{\partial z^2} + \frac{1}{c^2}\frac{\partial^2}{\partial t^2}. \tag{3.46}$$

The corresponding classical vector operator is

$$\Box^2 = \nabla \cdot \nabla - \frac{1}{c^2}\frac{\partial^2}{\partial t^2}$$

$$= \frac{\partial^2}{\partial x^2} + \frac{\partial^2}{\partial y^2} + \frac{\partial^2}{\partial z^2} - \frac{1}{c^2}\frac{\partial^2}{\partial t^2}. \tag{3.47}$$

■ *The D'Alembertian Of A Hypercomplex Function*—The D'Alembertian is a scalar operation. If applied to a hypercomplex (vector) function

$$\mathrm{F}(\mathbf{Z}) = \mathbf{1}X + \mathbf{i}Y + \mathbf{j}Z + \mathbf{k}T,$$

it is applied term-by-term, as follows:

$$\Box^2\mathrm{F} = \mathbf{1}\Box^2 X + \mathbf{i}\Box^2 Y + \mathbf{j}\Box^2 Z + \mathbf{k}\Box^2 T. \tag{3.48}$$

The corresponding classical vector operation is

$$\Box^2\mathbf{F} = \mathbf{i}\Box^2 X + \mathbf{j}\Box^2 Y + \mathbf{k}\Box^2 Z, \tag{3.49}$$

where $\Box$ has the classical definition, (3.47).

■ *Relationship To The Hypercomplex Second Derivative*—The hypercomplex D'Alembertian is related to the second derivative of a hypercomplex function in a way similar to its relationship to the first derivative; as a result of (2.168) one has

$$\frac{d\mathrm{F}}{d\mathbf{Z}} = \frac{\partial \mathrm{F}}{\partial x};$$

and, applying the same operation again,

$$\frac{d^2\mathrm{F}}{d\mathbf{Z}^2} = \frac{\partial^2 \mathrm{F}}{\partial x^2} \, . \tag{3.50}$$

This is probably the simplest definition, or interpretation, of the second derivativ operation. At the other extreme, one may view the operation as being simila to the quaternion product $\nabla^2\mathbf{F}$, as follows. From (3.45), one may write

$$\frac{d\mathrm{F}}{d\mathbf{Z}} = (1/4)\ \Box^{\mathrm{T}}\mathrm{F}\ ;$$

$$\frac{d^2\mathbf{F}}{d\mathbf{Z}^2} = (1/16)\ (\Box^2)^{\mathrm{T}}\mathrm{F}\ ; \tag{3.51}$$

Form (3.51) is the result that we were seeking, but it is interesting to se how it expands:

$$\begin{aligned} \frac{\mathbf{d}^2\mathbf{F}}{d\mathbf{Z}^2} = (1/16)\ [\mathbf{i}\ &(\frac{\partial^2}{\partial x^2} - \frac{\partial^2}{\partial y^2} - \frac{\partial^2}{\partial z^2} + \frac{\partial^2}{\partial c^2 t^2}) \\ + \mathbf{i}\ &(\frac{\partial^2}{\partial y \partial x} + \frac{\partial^2}{\partial x \partial y} - \frac{\partial^2}{\partial ct \partial z} - \frac{\partial^2}{\partial z \partial ct}) \\ + \mathbf{j}\ &(\frac{\partial^2}{\partial z \partial x} - \frac{\partial^2}{\partial ct \partial y} + \frac{\partial^2}{\partial x \partial z} - \frac{\partial^2}{\partial y \partial ct}) \\ + \mathbf{k}\ &(\frac{\partial^2}{\partial ct \partial x} + \frac{\partial^2}{\partial z \partial y} + \frac{\partial^2}{\partial y \partial z} + \frac{\partial^2}{\partial x \partial ct})\ ]^{\mathrm{T}}\mathrm{F}\, . \end{aligned}$$

Now consider the unitary transformation of coordinates

$$\begin{bmatrix} x' \\ y' \\ z' \\ ct' \end{bmatrix} = \begin{bmatrix} 1 & 0 & 0 & 0 \\ 0 & i & 0 & 0 \\ 0 & 0 & i & 0 \\ 0 & 0 & 0 & 1 \end{bmatrix} \begin{bmatrix} x \\ y \\ z \\ ct \end{bmatrix} , \tag{3.52}$$

where "i" is the classical pure imaginary, distinct from the hypercomplex **i**. This transformation takes (3.51) into

$$\frac{d^2\mathrm{F}}{d\mathbf{Z}'^2} = (1/16)\ (\square'^2)^{\mathrm{T}}\mathrm{F} \tag{3.53}$$

$$\begin{aligned} \rightarrow (1/16)\ [\mathbf{1} & \left(\frac{\partial^2}{\partial x^2} + \frac{\partial^2}{\partial y^2} + \frac{\partial^2}{\partial z^2} + \frac{\partial^2}{\partial c^2 t^2}\right) \\ & - \mathbf{i}\,i \left(\frac{\partial^2}{\partial y \partial x} + \frac{\partial^2}{\partial x \partial y} - \frac{\partial^2}{\partial ct \partial z} - \frac{\partial^2}{\partial z \partial ct}\right) \\ & - \mathbf{j}\,i \left(\frac{\partial^2}{\partial z \partial x} - \frac{\partial^2}{\partial ct \partial y} + \frac{\partial^2}{\partial x \partial z} - \frac{\partial^2}{\partial y \partial ct}\right) \\ & - \mathbf{k}\,i \left(\frac{\partial^2}{\partial ct \partial x} + \frac{\partial^2}{\partial z \partial y} + \frac{\partial^2}{\partial y \partial z} + \frac{\partial^2}{\partial x \partial ct}\right)]^{\mathrm{T}}\mathrm{F}\,. \end{aligned}$$

We have used the → to avoid the messiness of so many (′) marks. With analytic functions, the order of taking the partial derivatives does not matter, hence one may collect terms:

$$\begin{aligned} \frac{d^2\mathrm{F}}{d\mathbf{Z}'^2} \rightarrow (1/16)\ [\mathbf{1} & \left(\frac{\partial^2}{\partial x^2} + \frac{\partial^2}{\partial y^2} + \frac{\partial^2}{\partial z^2} + \frac{\partial^2}{\partial c^2 t^2}\right) \\ & - \mathbf{i}\ (2i) \left(\frac{\partial^2}{\partial y \partial x} - \frac{\partial^2}{\partial z \partial ct}\right) \\ & - \mathbf{j}\ (2i) \left(\frac{\partial^2}{\partial z \partial x} - \frac{\partial^2}{\partial ct \partial y}\right) \\ & - \mathbf{k}\ (2i) \left(\frac{\partial^2}{\partial ct \partial x} + \frac{\partial^2}{\partial z \partial y}\right)]^{\mathrm{T}}\mathrm{F} \end{aligned} \tag{3.54}$$

$$= (1/16)\ [\mathbf{1}\ \Box^2 \mathrm{F}$$

$$+\ \mathbf{i}\ (2i)\left(\frac{\partial^2 \mathrm{F}}{\partial y \partial x} - \frac{\partial^2 \mathrm{F}}{\partial z \partial ct}\right)$$

$$+\ \mathbf{j}\ (2i)\left(\frac{\partial^2 \mathrm{F}}{\partial z \partial x} - \frac{\partial^2 \mathrm{F}}{\partial ct \partial y}\right) \qquad \text{(F is hypercomplex)}$$

$$-\ \mathbf{k}\ (2i)\left(\frac{\partial^2 \mathrm{F}}{\partial ct \partial x} + \frac{\partial^2 \mathrm{F}}{\partial z \partial y}\right)]\ .$$

We shall see later that $\Box^2\ \mathrm{F} \equiv 0$, hence under this particular transformational viewpoint the expansion of the second derivative of every analytic hypercomplex function always has a term which explicitly satisfies four dimensional wave behavior.

■ *The D'Alembertian Of A Scalar Analytic Function*—Suppose one has a scalar analytic function $\Psi(x,y,z,ct)$ of four real variables; then the hypercomplex D'Alembertian operation is defined to be

$$\Box^2\ \Psi = \frac{\partial^2 \Psi}{\partial x^2} + \frac{\partial^2 \Psi}{\partial y^2} + \frac{\partial^2 \Psi}{\partial z^2} + \frac{\partial^2 \Psi}{\partial c^2 t^2}\ . \qquad (3.55)$$

The classical D'Alembertian operation is similar, with only a sign difference

$$\Box^2\ \Psi = \frac{\partial^2 \Psi}{\partial x^2} + \frac{\partial^2 \Psi}{\partial y^2} + \frac{\partial^2 \Psi}{\partial z^2} - \frac{\partial^2 \Psi}{\partial c^2 t^2}\ . \qquad (3.56)$$

3.1.8 Analytic Consequences Of The Cauchy-Riemann Conditions

The stage is now sufficiently set to show that the four-dimensional Cauchy-Riemann (C-R) conditions have the same kinds of extensive consequences in four dimensions that the classical C-R conditions have in only two. Some new consequences appear which have only trivial expression in two dimensions but make quite revealing statements about analytic functions in four dimensions.

A new aspect of the $\mathbb{D}$-space algebra will be revealed: that functions and derivatives defined on it have implicit functional relationships among their four vector components such that a change in one component is accompanied by complementary changes in all the rest. Recall that the ring $\mathbb{D}$ was shown to be isomorphic to the complex direct product ring, $\mathbb{C}^2$, hence behaves somewhat like two disassociated copies of the classical complex algebra. One might expect that the mathematics are separated into two isolated, classical complex compartments, never interacting. That is true, to a significant degree, but it is not the whole story.

■ *Component Four-Gradients Are Not All Mutually Orthogonal*—Recall that in the classical vector analysis, a vector function

$$\mathbf{F} = \mathbf{i}X + \mathbf{j}Y + \mathbf{k}Z \tag{3.57}$$

representing a conservative force field in the *xyz*-space has the gradients of its components mutually orthogonal:

$$\nabla X \cdot \nabla Y = \nabla X \cdot \nabla Z = \nabla Y \cdot \nabla Z = 0. \tag{3.58}$$

We shall now show how the same behavior mainfests itself in the $\mathbb{D}$-space theory in four dimensions. A vector function representing a conservative field in three dimensions is the nearest analogue of an analytic hypercomplex function in four dimensions. One might expect that the four-gradients of the components of an analytic function

$$\mathrm{F}(\mathbf{Z}) = \mathbf{1}X + \mathbf{i}Y + \mathbf{j}Z + \mathbf{k}T \tag{3.59}$$

would be mutually orthogonal. Most are, but it is significant that some are not. If we start with the first two components X, Y and the hypercomplex C-R conditions (2.156), we can obtain

$$\begin{aligned}\square X \cdot \square Y &= (\mathbf{1}\frac{\partial X}{\partial x} + \mathbf{i}\frac{\partial X}{\partial y} + \mathbf{j}\frac{\partial X}{\partial z} + \mathbf{k}\frac{\partial X}{\partial ct}) \\ &\quad \cdot (\mathbf{1}\frac{\partial Y}{\partial x} + \mathbf{i}\frac{\partial Y}{\partial y} + \mathbf{j}\frac{\partial Y}{\partial z} + \mathbf{k}\frac{\partial Y}{\partial ct}) \\ &= \frac{\partial X}{\partial x}\frac{\partial Y}{\partial x} + \frac{\partial X}{\partial y}\frac{\partial Y}{\partial y} + \frac{\partial X}{\partial z}\frac{\partial Y}{\partial z} + \frac{\partial X}{\partial ct}\frac{\partial Y}{\partial ct} \\ &= \frac{\partial X}{\partial x}\frac{(-\partial X)}{\partial y} + \frac{\partial X}{\partial y}\frac{\partial X}{\partial x} + \frac{(-\partial Z)}{\partial x}\frac{(-\partial T)}{\partial x} + \frac{\partial T}{\partial x}\frac{(-\partial Z)}{\partial x} = 0.\end{aligned} \tag{3.60}$$

Similarly, the gradients for the component pairs (X,Z), (Y,T), and (Z,T) are orthogonal (have zero dot products). However,

$$\square X \bullet \square T = (\mathbf{1}\frac{\partial X}{\partial x} + \mathbf{i}\frac{\partial X}{\partial y} + \mathbf{j}\frac{\partial X}{\partial z} + \mathbf{k}\frac{\partial X}{\partial ct}) \bullet (\mathbf{1}\frac{\partial T}{\partial x} + \mathbf{i}\frac{\partial T}{\partial y} + \mathbf{j}\frac{\partial T}{\partial z} + \mathbf{k}\frac{\partial T}{\partial ct})$$

$$= \frac{\partial X}{\partial x}\frac{\partial T}{\partial x} + \frac{\partial X}{\partial y}\frac{\partial T}{\partial y} + \frac{\partial X}{\partial z}\frac{\partial T}{\partial z} + \frac{\partial X}{\partial ct}\frac{\partial T}{\partial ct}$$

$$= \frac{\partial T}{\partial ct}\frac{\partial T}{\partial x} + \frac{(-\partial T)}{\partial z}\frac{\partial T}{\partial y} + \frac{(-\partial T)}{\partial y}\frac{\partial T}{\partial z} + \frac{\partial T}{\partial x}\frac{\partial T}{\partial ct}$$

$$= 2\left(\frac{\partial T}{\partial ct}\frac{\partial T}{\partial x} - \frac{\partial T}{\partial z}\frac{\partial T}{\partial y}\right), \tag{3.61}$$

and similarly for the component pair (Y,Z), except for an overall negative sign on the right. These results may be summarized as follows:

$$\square X \bullet \square Y = \square X \bullet \square Z = \square Z \bullet \square T = \square Y \bullet \square T = 0$$

$$\square X \bullet \square T = -\square Y \bullet \square Z = 2\left(\frac{\partial T}{\partial ct}\frac{\partial T}{\partial x} - \frac{\partial T}{\partial z}\frac{\partial T}{\partial y}\right) \tag{3.62}$$

If one considers the families of hypersurfaces denoted by

$$X(x,y,z,ct) = C_1$$
$$Y(x,y,z,ct) = C_2 \tag{3.63}$$
$$Z(x,y,z,ct) = C_3$$
$$T(x,y,z,ct) = C_4 ,$$

with C_i constants, then (3.62) asserts that they are orthogonal except for the pairs X, T and Y, Z. The latter pairs do not appear in the classical complex variable case (there is no Z or T), hence the components there always form orthogonal grid lines. This is another instance showing that the four components of an analytic, hypercomplex function have intricate, interlocking behavior on the global scale. A look back at the definition of the components, (2.99), recalling that the eigenvalues ξ and η are themselves interrelated functions of x,y,z,ct, now allows one to see some consequences of their structure.

■ *Component Four-Gradients Are Rotated Equivalents*—The hypercomplex gradient of the X component of a hypercomplex function is

$$\Box X = \mathbf{1}\frac{\partial X}{\partial x} + \mathbf{i}\frac{\partial X}{\partial y} + \mathbf{j}\frac{\partial X}{\partial z} + \mathbf{k}\frac{\partial X}{\partial ct}, \tag{3.64}$$

and that for the Y component is

$$\Box Y = \mathbf{1}\frac{\partial Y}{\partial x} + \mathbf{i}\frac{\partial Y}{\partial y} + \mathbf{j}\frac{\partial Y}{\partial z} + \mathbf{k}\frac{\partial Y}{\partial ct}. \tag{3.65}$$

By use of the C-R conditions, (2.156), one obtains

$$\begin{aligned}\Box Y &= -\mathbf{1}\frac{\partial X}{\partial y} + \mathbf{i}\frac{\partial X}{\partial x} - \mathbf{j}\frac{\partial X}{\partial ct} + \mathbf{k}\frac{\partial X}{\partial z} \\ &= \mathbf{i}\,(\mathbf{1}\frac{\partial X}{\partial x} + \mathbf{i}\frac{\partial X}{\partial y} + \mathbf{j}\frac{\partial X}{\partial z} + \mathbf{k}\frac{\partial X}{\partial ct}) = \mathbf{i}\,\Box X\end{aligned} \tag{3.66}$$

Continuing in a similar fashion, one obtains the following:

$$\boxed{\mathbf{1}\,\Box X = -\mathbf{i}\,\Box Y = -\mathbf{j}\,\Box Z = \mathbf{k}\,\Box T} \tag{3.67}$$

Now recall that $\mathbf{1},\mathbf{i},\mathbf{j},\mathbf{k}$ correspond to 4 X 4 orthogonal matrices (2.2), hence the gradients of the components X, Y, Z, T can be interpreted as equivalent vectors rotated in the hypercomplex four-space.

■ *Component Four-Gradients Have Equal Magnitudes*—The hypercomplex gradient of the X component of a hypercomplex function is

$$\Box X = \mathbf{1}\frac{\partial X}{\partial x} + \mathbf{i}\frac{\partial X}{\partial y} + \mathbf{j}\frac{\partial X}{\partial z} + \mathbf{k}\frac{\partial X}{\partial ct}, \tag{3.68}$$

and that for the Y component is

$$\Box Y = \mathbf{1}\frac{\partial Y}{\partial x} + \mathbf{i}\frac{\partial Y}{\partial y} + \mathbf{j}\frac{\partial Y}{\partial z} + \mathbf{k}\frac{\partial Y}{\partial ct}. \tag{3.69}$$

By use of the C-R conditions, (2.156), one obtains

$$\Box Y = -\mathbf{1}\frac{\partial X}{\partial y} + \mathbf{i}\frac{\partial X}{\partial x} - \mathbf{j}\frac{\partial X}{\partial ct} + \mathbf{k}\frac{\partial X}{\partial z}; \tag{3.70}$$

then

$$\begin{aligned} |\Box Y|^2 &= \left(\frac{\partial X}{\partial x}\right)^2 + \left(\frac{\partial X}{\partial y}\right)^2 + \left(\frac{\partial X}{\partial z}\right)^2 + \left(\frac{\partial X}{\partial ct}\right)^2 \\ &= |\Box X|^2 . \end{aligned} \tag{3.71}$$

Continuing in a similar fashion, one obtains the following:

$$\boxed{|\Box X|^2 = |\Box Y|^2 = |\Box Z|^2 = |\Box T|^2} \tag{3.72}$$

■ *The Component Gradients Have Global Rotational Invariants*—We want to show that the gradients of the components of an analytic hypercomplex function, individually, have invariants under orthogonal transformations of the independent variables, and that the invariants are identical among the four components. We do so as follows. The typical element in $\mathbb{D}$,

$$\mathbf{Z} = \mathbf{1}x + \mathbf{i}y + \mathbf{j}z + \mathbf{k}ct ,$$

has a matrix interpretation

$$\mathbf{Z} = \begin{bmatrix} x & -y & -z & ct \\ y & x & -ct & -z \\ z & -ct & x & -y \\ ct & z & y & x \end{bmatrix}, \tag{3.73}$$

with the attendant matrix invariants under coordinate transformations. For example, if one applies an orthogonal transformation A to the coordinate vector **Z**, then

$$\mathbf{Z}' = \mathrm{A}\mathbf{Z},$$

and, in the matrix interpretation,

$$\begin{aligned} det(\mathbf{Z}') &= det(\mathrm{A}) \;\; det(\mathbf{Z}) \\ &= det(\mathbf{Z}) \,. \end{aligned} \tag{3.74}$$

Now consider the coordinate transformation A in the form

$$\begin{aligned} x' &= a_{11}x + a_{12}y + a_{13}z + a_{14}ct, \\ y' &= a_{21}x + a_{22}y + a_{23}z + a_{24}ct, \\ z' &= a_{31}x + a_{32}y + a_{33}z + a_{34}ct, \\ ct' &= a_{41}x + a_{42}y + a_{43}z + a_{44}ct, \end{aligned} \tag{3.75}$$

where the a_{ij}s are constrained by the orthogonality conditions; then one has

$$\frac{\partial x'}{\partial x} = a_{11}, \qquad \frac{\partial x'}{\partial y} = a_{12}, \text{ etc.}$$

The components X, Y, Z, T are analytic in the independent variables x, y, z, ct, hence one may use the chain rule for partial derivatives to obtain

$$\frac{\partial X}{\partial x} = \frac{\partial X}{\partial x'}\frac{\partial x'}{\partial x} + \frac{\partial X}{\partial y'}\frac{\partial y'}{\partial x} + \frac{\partial X}{\partial z'}\frac{\partial z'}{\partial x} + \frac{\partial X}{\partial ct'}\frac{\partial ct'}{\partial x},$$

$$\frac{\partial X}{\partial y} = \frac{\partial X}{\partial x'}\frac{\partial x'}{\partial y} + \frac{\partial X}{\partial y'}\frac{\partial y'}{\partial y} + \frac{\partial X}{\partial z'}\frac{\partial z'}{\partial y} + \frac{\partial X}{\partial ct'}\frac{\partial ct'}{\partial y},$$

$$\frac{\partial X}{\partial z} = \frac{\partial X}{\partial x'}\frac{\partial x'}{\partial z} + \frac{\partial X}{\partial y'}\frac{\partial y'}{\partial z} + \frac{\partial X}{\partial z'}\frac{\partial z'}{\partial z} + \frac{\partial X}{\partial ct'}\frac{\partial ct'}{\partial z}, \tag{3.76}$$

$$\frac{\partial X}{\partial ct} = \frac{\partial X}{\partial x'}\frac{\partial x'}{\partial ct} + \frac{\partial X}{\partial y'}\frac{\partial y'}{\partial ct} + \frac{\partial X}{\partial z'}\frac{\partial z'}{\partial ct} + \frac{\partial X}{\partial ct'}\frac{\partial ct'}{\partial ct};$$

then, using (3.75),

$$\begin{aligned}
\frac{\partial X}{\partial x} &= \frac{\partial X}{\partial x'}a_{11} + \frac{\partial X}{\partial y'}a_{12} + \frac{\partial X}{\partial z'}a_{13} + \frac{\partial X}{\partial ct'}a_{14}, \\
\frac{\partial X}{\partial y} &= \frac{\partial X}{\partial x'}a_{21} + \frac{\partial X}{\partial y'}a_{22} + \frac{\partial X}{\partial z'}a_{23} + \frac{\partial X}{\partial ct'}a_{24}, \\
\frac{\partial X}{\partial z} &= \frac{\partial X}{\partial x'}a_{31} + \frac{\partial X}{\partial y'}a_{32} + \frac{\partial X}{\partial z'}a_{33} + \frac{\partial X}{\partial ct'}a_{34}, \\
\frac{\partial X}{\partial ct} &= \frac{\partial X}{\partial x'}a_{41} + \frac{\partial X}{\partial y'}a_{42} + \frac{\partial X}{\partial z'}a_{43} + \frac{\partial X}{\partial ct'}a_{44},
\end{aligned} \tag{3.77}$$

i.e.,

$$\Box X = \mathrm{A}\Box_1 X, \tag{3.78}$$

where

$$\Box_1 = \mathbf{1}\frac{\partial}{\partial x'} + \mathbf{i}\frac{\partial}{\partial y'} + \mathbf{j}\frac{\partial}{\partial z'} + \mathbf{k}\frac{\partial}{\partial ct'},$$

and similarly for the other components Y, Z, T. Comparison with (3.74) and (3.75) shows that *the gradient of a component of an analytic hypercomplex function transforms covariantly under a change in the frame of reference.* It follows that

$$det(\Box X) = det(\Box_1 X), \tag{3.79}$$

and similarly for the other components Y, Z, T. Combining this result with (3.67), one has

$$\begin{aligned} det(\Box X) &= det(\Box Y) = det(\Box Z) = det(\Box T) \\ &= \text{Invariant under orthogonal transformations of the coordinates x,y,z,ct} \end{aligned} \tag{3.80}$$

But (3.80) is not all concerning the invariance properties of the gradients. The gradient forms are elements of $\mathbb{D}$, hence have determinants of the form

$$\begin{aligned} det(\Box X) &= \left[\left(\frac{\partial X}{\partial x} - \frac{\partial X}{\partial ct}\right)^2 + \left(\frac{\partial X}{\partial y} + \frac{\partial X}{\partial z}\right)^2\right]\left[\left(\frac{\partial X}{\partial x} + \frac{\partial X}{\partial ct}\right)^2 + \left(\frac{\partial X}{\partial y} - \frac{\partial X}{\partial z}\right)^2\right] \\ &= |\Box X|^4 - 4\left(\frac{\partial X}{\partial x}\frac{\partial X}{\partial ct} - \frac{\partial X}{\partial y}\frac{\partial X}{\partial z}\right)^2 \end{aligned} \tag{3.81}$$

The absolute value (Euclidean norm) of a vector is not affected by an orthogonal transformation of the underlying coordinates, hence the gradient norm quantities in (3.72) are not only equivalent, but invariant. That being so, and the determinantal forms in (3.80) and (3.81) being equivalent and invariant, one must conclude

$$\begin{aligned} &\frac{\partial X}{\partial x}\frac{\partial X}{\partial ct} - \frac{\partial X}{\partial y}\frac{\partial X}{\partial z} = \frac{\partial Y}{\partial x}\frac{\partial Y}{\partial ct} - \frac{\partial Y}{\partial y}\frac{\partial Y}{\partial z} \\ &= \frac{\partial Z}{\partial x}\frac{\partial Z}{\partial ct} - \frac{\partial Z}{\partial y}\frac{\partial Z}{\partial z} = \frac{\partial T}{\partial x}\frac{\partial T}{\partial ct} - \frac{\partial T}{\partial y}\frac{\partial T}{\partial z} \\ &= \text{Invariant under orthogonal transformations of the coordinates } x, y, z, ct \end{aligned} \tag{3.82}$$

The equivalence of the forms in (3.82) may also be verified directly from the C-R conditions, (2.156). Some interpretation of these forms is available from (2.165), from which it follows that

$$\Box X \cdot (\mathbf{k}\Box X) = 2\left(\frac{\partial X}{\partial x}\frac{\partial X}{\partial ct} - \frac{\partial X}{\partial y}\frac{\partial X}{\partial z}\right). \tag{3.83}$$

The discussion following (2.165) interprets the vector $\mathbf{k}\,\Box X$ as lying in a direction which is an hypercomplex 180 degrees from that of $\Box X$, thus (3.83) is the square of the projection of $\Box X$ onto its hypercomplex "opposite" direction. An "oppositely-directed" vector is not merely the negative of the original, in a space of four dimensions.

■ *Analytic Function Components Satisfy The Wave Equation*—In the classical complex variables, if one has a function of the form

$$f(z) = u(x, y) + iv(x, y) ,$$

then it is a consequence of the Cauchy-Riemann conditions that

$$\frac{\partial^2 u}{\partial x^2} + \frac{\partial^2 u}{\partial y^2} = 0 ,$$
$$\frac{\partial^2 v}{\partial x^2} + \frac{\partial^2 v}{\partial y^2} = 0 . \tag{3.84}$$

For analytic, hypercomplex functions (3.84) generalizes straightforwardly, as follows. One may use the C-R conditions, (2.156), and the classical result that for an analytic function it does not matter in what order one takes multiple partial derivatives, to assert

$$\frac{\partial^2 X}{\partial x^2} + \frac{\partial^2 X}{\partial y^2} + \frac{\partial^2 X}{\partial z^2} + \frac{\partial^2 X}{\partial c^2 t^2}$$
$$= \frac{\partial^2 Y}{\partial y \partial x} - \frac{\partial^2 Y}{\partial x \partial y} + \frac{\partial^2 Y}{\partial ct \partial z} - \frac{\partial^2 Y}{\partial z \partial ct} = 0 \tag{3.85}$$

The operations performed in (3.85) are symmetric, because

$$\frac{\partial^2 Y}{\partial x^2} + \frac{\partial^2 Y}{\partial y^2} + \frac{\partial^2 Y}{\partial z^2} + \frac{\partial^2 Y}{\partial c^2 t^2}$$
$$= \frac{\partial^2 X}{\partial x \partial y} - \frac{\partial^2 X}{\partial y \partial x} - \frac{\partial^2 X}{\partial ct \partial z} + \frac{\partial^2 X}{\partial z \partial ct} = 0 \tag{3.86}$$

Similar results hold for the Z and T components, with the result

$$\Box^2 X = \Box^2 Y = \Box^2 Z = \Box^2 T = 0 \tag{3.87}$$

Although the forms in (3.87) are not strictly wave equations, they are usually treated as being equivalent to the wave equation forms because of their four dimensionality including time. The usual device for reconciling one form with the other is to apply the unitary transformation $x'=x$, $y'=y$, $z'=z$, $t'=it$, where "i" is the classical complex imaginary, distinct from the hypercomplex **i**. This produces the desired change in sign of the fourth term involving differentiation with respect to time.

■ *The Gradient Of A Hypercomplex Function Is Null*—The four-gradient of an analytic, hypercomplex function is given by (3.33). If one substitutes the C-R conditions (2.156) into (3.33), one obtains

$$\begin{aligned}\Box\, F(Z) = \;& \mathbf{1}\left(\frac{\partial X}{\partial x} - \frac{\partial X}{\partial x} - \frac{\partial X}{\partial x} - \frac{\partial X}{\partial x}\right)\\ &+ \mathbf{i}\left(-\frac{\partial Y}{\partial x} + \frac{\partial Y}{\partial x} - \frac{\partial Y}{\partial x} + \frac{\partial Y}{\partial x}\right)\\ &+ \mathbf{j}\left(-\frac{\partial Z}{\partial x} - \frac{\partial Z}{\partial x} + \frac{\partial Z}{\partial x} + \frac{\partial Z}{\partial x}\right)\\ &+ \mathbf{k}\left(\frac{\partial T}{\partial x} - \frac{\partial T}{\partial x} - \frac{\partial T}{\partial x} + \frac{\partial T}{\partial x}\right) = 0\,.\end{aligned} \tag{3.88}$$

This result makes an unusual statement about the overall variation of an analytic, hypercomplex function at a point: *it is uniformly zero*; if one component initiates some variation, all the others vary in an interlocked, complementary way that nulls out the first variation and mutually nulls the reactionary variations. The nearest analogy that occurs to the author is the concept of a closed spacetime universe from the field of physics.

The hypercomplex derivative is related to the four-gradient of a hypercomplex function by (3.45) in such a way that the derivative is not null in general. In fact, one can show that the derivative is null everywhere only if the subject function is a constant, as follows: from (2.169) we have

$$\frac{d\mathrm{F}}{d\mathbf{Z}} = \frac{\partial \mathrm{F}}{\partial x} = \mathbf{1}\frac{\partial X}{\partial x} + \mathbf{i}\frac{\partial Y}{\partial x} + \mathbf{j}\frac{\partial Z}{\partial x} + \mathbf{k}\frac{\partial T}{\partial x}, \tag{3.89}$$

which is zero everywhere only if all the components are zero everywhere; that is, only if all variation along the x-axis is zero. We have seen earlier that the underlying coordinates may be reoriented by means of an orthogonal transformation similar to (3.75) with the result

$$\begin{aligned} x &= a_{11}\mathrm{x}' + a_{12}\mathrm{y}' + a_{13}\mathrm{z}' + a_{14}\mathrm{ct}' \\ \frac{\partial F}{\partial x'} &= \frac{\partial F}{\partial x}\frac{\partial x}{\partial x'} = a_{11}\frac{\partial F}{\partial x}. \end{aligned} \tag{3.90}$$

It follows that if the variation is zero along one line, then it is zero in all directions; i.e., the function is a constant.

■ *The Wave Equation Is Preserved Under Analytic Transformations*—If one applies two analytic functions F and G successively to an independent variable **Z**, i.e., G(F(**Z**)), then one may view F(**Z**) as an analytic transformation of the underlying coordinates **Z**. The transformation takes the form

$$\begin{aligned} \mathbf{Z} &= \mathbf{1}x + \mathbf{i}y + \mathbf{j}z + \mathbf{k}ct, \\ x &\to X(x,y,z,ct) \\ y &\to Y(x,y,z,ct) \\ z &\to Z(x,y,z,ct) \\ ct &\to T(x,y,z,ct), \end{aligned} \tag{3.91}$$

and

$$\mathbf{Z}' = \mathbf{1}X + \mathbf{i}Y + \mathbf{j}Z + \mathbf{k}T.$$

The question naturally arises: what effect does such a transformation have on the more important vector field operations? We cannot investigate all cases but we will prove the following important result:

Let

$$F(\mathbf{Z}) = \mathbf{1}X + \mathbf{i}Y + \mathbf{j}Z + \mathbf{k}T$$

and

$$G(\mathbf{Z}') = \mathbf{1}U + \mathbf{i}V + \mathbf{j}W + \mathbf{k}S \tag{3.92}$$

be any two analytic, hypercomplex functions with which we will work in relation to the transformation indicated in (3.91). Consider the notation

$$\Box = \mathbf{1}\frac{\partial}{\partial x} + \mathbf{i}\frac{\partial}{\partial y} + \mathbf{j}\frac{\partial}{\partial z} + \mathbf{k}\frac{\partial}{\partial ct}$$

and (3.93)

$$\Box_1 = \mathbf{1}\frac{\partial}{\partial X} + \mathbf{i}\frac{\partial}{\partial Y} + \mathbf{j}\frac{\partial}{\partial Z} + \mathbf{k}\frac{\partial}{\partial T},$$

then

$$\Box^2 U = \Box_1^2 U = 0, \tag{3.94}$$

and similarly for the V, W, S components of the function G. Put another way, *the wave equation is invariant under analytic, hypercomplex transformations* of the independent variables x, y, z, ct.

Proof: We have that

$$\Box^2 U = 0$$

from (3.87) which in turn follows directly from the C-R conditions, (2.156). From classical complex variable theory, it is known that the result of composing two analytic functions into one, as in $G(F(\mathbf{Z}))$, is analytic. In the present case, this makes the function G analytic in the "independent" variables X, Y, Z, T; consequently

$$\Box_1^2 U = 0,$$

and the proof is concluded.

We have the means to verify (3.94) directly by use of the C-R conditions and the chain rule for differentiation. We shall do so as an illustration of how the C-R conditions can simplify very complex expressions. First, assume that the transformation (3.91) involves functions X, Y, Z, T which are analytic but not necessarily conjugate; then the reader may verify by the chain rule that the hypercomplex wave function operator transforms as follows:

$$
\begin{aligned}
\Box^2 U = {} & |\Box X|^2 \frac{\partial^2 U}{\partial X^2} + |\Box Y|^2 \frac{\partial^2 U}{\partial Y^2} \\
& + |\Box Z|^2 \frac{\partial^2 U}{\partial Z^2} + |\Box T|^2 \frac{\partial^2 U}{\partial T^2} \\
& + (\Box^2 X) \frac{\partial U}{\partial X} + (\Box^2 Y) \frac{\partial U}{\partial Y} \\
& + (\Box^2 Z) \frac{\partial U}{\partial Z} + (\Box^2 T) \frac{\partial U}{\partial T} \\
& + 2(\Box X \cdot \Box Y) \frac{\partial^2 U}{\partial X \partial Y} + 2(\Box X \cdot \Box Z) \frac{\partial^2 U}{\partial X \partial Z} \\
& + 2(\Box X \cdot \Box T) \frac{\partial^2 U}{\partial X \partial T} + 2(\Box Y \cdot \Box Z) \frac{\partial^2 U}{\partial Y \partial Z} \\
& + 2(\Box Y \cdot \Box T) \frac{\partial^2 U}{\partial Y \partial T} + 2(\Box Z \cdot \Box T) \frac{\partial^2 U}{\partial Z \partial T}
\end{aligned}
\tag{3.95}
$$

Now assume that X, Y, Z, T <u>are</u> conjugate functions and apply the results given in (3.62), (3.72), and (3.87) and collect terms to obtain

$$
\begin{aligned}
\Box^2 U = {} & |\Box \mathrm{X}|^2 \, \Box_1^2 U \\
& + (\Box X \cdot \Box T) \left(\frac{\partial^2 U}{\partial X \partial T} - \frac{\partial^2 U}{\partial Y \partial Z} \right) .
\end{aligned}
\tag{3.96}
$$

Finally, we use the fact that the order of taking mixed partial derivatives of analytic functions is immaterial and also use the C-R conditions (2.156) on the last term on the right to obtain

$$\frac{\partial}{\partial T}\frac{\partial U}{\partial X} - \frac{\partial}{\partial Z}\frac{\partial U}{\partial Y} = \frac{\partial}{\partial T}\frac{\partial U}{\partial X} + \frac{\partial}{\partial Z}\frac{\partial V}{\partial X}$$
$$= \frac{\partial}{\partial X}\left(\frac{\partial U}{\partial T} + \frac{\partial V}{\partial Z}\right) = \frac{\partial}{\partial X}\left(\frac{\partial U}{\partial T} - \frac{\partial U}{\partial T}\right) = 0 \ , \tag{3.97}$$

and we are left with

$$\Box^2 U = |\Box X|^2 \Box_1^2 U \ . \tag{3.98}$$

By (3.72). the gradient norm on the right-hand side is zero only if the gradient of all the components X, Y, Z, T are zero, and the left-hand side is zero by (3.87). The desired result follows.

■ *Four-Gradients Transform Into Gradient Products*—As in the previous section, we will use the notation in (3.91) and (3.93) and investigate the effect on a hypercomplex gradient expression when an analytic, hypercomplex transformation is applied to the independent variables x,y,z,ct. Let $U(x,y,z,ct)$ be any analytic function of four independent variables; then

$$\Box\ U = \mathbf{1}\frac{\partial U}{\partial x} + \mathbf{i}\frac{\partial U}{\partial y} + \mathbf{j}\frac{\partial U}{\partial z} + \mathbf{k}\frac{\partial U}{\partial ct} \ .$$

After the transformation $U(x,y,z,ct) \rightarrow U(X,Y,Z,T)$ is made, then by the chain rule for differentiation,

$$\frac{\partial U}{\partial x} = \frac{\partial U}{\partial X}\frac{\partial X}{\partial x} + \frac{\partial U}{\partial Y}\frac{\partial Y}{\partial x} + \frac{\partial U}{\partial Z}\frac{\partial Z}{\partial x} + \frac{\partial U}{\partial T}\frac{\partial T}{\partial x}$$

$$\frac{\partial U}{\partial y} = \frac{\partial U}{\partial X}\frac{\partial X}{\partial y} + \frac{\partial U}{\partial Y}\frac{\partial Y}{\partial y} + \frac{\partial U}{\partial Z}\frac{\partial Z}{\partial y} + \frac{\partial U}{\partial T}\frac{\partial T}{\partial y} \tag{3.99}$$

$$\frac{\partial U}{\partial z} = \frac{\partial U}{\partial X}\frac{\partial X}{\partial z} + \frac{\partial U}{\partial Y}\frac{\partial Y}{\partial z} + \frac{\partial U}{\partial Z}\frac{\partial Z}{\partial z} + \frac{\partial U}{\partial T}\frac{\partial T}{\partial z}$$

$$\frac{\partial U}{\partial ct} = \frac{\partial U}{\partial X}\frac{\partial X}{\partial ct} + \frac{\partial U}{\partial Y}\frac{\partial Y}{\partial ct} + \frac{\partial U}{\partial Z}\frac{\partial Z}{\partial ct} + \frac{\partial U}{\partial T}\frac{\partial T}{\partial ct} \ .$$

This can be written in vector-matrix form as

$$\begin{bmatrix} \frac{\partial U}{\partial x} \\ \frac{\partial U}{\partial y} \\ \frac{\partial U}{\partial z} \\ \frac{\partial U}{\partial ct} \end{bmatrix} = \begin{bmatrix} \frac{\partial X}{\partial x} & \frac{\partial Y}{\partial x} & \frac{\partial Z}{\partial x} & \frac{\partial T}{\partial x} \\ \frac{\partial X}{\partial y} & \frac{\partial Y}{\partial y} & \frac{\partial Z}{\partial y} & \frac{\partial T}{\partial y} \\ \frac{\partial X}{\partial z} & \frac{\partial Y}{\partial z} & \frac{\partial Z}{\partial z} & \frac{\partial T}{\partial z} \\ \frac{\partial X}{\partial ct} & \frac{\partial Y}{\partial ct} & \frac{\partial Z}{\partial ct} & \frac{\partial T}{\partial ct} \end{bmatrix} \begin{bmatrix} \frac{\partial U}{\partial X} \\ \frac{\partial U}{\partial Y} \\ \frac{\partial U}{\partial Z} \\ \frac{\partial U}{\partial T} \end{bmatrix} . \tag{3.100}$$

Now we use the C-R conditions (2.156) on the elements of the 4 X 4 matri in (3.100) to obtain

$$\begin{bmatrix} \frac{\partial U}{\partial x} \\ \frac{\partial U}{\partial y} \\ \frac{\partial U}{\partial z} \\ \frac{\partial U}{\partial ct} \end{bmatrix} = \begin{bmatrix} \frac{\partial X}{\partial x} & -\frac{\partial X}{\partial y} & -\frac{\partial X}{\partial z} & \frac{\partial X}{\partial ct} \\ \frac{\partial X}{\partial y} & \frac{\partial X}{\partial x} & -\frac{\partial X}{\partial ct} & -\frac{\partial X}{\partial z} \\ \frac{\partial X}{\partial z} & -\frac{\partial X}{\partial ct} & \frac{\partial X}{\partial x} & -\frac{\partial X}{\partial y} \\ \frac{\partial X}{\partial ct} & \frac{\partial X}{\partial z} & \frac{\partial X}{\partial y} & \frac{\partial X}{\partial x} \end{bmatrix} \begin{bmatrix} \frac{\partial U}{\partial X} \\ \frac{\partial U}{\partial Y} \\ \frac{\partial U}{\partial Z} \\ \frac{\partial U}{\partial T} \end{bmatrix} . \tag{3.101}$$

One observes that the 4 X 4 matrix has the form of an element of $\mathbb{D}$; the we use the vector-matrix formulation of Section 2.3.6 to assert that (3.101 is the same as

$$\Box U = \Box X \Box_1 U . \tag{3.102}$$

Finally, one may use (3.67) to assert that

$$\boxed{\begin{aligned} \Box U &= \Box X \Box_1 U = -\mathbf{i} \Box Y \Box_1 U \\ &= -\mathbf{j} \Box Z \Box_1 U = k \Box T \Box_1 U \end{aligned}} , \tag{3.103}$$

In view of the relationship between the hypercomplex derivative and the gradient, (3.45), the forms in (3.103) are tantamount to the chain rule for derivatives:

$$\frac{d\mathrm{F}}{d\mathbf{Z}} = \frac{d\mathrm{F}}{d\mathbf{Z}'}\,\frac{d\mathbf{Z}'}{d\mathbf{Z}} . \tag{3.104}$$

3.2 Maxwell's Equations In D-Space Notation

In the classical complex variable theory, analytic functions $f(z) = u(x,y) + i v(x,y)$ are called *harmonic* as a reminder that the components u and v always obey the two-dimensional LaPlace's equation,

$$\frac{\partial^2 u}{\partial x^2} + \frac{\partial^2 u}{\partial y^2} = \frac{\partial^2 v}{\partial x^2} + \frac{\partial^2 v}{\partial y^2} = 0 .$$

As shown in (3.87), this behavior carries over into the four-dimensional D-space. The two-dimensional LaPlace equation becomes the four-dimensional D'Alembertian equation, which has a wave equation interpretation. Additionally, the gradients of u and v are orthogonal to each other away from singularities and discontinuities of the function. In the D-space formulation, four pairs of the four-dimensional gradients are mutually orthogonal, and the two that are not orthogonal produce dot products that are invariant under rotations of the frame of reference. We are led to hypothesize that the function space over D can be used to describe electromagnetic and other conservative force fields in three and four dimensions, as is done in the classical complex variable case for two dimensions. The following sections will investigate that notion and will yield a D-space formulation of Maxwell's equations for electromagnetic fields.

3.2.1 Hypercomplex Functions Describe Conservative Force Fields

In physics, a conservative force field is a vector field derived fron a scalar analytic function Φ, called the *potential*, by means of the gradient operator, ∇. Typical notation is

$$\mathbf{E} = -\nabla \Phi , \tag{3.105}$$

which makes $\mathbf{E}$ a three-dimensional vector function. If Φ is not a function of time, then $\mathbf{E}$ represents a static field characterized by having both its divergence $\nabla \cdot \mathbf{E}$ and its curl $\nabla \times \mathbf{E}$ equal to zero away from its "sources," discontinuities, and singularities. As shown in (3.38), the quaternion product of ∇ and $\mathbf{E}$ is composed of the divergence and the curl, consequently

$$\nabla \mathbf{E} = -\nabla \cdot \mathbf{E} + \nabla \times \mathbf{E} = 0 \tag{3.106}$$

is one characterization of a static, conservative force field in a free space of three dimensions. If a time variation of Φ is allowed (thereby moving the problem into a four-dimensional domain), then classical treatments show that an equivalent formulation of (3.106) is

$$\nabla^2 \Phi - \frac{1}{c^2} \frac{\partial^2 \Phi}{\partial t^2} = -4\pi\sigma , \tag{3.107}$$

where $\sigma(x,y,z,t)$ is a source of the field and may be a function of the coordinates and time, or of the coordinates only. In free space, there is no field source σ, hence under those conditions,

$$\Box^2 \Phi = 0 , \tag{3.108}$$

where the D'Alembertian has the classical definition with a negative sign in front of the time derivative.

The $\mathbb{D}$-space equivalent of (3.106) is

$$\Box \mathbf{E} = 0 , \tag{3.109}$$

which holds for all analytic, $\mathbb{D}$-space functions $\mathbf{E}$. We have observed earlier (Sec. 3.1.8) that condition (3.109) is "conservative" in the strictest sense: the field variation is uniformly zero at all free-space points and in all directions when four dimensions are considered. Even if the independent variables are transformed by some analytic, hypercomplex function then (3.109) still holds as a result of (3.103) and distributivity in $\mathbb{D}$.

For the second half of the problem (an analogue of (3.108) in $\mathbb{D}$), the question really reduces to: for a given $\mathbf{E}$, can we find a $\Phi(x,y,z,ct)$ such that

$$\mathbf{E} = -\Box \Phi \ ? \tag{3.110}$$

If so, the rest of the derivation will be simple. We prove that the requisite Φ exists, as follows. Recall that the $\mathbb{D}$-space with its function definition (2.96) is a space of analytic functions having derivatives (2.129) and integrals (2.132). It follows from classical complex variable theory that for any analytic function $\mathbf{E}(\mathbf{Z})$, we can find a function $G(\mathbf{Z})$ such that

$$\mathbf{E}(\mathbf{Z}) = \frac{dG}{d\mathbf{Z}} ; \tag{3.111}$$

then by (2.168),

$$\mathbf{E}(\mathbf{Z}) = \mathbf{1}\frac{\partial U}{\partial x} + \mathbf{i}\frac{\partial V}{\partial x} + \mathbf{j}\frac{\partial W}{\partial x} + \mathbf{k}\frac{\partial S}{\partial x} , \tag{3.112}$$

where we have used the notation

$$\mathrm{G}(\mathbf{Z}) = \mathbf{1}U + \mathbf{i}V + \mathbf{j}W + \mathbf{k}S . \tag{3.113}$$

Now one may apply the C-R conditions (2.156) to (3.112) to obtain

$$\mathbf{E}(\mathbf{Z}) = \mathbf{1}\frac{\partial U}{\partial x} + \mathbf{i}\frac{\partial U}{\partial y} + \mathbf{j}\frac{\partial U}{\partial z} + \mathbf{k}\frac{\partial U}{\partial ct} , \tag{3.114}$$

$$= \Box^{\mathrm{T}} U . \tag{3.115}$$

Now consider the orthogonal transformation

$$A = \begin{bmatrix} -1 & 0 & 0 & 0 \\ 0 & 1 & 0 & 0 \\ 0 & 0 & 1 & 0 \\ 0 & 0 & 0 & -1 \end{bmatrix} , \tag{3.116}$$

$$\mathbf{Z}' = \mathrm{A} \;\; \mathbf{Z} = - \mathbf{Z}^{\mathrm{T}} ; \tag{3.117}$$

then

$$\Box^{\mathrm{T}} U(x,y,z,ct) \rightarrow -\Box_{1} U(x',y',z',ct') \tag{3.118}$$

and

$$\mathbf{E}' = -\Box_{1} U(x',y',z',ct') . \tag{3.119}$$

Finally, as a consequence of (3.87) and the fact that U is a component of an analytic, hypercomplex function, we have

$$\square_1^2 U(x', y', z', ct') = 0 . \tag{3.120}$$

We have shown that, in the proper frame of reference, **E** may be expresse as the negative of the hypercomplex gradient of a scalar function U, wher U obeys the hypercomplex wave equation. We conclude that analytic, hyper complex functions may be viewed as representations of conservative force fields

As a side result, it is now apparent that *any one scalar component U, V, W or S plus the C-R conditions are sufficient to reconstruct the entire hypercomple function.*

3.2.2 A Hypercomplex Representation Of Maxwell's Equations

The theory of the $\mathbb{D}$ analytic function space is looking very much like th essence of classical electromagnetic theory. In particular, the consequences c the Cauchy-Riemann conditions, as outlined in Section 3.1.8 and its subsection are properties characteristic of conservative force fields in general, as we showe in Section 3.2.1. Basically, all we have to do here is cast the electromagneti potential as an analytic, hypercomplex function in a way that relates easil to the classical theory.

We shall restrict our attention to electromagnetic fields in a vacuum, awa from sources, sinks, discontinuities, or singularities. This specifically avoid consideration of material effects such as polarization. We shall also use notatio that corresponds to the usual scientific and engineering treatments of the subjec Let **E** represent the electric field and let **B** denote the magnetic field. In classic treatments, these are derivable from a scalar electrostatic potential functio Φ, and a vector magnetic potential function, **A**, as follows:

$$\mathbf{E} = -\nabla \Phi - \frac{1}{c}\frac{\partial \mathbf{A}}{\partial t} , \tag{3.121}$$

$$\mathbf{B} = \nabla \times \mathbf{A} ;$$

moreover, classical treatments specify the *Lorentz condition* on the potenti functions, as follows:

$$\nabla \cdot \mathbf{A} + \frac{1}{c}\frac{\partial \Phi}{\partial t} = 0 . \tag{3.122}$$

Equation (3.122) suggests a natural way to define the *electromagnetic potenti function*, denoted by Γ, for the $\mathbb{D}$-space treatment: let

$$\Gamma = \mathbf{A} + \mathbf{k}\Phi \ , \tag{3.123}$$

with

$$\mathbf{A} = \mathbf{1}A_1 + \mathbf{i}A_2 + \mathbf{j}A_3 \ .$$

Tolman[43] calls (3.123) the *generalized potential.* If we take the four-divergence, we get the Lorentz condition:

$$\Box \bullet \Gamma = \frac{\partial A_1}{\partial x} + \frac{\partial A_2}{\partial y} + \frac{\partial A_3}{\partial z} + \frac{\partial \Phi}{\partial ct} = 0 \ ; \tag{3.124}$$

however, we do not stop here. We recognize that the four-divergence is the same as the first component of the full four-gradient product (within an orthogonal transformation of x,y,z,t), and invoke the considerations leading to (3.106) and (3.109) to define as a basic requirement that the full four-gradient product is equal to zero:

$$\Box \ \Gamma = 0 \ . \tag{3.125}$$

By doing so, we force Γ to be an analytic function in the $\mathbb{D}$-space. We have seen in Section 3.1.8 that analytic function components satisfy the four-dimensional D'Alembertian equation, which has a wave equation interpretation [see (3.87) and the discussion immediately following]. We have distributivity in $\mathbb{D}$, hence we may write

$$\Box^2\Gamma = \Box^2\mathbf{A} + \mathbf{k}\,\Box^2\Phi = 0 \ ; \tag{3.126}$$

consequently,

$$\begin{aligned} \Box^2\mathbf{A} &= 0 \\ \Box^2\Phi &= 0 \ , \end{aligned} \tag{3.127}$$

where the D'Alembertian operator has the $\mathbb{D}$-space definition with a plus sign in front of the ct-component. If we accept that Equations (3.127) are equivalent to wave equations, then Jackson[27], for example, has shown that they are equivalent to Maxwell's equations in free space.

In one view, (3.125) is a more fundamental form of Maxwell's equations because (3.127) follows directly from (3.125) and the analytic function theory in $\mathbb{D}$. *Maxwell's equations are intrinsic to the* $\mathbb{D}$*-space function theory.*

Formulation (3.125) has import for the numerical solution of electromagnetic field equations, because one need only solve the first-order system of C-R conditions with specified boundary conditions instead of one or more second-order partial differential equations.

Electromagnetic point sources and equipotential surfaces correspond to analytic function singularities and branch cuts, respectively, as is done in the two-dimensional case. There is a four-dimensional conformal mapping theory based, as is any $\mathbb{D}$-space function theory, on the corresponding classical complex variable theory. Even better, as a result of Γ meeting all the conditions for an analytic function in $\mathbb{D}$, one may apply complex analysis techniques, for example Cauchy's integral theorem and Laurent series approximations, in all calculations.

No attempt will be made to accomodate material effects such as polarization in the present theory; that will be left to others as a separate study.

3.2.3 A Tensor Interpretation Of The Gradient Of An Analytic Function

We have presumed above to give another expression for Maxwell's equations (3.123), in the form of the gradient of an analytic, hypercomplex function. This formulation is expected to hold only within the $\mathbb{D}$-space mathematical system. Under any circumstances, however, any such formulation is of no utility unless it retains form invariance under changes of the independent variables x,y,z,ct, i.e., is a tensor formulation. If it does not, the associated physics will appear to be different in different frames of reference, in contradiction to experimental reality. Fortunately, our formulation has taken the form of the gradient of an analytic, hypercomplex function (the electromagnetic potential function), and we already have results at hand to show form invariance, as follows.

Elementary results of tensor theory assert that the gradient of a scalar function is a tensor, and a sum of tensors is again a tensor. We may use these results and distributivity in $\mathbb{D}$ to conclude that the hypercomplex gradient of an analytic function is a tensor. That is, if

$$\mathrm{F} = \mathbf{1}X + \mathbf{i}Y + \mathbf{j}Z + \mathbf{k}T \ ,$$

then we can always write $\Box\,\mathrm{F}$ as

$$\Box\,\mathrm{F} = \mathbf{1}\Box\,X + \mathbf{i}\Box\,Y + \mathbf{j}\Box\,Z + \mathbf{k}\Box\,T \ ,$$

which is a tensor by inspection.

One may show explictly how form invariance occurs for two important classes of transformations. Equation (3.123) is invariant in form under any orthogonal transformation and even under any analytic function transformation of the independent variable in $\mathbb{D}$, as follows: For the general orthogonal transformation case, one may use (3.78) and the distributivity property to assert that

$$\Box \Gamma = \mathrm{A} \Box_1 \Gamma = 0 \,, \tag{3.128}$$

where A is the transformation matrix such that

$$\mathbf{Z}' = \mathrm{A}\mathbf{Z}$$

and (3.129)

$$\Box_1 = \mathbf{1}\frac{\partial}{\partial x'} + \mathbf{i}\frac{\partial}{\partial y'} + \mathbf{j}\frac{\partial}{\partial z'} + \mathbf{k}\frac{\partial}{\partial ct'} \,.$$

For the second part involving analytic function transformations of the independent variables, we use the notation in (3.91)–(3.93), the results in (3.103), and distributivity to assert that

$$\Box \Gamma = \Box X \Box_1 \Gamma = 0 \,, \tag{3.130}$$

where the independent variables are transformed according to an analytic hypercomplex function:

$$\mathbf{Z}' = \mathrm{F}(\mathbf{Z}) = \mathbf{1}X + \mathbf{i}Y + \mathbf{j}Z + \mathbf{k}T \,;$$

then (3.131)

$$\Box_1 = \mathbf{1}\frac{\partial}{\partial X} + \mathbf{i}\frac{\partial}{\partial Y} + \mathbf{j}\frac{\partial}{\partial Z} + \mathbf{k}\frac{\partial}{\partial T} \,.$$

It is a consequence of (3.67) that $\Box X = 0$ only if the four-gradients of the three other conjugate functions are zero (i.e., only if F is a constant). The desired result,

$$\Box_1 \Gamma = 0 ,$$

follows from (3.130). Put another way, *the form of (3.123) is invariant throughou the $\mathbb{D}$ analytic function space and under any orthogonal transformation i four dimensions.*

3.3 Some Ramifications For The Theory Of Partial Differential Equations

This section will present some nontraditional results concerning the solutio of partial differential equations. We shall find a new class of objects that satisf the given PDEs excluding boundary and initial conditions. We shall call thes objects *elementary Cartesian solutions*, or simply *elementary solutions*, becaus they will be expressed in the same coordinates as for the original PDE, whic are Cartesian in our case. The significance of these solutions is the same a that of the original PDE: they embody the space variation of any allowe formal solution including boundary conditions, about any given point in th solution space. These elementary solutions can give insight into the form tha an initial/boundary-value problem solution must assume. In the linear cases the elementary solutions are recognizable as combinations of already-know eigenfunctions of the differential operator. In the nonlinear cases, no comparabl solution may exist.

By "new class of objects" we mean functions of one hypercomplex variabl of dimension four, which may be expanded into a four dimensional vector valued function. This is an extension of the case wherein a complex-value function is a solution of some linear or nonlinear PDE having real scala coefficients. For a linear PDE, the vector components of the elementar Cartesian solutions are themselves scalar solutions of the PDE. For a nonlinea PDE, the vector components are usually not separate solutions of the give PDE. The corresponding situation in existing theory is any case of a nonlinea PDE that has a complex-valued solution. We are not at liberty to discar the imaginary component and expect that the real component, alone, will b a solution of the nonlinear equation. We shall see, also, that the existenc of the hypercomplex solutions assures the existence of pairs of classical complex valued solutions.

The results of this section are given with little discussion or suggeste applications, in the hope that someone will find some significance or usefulnes No attempt is made to tie the results into the existing theoretical framewor for partial differential equations. The technical difficulty in doing so is beyon the scope of this work. We also shall not address real-world problems an solutions involving boundary and initial conditions.

This section will illustrate a simple technique by which *partial differential equations may be converted into ordinary differential equations* and then may be easily solved for the elementary Cartesian solutions in the hypercomplex form. For the case of a linear differential operator, the vector components of the hypercomplex elementary solutions are themselves scalar solutions, obtained by a simpler method than separation of variables. We shall examine several of the more fundamental physics field theory equations, using the following notation:

$$\mathbf{Z} = \mathbf{1}x + \mathbf{i}y + \mathbf{j}z + \mathbf{k}ct \tag{3.132}$$

will represent the independent variable (note the use of ct for the **k**-component, because we shall be dealing with the real, physical four-space);

$$\mathbf{W(Z)} = \mathbf{1}U + \mathbf{i}R + \mathbf{j}V + \mathbf{k}S \tag{3.133}$$

with U, R, V, S real, scalar functions, will indicate an analytic field or vector function;

$$\Box = \mathbf{1}\frac{\partial}{\partial x} + \mathbf{i}\frac{\partial}{\partial y} + \mathbf{j}\frac{\partial}{\partial z} + \mathbf{k}\frac{\partial}{\partial ct} \tag{3.134}$$

will represent the four-dimensional gradient operator;

$$\Box^2 = \frac{\partial^2}{\partial x^2} + \frac{\partial^2}{\partial y^2} + \frac{\partial^2}{\partial z^2} + \frac{\partial^2}{\partial (ct)^2} \tag{3.135}$$

is the scalar quad squared operator in the $\mathbb{D}$-space; and

$$\Psi = \Psi(x,y,z,ct) \tag{3.136}$$

will indicate a scalar analytic function. We shall be concerned, with only two exceptions, with classical field equations. The reader may see Eisele[29] for a detailed presentation and analysis of relativistic electromagnetic and quantum physics equations in classical vector notation, especially the D'Alembertian, in forms that are easily translated into $\mathbb{D}$-space notation.

In the following, we shall start with some of the simpler linear, four-dimensional cases to illustrate the method, then work into nonlinear examples, both two and four-dimensional including time.

3.3.1 The Wave Equation

As a consequence of (3.87) and the linearity of the $\mathbb{D}$-space wave equation operator,

$$\Box^2 = \frac{\partial^2}{\partial x^2} + \frac{\partial^2}{\partial y^2} + \frac{\partial^2}{\partial z^2} + \frac{\partial^2}{\partial (ct)^2} ,$$

any analytic function satisfies the four-dimensional wave equation. This result in in agreement with existing theory wherein, for example, it is easy to show that any differentiable function $f(x-ct)$ or $f(x+ct)$ is a solution of the wave equation in one space dimension and time. We shall see, below, that this is not the case for most of the other PDEs that we shall examine.

3.3.2 Helmholtz's Equation

The Helmholtz equation for a scalar function U is

$$\nabla^2 U + \kappa^2 U = 0 , \tag{3.137}$$

where κ is a scalar. It occurs repeatedly when the more familiar field theory equations are being solved for their eigenfunctions by means of the separation of variables technique. We remarked earlier that one scalar, analytic component U plus the Cauchy-Riemann conditions (2.156) are sufficient to reconstruct a hypercomplex function. Accordingly, we first broaden the equation to operate on a vector function:

$$\mathbf{W}(\mathbf{Z}) = \mathbf{1}U + \mathbf{i}R + \mathbf{j}V + \mathbf{k}S . \tag{3.138}$$

The Helmholtz operator is linear and we have distributivity in $\mathbb{D}$, hence

$$\nabla^2 \mathbf{W} + \kappa^2 \mathbf{W} = 0 . \tag{3.139}$$

Equation (3.137) is implicit in (3.139) as the first vector component. We add and subtract the same time derivative quantity to complete a D'Alembertian operator from the scalar del operator and obtain

$$\Box^2\mathbf{W} - \frac{1}{c^2}\frac{\partial^2 \mathbf{W}}{\partial t^2} + \kappa^2 \mathbf{W} = 0 . \tag{3.140}$$

We now assume that we are dealing with an analytic function **W**. This is a reasonable assumption for most physical problems, inasmuch as it merely requires that **W** shall be continuous and single-valued in the four-space within some region of interest. As in complex variable theory, it does not matter that **W** globally may have some discontinuities; the region of interest is, typically, away from any discontinuities. By (2.169), taking account that *ct* is the time coordinate here, the isolated time partial derivative term converts to a full derivative of the hypercomplex variable **Z**, as follows.

$$\Box^2 \mathbf{W} - \frac{d^2\mathbf{W}}{d\mathbf{Z}^2} + \kappa^2 \mathbf{W} = 0 \; . \qquad (3.141)$$

The D'Alembertian term drops off because it is uniformly zero for any analytic function, leaving only

$$\frac{d^2\mathbf{W}}{d\mathbf{Z}^2} - \kappa^2 \mathbf{W} = 0 \; . \qquad (3.142)$$

One may integrate (3.142) to obtain

$$\mathbf{W}(\mathbf{Z}) = \mathbf{C}\ \mathrm{EXP}(-\kappa\mathbf{Z}) + \mathbf{D}\ \mathrm{EXP}(+\kappa\mathbf{Z}), \qquad (3.143)$$

where **C** and **D** are hypercomplex constants of integration. Form (3.143) is the general solution of (3.142) because of the two arbitrary constants. We have introduced time as an additional independent coordinate over the three in the original equation, but we shall show that **W** is nevertheless an elementary solution of (3.139) and implicitly contains an elementary solution of the original equation, (3.137). The extra coordinate may be used as a parameter, giving a one-parameter family of solutions.

Recall that for the wave equation any analytic function is an elementary Cartesian solution. There are an infinity of solutions. This does not appear to be the case for the Helmholtz equation, because (3.143) is an elementary Cartesian solution of the Helmholtz equation and is also a general solution of the associated ordinary differential equation, (3.142). One might logically ask: does (3.143) implicitly contain all elementary solutions of the Helmholtz equation, including all eigenfunctions? We shall see below that (3.143) expands into linear combinations of exponentially-decreasing and -increasing functions of sines and cosines that can be reduced in one space dimension and time to sums and differences of exponentials (hence sinh and cosh hyperbolic functions) or pure sine and cosine terms. All these are classical eigenfunctions of the Helmholtz equation.

To explicitly show that **W** satisfies equation (3.139), it is sufficient to show that the first hypercomplex term of **W**, which we shall denote by **Y**, satisfies (3.139). We may use ordinary exponential rules and write the first term of **W** in the form

$$\mathbf{Y} = \mathbf{C}\, e^{-\mathbf{1}\kappa x}\, e^{-\mathbf{i}\kappa y}\, e^{-\mathbf{j}\kappa z}\, e^{-\mathbf{k}\kappa ct} , \tag{3.144}$$

where the lower-case e denotes the exponential function, and note that we can use real or complex variable rules for taking partial derivatives; then

$$\begin{aligned}
\frac{\partial \mathbf{Y}}{\partial x} &= -\mathbf{1}\kappa \mathbf{Y} & \qquad \frac{\partial^2 \mathbf{Y}}{\partial x^2} &= \kappa^2 \mathbf{Y} \\
\frac{\partial \mathbf{Y}}{\partial y} &= -\mathbf{i}\kappa \mathbf{Y} & \qquad \frac{\partial^2 \mathbf{Y}}{\partial y^2} &= -\kappa^2 \mathbf{Y} \\
\frac{\partial \mathbf{Y}}{\partial z} &= -\mathbf{j}\kappa \mathbf{Y} & \qquad \frac{\partial^2 \mathbf{Y}}{\partial z^2} &= -\kappa^2 \mathbf{Y} ,
\end{aligned} \tag{3.145}$$

hence

$$\nabla^2 \mathbf{Y} + \kappa^2 \mathbf{Y} = 0 .$$

To show that U satisfies equation (3.137), we note that **W** is an analytic function that satisfies (3.137) and can be expanded in the form (3.138) [see (2.98) – (2.100)]. The Helmholtz operator is a linear operator which can operate on each component of **W** separately, hence we conclude that the first component, U, satisfies (3.137).

It is informative to see the specific form that **W** takes upon its expansion into vector components. Again, it is sufficiently illuminating to examine the first hypercomplex term, only, denoting it by **Y**. We first expand the exponential function:

$$\begin{aligned}
e^{-\kappa \mathbf{Z}} = \mathbf{1}\ &\{e^{-\kappa(x-ct)} \cos[\kappa(y+z)] \\
&\quad + e^{-\kappa(x+ct)} \cos[\kappa(y-z)]\} / 2 \\
&+ \mathbf{i}\ \{e^{-\kappa(x-ct)} \sin[\kappa(y+z)]
\end{aligned}$$

$$
\begin{aligned}
&\quad + e^{-\kappa(x+ct)}\sin[\kappa(y+z)]\}/2 \\
&+ \mathbf{j}\ \{e^{-\kappa(x-ct)}\sin[\kappa(y+z)] \\
&\quad - e^{-\kappa(x+ct)}\sin[\kappa(y-z)]\}/2 \\
&+ \mathbf{k}\ \{-\ e^{-\kappa(x-ct)}\cos[\kappa(y+z)] \\
&\quad + e^{-\kappa(x+ct)}\cos[\kappa(y-z)]\}/2\ ,
\end{aligned}
\tag{3.146}
$$

and if we use the notation

$$
\begin{aligned}
e^{-\kappa\mathbf{Z}} &= \mathbf{1}u + \mathbf{i}r + \mathbf{j}v + \mathbf{k}s \\
\mathbf{C} &= \mathbf{1}c_1 + \mathbf{i}c_2 + \mathbf{j}c_3 + \mathbf{k}c_4\ ,
\end{aligned}
\tag{3.147}
$$

then

$$
\begin{aligned}
\mathbf{Y} = \mathbf{1}\ &[c_1u - c_2r - c_3v + c_4s] \\
+ \mathbf{i}\ &[c_2u + c_1r - c_4v - c_3s] \\
+ \mathbf{j}\ &[c_3u - c_4r + c_1v - c_2s] \\
+ \mathbf{k}\ &[c_4u + c_3r + c_2v + c_1s]\ .
\end{aligned}
\tag{3.148}
$$

The components c_i of the hypercomplex constant $\mathbf{C}$ are abitrary, and can be selected to suit the boundary conditions. This being so, equation (3.148) and the linearity of the Helmholtz operator implies that *any component of the hypercomplex exponential (3.146) or any linear combination of the components is an elementary solution of Helmholtz' equation.* Moreover, (3.148) gives us the ability to take sums and differences of the components of (3.146), and the components themselves are sums and differences of the components of the complex eigenvalues $f(\xi)$ and $f(\eta)$, hence any term of any component in (3.146) is an elementary solution of Helmholtz' equation. The same statements hold for the $\mathbf{D}\ \mathrm{EXP}(+\kappa\mathbf{Z})$ term.

It is known that the Helmholtz equation does not have a single, simple solution such as (3.143) for all boundary conditions, so what are we to make of the present results? In keeping with the analogy with the real and complex analysis, the elementary Cartesian solution $\mathbf{W}$ in the form of (3.143) is an *hypercomplex eigenfunction of the Helmholtz operator* with an eigenvalue of $-\kappa^2$, and the components and separate terms of the components of (3.148) are real eigenfunctions with the same eigenvalue. As such, the form of **W** contains the essence of the Helmholtz equation and the physics upon which it is based. In a multidimensional problem, one would build up a series solution with terms of the form (3.143) or any of its vector components, but with different values of κ, just as in real analysis. *We have discovered a new means of finding eigenfunctions for a linear partial differential operator.*

Another interpretation of (3.143) is that it is a *point solution*: it describes the behavior of a Helmholtz solution about any fixed point in the medium. In the present case, the fixed, observer's point is the origin of coordinates, which can be moved about at will. In relation to the value of the solution at the origin, the solution in the surrounding medium varies as a function of relative position **Z** as given by (3.143). This should be of significance to numerical analysis of Helmholtz problems because, for example, (3.143) can be used to devise better predictor-corrector methods. One could use (3.143) itself for this purpose, but it would be a rather compute-intensive process. Instead, the function approximation techniques from complex analysis could be used to devise a compute- efficient approximation of (3.143).

So far, no conditions have been put upon the possible values of κ. *It is the boundary conditions that force certain values of the parameter* κ.

The technique of completing the D'Alembertian operator and then converting partial derivatives into full hypercomplex derivatives in terms of one hypercomplex variable **Z** has wide applicability in physics field theory, because so many physics equations include the scalar del operator.

3.3.3 Klein-Gordon Equation

The Klein-Gordon equation for a free subatomic particle of spin zero has the form

$$\Box^2 \Psi - \kappa^2 \Psi = 0, \tag{3.149}$$

where κ is a scalar. Classically, the D'Alembertian in (3.149) has a minus sign in front of the time derivative; but it is only a matter of a unitary transformation to change the sign to the positive. We now replace Ψ with an analytic vector function **W** in (3.149), obtaining

$$\Box^2 \mathbf{W} - \kappa^2 \mathbf{W} = 0\,, \tag{3.150}$$

and we still have (3.149) as the first vector component. The D'Alembertian term is uniformly zero for any analytic function **W**, leaving only

$$\mathbf{W} = 0 . \tag{3.151}$$

Physics experiments indicate that **W** is not a null function in three dimensions. One concludes that **W** is either not analytic, or is the hypercomplex gradient of some analytic potential function **P**, which is uniformly zero:

$$\mathbf{W} = \Box \mathbf{P} \equiv 0 . \tag{3.152}$$

If (3.152) holds, then any analytic function satisfies the Klein-Gordon equation.

3.3.4 The Diffusion Equation In Three Spatial Dimensions

The three-dimensional diffusion equation is of the form

$$\nabla^2 U - \kappa \frac{\partial U}{\partial t} = 0 , \tag{3.153}$$

where κ is a scalar. The symbol U represents a scalar field, typically representing temperature in a solid. One may use the Cauchy-Riemann conditions (2.156) and the scalar analytic function U to assert the existence of an analytic, hypercomplex function **W** such that

$$\nabla^2 \mathbf{W} - \kappa \frac{\partial \mathbf{W}}{\partial t} = 0 . \tag{3.154}$$

Equation (3.153) is implicit in (3.154) as the first vector component. As we did for the Helmholtz equation, we complete the D'Alembertian from the scalar del term to obtain

$$\Box^2 \mathbf{W} - \frac{\partial^2 \mathbf{W}}{\partial (ct)^2} - \kappa c \frac{\partial \mathbf{W}}{\partial (ct)} = 0 . \tag{3.155}$$

We eliminate the D'Alembertian term because it is uniformly zero for any analytic function, then convert the partial derivatives to full hypercomplex derivatives by means of (2.169):

$$\frac{d^2\mathbf{W}}{d\mathbf{Z}^2} + \kappa c\mathbf{k}\,\frac{d\mathbf{W}}{d\mathbf{Z}} = 0\ . \tag{3.156}$$

This reduces to

$$\frac{d}{d\mathbf{W}}\left[\frac{d\mathbf{W}}{dZ} + \kappa c\mathbf{k}\mathbf{W}\right] = 0\ ,$$

(3.157)

$$\frac{d\mathbf{W}}{d\mathbf{Z}} + \kappa c\mathbf{k}\mathbf{W} = \kappa c\mathbf{k}\mathbf{G}\ , \qquad \text{(a constant)}$$

with **G** arbitrary and $\kappa c\mathbf{k}\mathbf{G}$ being a convenient form for the hypercomplex constant of integration. We now integrate (3.157) to obtain the elementary Cartesian solution for the diffusion equation:

$$\mathbf{W}(\mathbf{Z}) = \mathbf{G} + \mathbf{C}\ \mathrm{EXP}(-\kappa c\mathbf{k}\mathbf{Z})\ , \tag{3.158}$$

where **C** is another hypercomplex constant of integration. Form (3.158) is the general solution of (3.156) because of the two arbitrary constants. Evidently, the set of elementary Cartesian solutions of the diffusion equation is not infinite in extent. As in the case of the Helmholtz equation, the explicit solution **W** of the associated hypercomplex ordinary differential equation is an elementary solution of the vector diffusion equation, (3.154), and its vector components are elementary solutions of the scalar diffusion equation, (3.153). It is not clear whether or not **W** is an eigenfunction of the diffusion operator. One could view (3.158) as a point solution and use a process reminiscent of complex analytic continuation to numerically "bridge" a solution between the boundaries.

The hypercomplex elementary solutions (3.158) for the diffusion equation are very similar to (3.143), the elementary solutions for the the Helmholtz equation, differing principally in the presence of the **k** factor in the exponential argument. Recall that in the matrix interpretation, **k** is an orthogonal transformation; when applied to **Z**, it merely produces a rotation, which will leave the exponential expression in the same form. Form (3.158) is expanded as follows:

$$e^{-\kappa c\mathbf{k}\mathbf{Z}} = \mathbf{1}\ \{e^{+\kappa c(x-ct)}\cos\left[\kappa c(y+z)\right]$$

$$
\begin{aligned}
&\quad + e^{-\kappa c(x+ct)} \cos[\kappa c(y-z)]\}/2 \\
&+ \mathbf{i}\{-e^{+\kappa c(x-ct)} \sin[\kappa c(y+z)] \\
&\quad + e^{-\kappa c(x+ct)} \sin[\kappa c(y-z)]\}/2 \\
&+ \mathbf{j}\{-e^{+\kappa c(x-ct)} \sin[\kappa c(y+z)] \\
&\quad - e^{-\kappa c(x+ct)} \sin[\kappa c(y-z)]\}/2 \\
&+ \mathbf{k}\{-e^{+\kappa c(x-ct)} \cos[\kappa c(y+z)] \\
&\quad + e^{-\kappa c(x+ct)} \cos[\kappa c(y-z)]\}/2,
\end{aligned} \tag{3.159}
$$

and if we use the notation

$$
e^{-\kappa c\mathbf{k}\mathbf{Z}} = \mathbf{1}u + \mathbf{i}r + \mathbf{j}v + \mathbf{k}s \tag{3.160}
$$

$$
\mathbf{G} = \mathbf{1}g_1 + \mathbf{i}g_2 + \mathbf{j}g_3 + \mathbf{k}g_4
$$

$$
\mathbf{C} = \mathbf{1}c_1 + \mathbf{i}c_2 + \mathbf{j}c_3 + \mathbf{k}c_4 \ ,
$$

then

$$
\begin{aligned}
\mathbf{W} = \mathbf{1}&[g_1 + c_1 u - c_2 r - c_3 v + c_4 s] \\
&+ \mathbf{i}[g_2 + c_2 u + c_1 r - c_4 v - c_3 s] \\
&+ \mathbf{j}[g_3 + c_3 u - c_4 r + c_1 v - c_2 s] \\
&+ \mathbf{k}[g_4 + c_4 u + c_3 r + c_2 v + c_1 s] \ .
\end{aligned} \tag{3.161}
$$

Explicitly, the first component [a solution of the original equation, (3.153)] is:

$$
\begin{aligned}
U = g_1 &+ c_1\{e^{+\kappa c(x-ct)} cos[\kappa c(y+z)] \\
&\quad + e^{-\kappa c(x+ct)} cos[\kappa c(y-z)]\}/2 \\
&- c_2\{- e^{+\kappa c(x-ct)} sin[\kappa c(y+z)]
\end{aligned}
$$

$$+ \ e^{-\kappa c(x+ct)} sin[\kappa c(y-z)]\}/2 \qquad (3.162)$$

$$- \ c_3\{- \ e^{+\kappa c(x-ct)} sin[\kappa c(y+z)]$$

$$- \ e^{-\kappa c(x+ct)} sin[\kappa c(y-z)]\}/2$$

$$+ \ c_4\{- \ e^{+\kappa c(x-ct)} cos[\kappa c(y+z)]$$

$$+ \ e^{-\kappa c(x+ct)} cos[\kappa c(y-z)]\}/2 \ .$$

The components c_i and g_i of the hypercomplex constants **C** and **G**, respectivel are arbitrary, and can be selected to suit the boundary conditions. This bein so, equation (3.161) and the linearity of the diffusion operator implies th *any component of the hypercomplex exponential (3.159) or any linea combination of the components is an elementary solution of the diffusio equation.* Moreover, (3.161) gives us the ability to take sums and differenc of the components of (3.159), and the components themselves are sums an differences of the components of the complex eigenvalues $f(\xi)$ and $f(\eta)$, henc any term of any component in (3.159) is an elementary solution of the diffusio equation.

The constant c, the speed of light in a vacuum, was introduced when w converted the first partial derivative with respect to time to the same wit respect to ct in order to obtain dimensional consistency with the oth components of **Z**. In real material media, the relative scales could be chose such that c is the diffusion speed through the medium.

The similarity of the hypercomplex elementary solutions (3.143) and (3.15 indicates a close theoretical relationship between processes governed by th diffusion equation and those governed by the Helmholtz equation. In fac for certain values of their respective constants *the two forms can be the san* to within an orthogonal transformation of the independent variable.

3.3.5 The Diffusion Equation In One Spatial Dimension And Time

Up to now, our examples have concerned a dependent variable dimensionality four, whose components are scalar functions of four independe coordinates. We give the following example to show how to handle cases where the partial differential equation is for less than four dimensions (includi time). Generally, the method is to start from the given differential equati with the given dimensionality and and solve it for a dependent variable dimensionality four, then set the unneeded independent coordinates to ze for the reduced elementary solution. The one-dimensional (plus time) diffusion equation is of the form

$$\frac{\partial^2 U}{\partial x^2} - \kappa \frac{\partial U}{\partial t} = 0 \ , \qquad (3.163)$$

where κ is a scalar. The symbol U represents a scalar field, typically representing temperature in a solid. We go directly to the larger problem:

$$\frac{\partial^2 \mathbf{W}}{\partial x^2} - \kappa \frac{\partial \mathbf{W}}{\partial t} = 0 \ , \qquad (3.164)$$

with

$$\mathbf{W} = \mathbf{1}U + \mathbf{i}R + \mathbf{j}V + \mathbf{k}S \ .$$

Equation (3.163) is implicit in (3.164) as the first vector component. We next convert the partial derivatives to full hypercomplex derivatives by means of (2.169):

$$\frac{d^2 \mathbf{W}}{d\mathbf{Z}^2} - \kappa c \mathbf{k} \frac{d\mathbf{W}}{d\mathbf{Z}} = 0 \ . \qquad (3.165)$$

This reduces to

$$\frac{d}{d\mathbf{Z}} \left[\frac{d\mathbf{W}}{d\mathbf{Z}} - \kappa c \mathbf{k} \mathbf{W} \right] = 0 \ , \qquad (3.166)$$

$$\frac{d\mathbf{W}}{d\mathbf{Z}} - \kappa c \mathbf{k} \mathbf{W} = -\kappa c \mathbf{k} \mathbf{G} \ , \qquad \text{(a constant)}$$

with **G** arbitrary and $\kappa c \mathbf{k} \mathbf{G}$ being a convenient form for the hypercomplex constant of integration. We now integrate (3.166) to obtain the elementary solution for the diffusion equation:

$$\mathbf{W}(\mathbf{Z}) = \mathbf{G} + \mathbf{C} \ \mathrm{EXP}(+\kappa c \mathbf{k} \mathbf{Z}) \ , \qquad (3.167)$$

where **C** is another hypercomplex constant of integration. Form (3.167) is the general solution of (3.165) because of the two arbitrary constants. As in the case of the Helmholtz equation, the explicit solution **W** of the associated hypercomplex ordinary differential equation is an elementary solution of the vector diffusion equation, (3.164), and its vector components are elementary solutions of the scalar diffusion equation, (3.163). It is not clear whether or not **W** is an eigenfunction of the one-dimensional diffusion operator. Instead one could view (3.167) as a point solution and use a process reminiscent of complex analytic continuation to numerically "bridge" a solution between the boundaries.

The hypercomplex elementary solutions (3.167) for the one-dimensional diffusion equation are very similar to (3.143), the eigenfunctions for the the Helmholtz equation, differing principally in the presence of the **k** factor in the exponential argument. Recall that in the matrix interpretation, **k** is an orthogonal transformation; when applied to **Z**, it merely produces a rotation which will leave the exponential expression in the same form. Form (3.167) is expanded as follows:

$$
\begin{aligned}
e^{+\kappa c \mathbf{k}\mathbf{Z}} = \; & \mathbf{1}\{e^{-\kappa c(x-ct)} cos\,[\kappa c(y+z)] \\
& \quad + e^{+\kappa c(x+ct)} cos\,[\kappa c(y-z)]\}/2 \\
& + \mathbf{i}\{-e^{-\kappa c(x-ct)} sin\,[\kappa c(y+z)] \\
& \quad + e^{+\kappa c(x+ct)} sin\,[\kappa c(y-z)]\}/2 \\
& + \mathbf{j}\{-e^{-\kappa c(x-ct)} sin\,[\kappa c(y+z)] \\
& \quad - e^{+\kappa c(x+ct)} sin\,[\kappa c(y-z)]\}/2 \\
& + \mathbf{k}\{-e^{-\kappa c(x-ct)} cos\,[\kappa c(y+z)] \\
& \quad + e^{+\kappa c(x+ct)} cos\,[\kappa c(y-z)]\}/2,
\end{aligned}
\tag{3.168}
$$

and if we use the notation

$$e^{\kappa c \mathbf{k}\mathbf{Z}} = \mathbf{1}u + \mathbf{i}r + \mathbf{j}v + \mathbf{k}s \tag{3.169}$$

$$\mathbf{G} = \mathbf{1}g_1 + \mathbf{i}g_2 + \mathbf{j}g_3 + \mathbf{k}g_4$$

$$\mathbf{C} = \mathbf{1}c_1 + \mathbf{i}c_2 + \mathbf{j}c_3 + \mathbf{k}c_4 ,$$

then

$$\begin{aligned} \mathbf{W} = \mathbf{1}&[g_1 + c_1 u - c_2 r - c_3 v + c_4 s] \\ &+ \mathbf{i}[g_2 + c_2 u + c_1 r - c_4 v - c_3 s] \\ &+ \mathbf{j}[g_3 + c_3 u - c_4 r + c_1 v - c_2 s] \\ &+ \mathbf{k}[g_4 + c_4 u + c_3 r + c_2 v + c_1 s] . \end{aligned} \tag{3.170}$$

Explicitly, the first component [an elementary solution of the original equation, (3.163)] is:

$$\begin{aligned} U = g_1 &+ c_1\{e^{-\kappa c(x-ct)} \cos[\kappa c(y+z)] \\ &\qquad + e^{+\kappa c(x+ct)} \cos[\kappa c(y-z)]\}/2 \\ &- c_2\{-e^{-\kappa c(x-ct)} \sin[\kappa c(y+z)] \\ &\qquad + e^{\kappa c(x+ct)} \sin[\kappa c(y-z)]\}/2 \\ &- c_3\{-e^{-\kappa c(x-ct)} \sin[\kappa c(y+z)] \\ &\qquad - e^{\kappa c(x+ct)} \sin[\kappa c(y-z)]\}/2 \\ &+ c_4\{-e^{-\kappa c(x-ct)} \cos[\kappa c(y+z)] \\ &\qquad + e^{\kappa c(x+ct)} \cos[\kappa c(y-z)]\}/2 . \end{aligned} \tag{3.171}$$

We could use (3.171) as is for an elementary solution of (3.163) and consider y and z to be parameters, giving a two-parameter family of solutions. Specifically, if we set $y = z = 0$, we have an elementary solution in only x and ct:

$$U = g_1 + c_1[e^{-\kappa c(x-ct)} + e^{\kappa c(x+ct)}]/2 \tag{3.172}$$

$$+ \; c_4[- e^{-\kappa c(x-ct)} + e^{\kappa c(x+ct)}]/2$$

with g_1, c_1, and c_4 arbitrary constants.

3.3.6 Schrödinger's Equation For A Particle In A Cubic Box

If a subatomic particle, such as an electron, is constrained to motion in a perfect cube-shaped space whose walls are perfectly repelling, then the Schrödinger equation for the probability density function Ψ is

$$\nabla^2\Psi + \mathrm{i}\kappa^2 \frac{\partial\Psi}{\partial(ct)} = 0 \; , \tag{3.173}$$

with

$$\kappa = 2mc/\hbar \; ,$$

where m is the mass of the particle and $\hbar$ is a constant, proportional to Planck's constant. The function Ψ is known to be complex-valued. Before we attack the full equation, (3.173), let us consider a special case:

$$\frac{\partial^2\Psi}{\partial x^2} + \mathrm{i}\kappa^2 \frac{\partial\Psi}{\partial(ct)} = 0 \; , \tag{3.174}$$

and assume Ψ in the form

$$\Psi = u + \mathrm{i}v \; , \tag{3.175}$$

with u,v real, scalar functions. With this notation, Equation (3.174) becomes

$$\frac{\partial^2}{\partial x^2}(u+iv) + \mathrm{i}\kappa^2 \frac{\partial}{\partial(ct)}(u+iv) \tag{3.176}$$

$$= \left[\frac{\partial^2 u}{\partial x^2} - \kappa^2 \frac{\partial v}{\partial(ct)}\right] + i \left[\frac{\partial^2 v}{\partial x^2} + \kappa^2 \frac{\partial u}{\partial(ct)}\right] = 0 \; ,$$

or

$$\frac{\partial^2 u}{\partial x^2} - \kappa^2 \frac{\partial v}{\partial(ct)} = 0 \tag{3.177}$$

$$\frac{\partial^2 v}{\partial x^2} - \kappa^2 \frac{\partial u}{\partial(ct)} = 0 .$$

We have reduced the original equation to its complex components. We can now see that the "i" in (3.173) acts as a rotation operator, and the component equations (3.177) indicate some kind of exchange (a "current"?) between the components of Ψ. We want to preserve this vector-operator behavior in four dimensions.

If we replace the "i" in (3.173) with the four-dimensional "**i**," we shall see that the desired behavior is preserved in the higher-dimensional case. (The four-dimensional "**i**" has all the properties of the classical imaginary). We complete the D'Alembertian as we did for the Helmholtz equation and expand our equation to consider a four-dimensional field **W**, of which Ψ corresponds to the first two components, then eliminate the D'Alembertian term to obtain

$$-\frac{\partial^2 \mathbf{W}}{\partial(ct)^2} + \mathbf{i}\kappa^2 \frac{\partial \mathbf{W}}{\partial(ct)} = 0 . \qquad (3.178)$$

We next use (2.169) to convert the partial derivatives to ordinary derivatives:

$$\frac{d^2\mathbf{W}}{d\mathbf{Z}^2} - \mathbf{i}\kappa^2\, \mathbf{k}\frac{d\mathbf{W}}{d\mathbf{Z}} \qquad (3.179)$$

$$= \frac{d^2\mathbf{W}}{d\mathbf{Z}^2} + \mathbf{j}\kappa^2 \frac{d\mathbf{W}}{d\mathbf{Z}}$$

$$= \frac{d}{d\mathbf{Z}}\left[\frac{d\mathbf{W}}{d\mathbf{Z}} + \mathbf{j}\kappa^2\, \mathbf{W}\right] = 0 , \qquad (3.180)$$

which is the same as

$$\frac{d\mathbf{W}}{d\mathbf{Z}} + \mathbf{j}\kappa^2\mathbf{W} = \mathbf{j}\kappa^2\mathbf{G} . \qquad \text{(a constant)} \qquad (3.181)$$

This integrates immediately to

$$\mathbf{W}(\mathbf{Z}) = \mathbf{G} + \mathbf{C}\,\mathrm{EXP}(-\kappa^2\mathbf{j}\mathbf{Z}) , \qquad (3.182)$$

a hypercomplex elementary solution, with **C** and **G** being arbitrary hypercomplex constants of integration which we may use to satisfy the boundary conditions. Again, the two arbitrary constants in (3.182) indicate that we have a general solution of (3.180). Equation (3.181) is the same, within an orthogonal transformation of the independent variable **Z**, as the reduced form (3.157) of the diffusion equation.

The **W**(**Z**) functional form, (3.182), can be expanded exactly as we did for the corresponding diffusion equation form, (3.158), if we take account of the **j** in the exponential argument. The result is

$$
\begin{aligned}
e^{-\kappa^2 \mathbf{Z}} = \mathbf{1}\, \{ & e^{\kappa^2 (y+z)} \cos[\kappa^2(x-ct)] \\
& + \{e^{-\kappa^2 (y-z)} \cos[\kappa^2(x+ct)]\}/2 \\
+\ \mathbf{i}\, \{ & - e^{\kappa^2 (y+z)} \sin[\kappa^2(x-ct)] \\
& + \{e^{-\kappa^2 (y-z)} \sin[\kappa^2(x+ct)]\}/2 \\
+\ \mathbf{j}\, \{ & - e^{\kappa^2 (y+z)} \sin[\kappa^2(x-ct)] \\
& - e^{-\kappa^2 (y-z)} \sin[\kappa^2(x+ct)]\}/2 \\
+\ \mathbf{k}\, \{ & - e^{\kappa^2 (yz)} \cos[\kappa^2(x-ct)] \\
& + e^{-\kappa^2 (y-z)} \cos[\kappa^2(x+ct)]\}/2 \ ,
\end{aligned}
\tag{3.183}
$$

and if we use the notation

$$
\mathbf{e}^{-\kappa^2 \mathbf{jZ}} = \mathbf{1}u + \mathbf{i}r + \mathbf{j}v + \mathbf{k}s \tag{3.184}
$$

$$
\mathbf{G} = \mathbf{1}g_1 + \mathbf{i}g_2 + \mathbf{j}g_3 + \mathbf{k}g_4
$$

$$
\mathbf{C} = \mathbf{1}c_1 + \mathbf{i}c_2 + \mathbf{j}c_3 + \mathbf{k}c_4 \ ,
$$

then

$$
\mathbf{W} = \mathbf{1}\ [g_1 + \mathrm{c}_1\mathrm{u} - \mathrm{c}_2\mathrm{r} - \mathrm{c}_3\mathrm{v} + \mathrm{c}_4\mathrm{s}]
$$

$$+ \mathbf{i}\ [g_2 + c_2 u + c_1 r - c_4 v - c_3 s]$$

$$+ \mathbf{j}\ [g_3 + c_3 u - c_4 r + c_1 v - c_2 s]$$

$$+ \mathbf{k}\ [g_4 + c_4 u + c_3 r + c_2 v + c_1 s]\ . \qquad (3.185)$$

The components c_n and g_n of the hypercomplex constants **C** and **G**, respectively, are arbitrary, and can be selected to satisfy the boundary conditions. This being so, equation (3.185) and the linearity of the Schrödinger operator implies that *any component of the hypercomplex exponential (3.183) or any linear combination of the components is an elementary solution of this particular Schrödinger equation.* Moreover, (3.185) gives us the ability to take sums and differences of the components of (3.183), and the components themselves are sums and differences of the components of the complex eigenvalues $f(\xi)$ and $f(\eta)$, hence any term of any component in (3.183) is an elementary solution of this particular Schrödinger equation.

So far, no conditions have been put upon the possible values of κ. *It is the boundary conditions that force certain values of the parameter* κ. The hypercomplex elementary solution (3.182) is doubly periodic, as may be seen from the following: one may write (3.182) in the form

$$\mathbf{W}(\mathbf{Z}) = \mathbf{G} + \mathbf{C}\ e^{\kappa^2 z}\, e^{\mathbf{i}\kappa^2 ct}\, e^{-\mathbf{j}\kappa^2 x}\, e^{-\mathbf{k}\kappa^2 y}\ , \qquad (3.186)$$

and since **i** and **j** both have the properties of the classical complex imaginary "i," then **W** is periodic in x and ct. One can perform an orthogonal transformation on the independent coordinates x, y, z, ct in such a way that x and ct are each replaced by a linear combination of the transformed coordinates x', y', z', ct'; then, **W** is periodic in all four transformed coordinates.

3.3.7 Schrödinger's Equation For The Hydrogen Atom

The probability density Ψ for the three-space location of the electron in a hydrogen atom is determined by a particular case of the Schrödinger equation, commonly written

$$\frac{\hbar^2}{2\mu}\nabla^2\Psi + \left[\frac{e'^2}{r} + E\right]\Psi = 0\ , \qquad (3.187)$$

where r is the radial distance of the electron from the nucleus,

$$e'^2 = \frac{e^2}{2\pi\varepsilon_o}$$

represents the charge on the electron (and on the nucleus, but of opposite sign), μ is the reduced mass of the electron in center-of-mass coordinates, ε_o and h are physical constants, and E is the energy state of the electron. As we did for the earlier equations that we have examined, we expand the scalar (complex) function Ψ to a vector function indicated by a boldface **Ψ**, of which the complex Ψ represents the first two components. Our first action toward solution will be to replace the "r" in the denominator with the hypercomplex variable **Z**, recognizing the fact that, for any given position vector **r** we can align our coordinate frame such that $\mathbf{Z} = \mathbf{1}r + \mathbf{k}ct$; then

$$\frac{\hbar^2}{2\mu} \nabla^2 \Psi + \left[\frac{e'^2}{\mathbf{Z}} + E \right] \Psi = 0 \ , \tag{3.188}$$

Next, we complete and eliminate the D'Alembertian, leaving

$$\frac{\hbar^2}{2\mu} \left[- \frac{\partial^2 \Psi}{\partial (ct)^2} \right] + \left[\frac{e'^2}{\mathbf{Z}} + E \right] \Psi = 0 \ , \tag{3.189}$$

Lastly, we convert the partial derivative to an ordinary derivative by means of (2.169), rearrange, and solve, obtaining

$$\frac{d^2\Psi}{d\mathbf{Z}^2} - \frac{2\mu}{\hbar^2} \left[\frac{e'^2}{\mathbf{Z}} + E \right] \Psi = 0 \ , \tag{3.190}$$

$$\Psi(\mathbf{Z}) = \mathbf{C} \ \mathbf{iZ} \, \mathrm{EXP}(-\mathbf{iDZ}) \ , \tag{3.191}$$

with **C** an arbitrary hypercomplex constant of integration, available for normalization purposes. The hypercomplex constant **D** is not arbitrary, but is fixed by the form of the original equation, as follows. If (3.191) is to be an elementary solution of (3.190), we must require

$$\frac{d^2\Psi}{d\mathbf{Z}^2} - \left[\frac{2\mathbf{iD}}{\mathbf{Z}} + \mathbf{D}^2 \right] \Psi = 0 \ . \tag{3.192}$$

A comparison with (3.190) shows that we must have

$$\mathbf{D} = \frac{\mu e'^2}{\mathbf{i}\,\hbar^2} . \tag{3.193}$$

Another comparison with (3.190) shows that

$$\frac{2\mu E}{\hbar^2} = \mathbf{D}^2 , \tag{3.194}$$

hence E is also fixed by the form of the original equation to

$$E = -\frac{\mu e'^4}{2\,\hbar^2} . \tag{3.195}$$

This is the *ground state energy* of the electron in a hydrogen atom, hence we have found the *hypercomplex ground state wave function*, $\Psi(\mathbf{Z})$ in Cartesian coordinates. The other energy state wave functions are the same except with $\hbar$ replaced with $n\hbar$. The expression for the allowed energies is then

$$E = -\frac{\mu e^A}{2n^2\,\hbar^2} \quad , \quad n \quad 1, 2, 3, \ldots \qquad 3.196)$$

These are the *quantized energy states* of the electron in the hydrogen atom, the same as have been found by earlier methods and have been verified by experiment. We have specified that n should have only positive integer values because that is what nature apparently requires; the original equation holds true for noninteger values as well. Perhaps boundary conditions can be invoked to formally restrict n to integer values. Form (3.191) represents the *hypercomplex elementary solution* in Cartesian coordinates for this particular Schrödinger equation. Its components are scalar elementary solutions, stated in a Cartesian coordinate system. Statements of (3.191) in other coordinate systems may be obtained by transforming the independent coordinates x, y, z into the alternate system.

3.3.8 Burger's Equation

The Burger's equation is

$$\lambda\ U_{xx} - U\ U_x - U_t = 0\ , \tag{3.197}$$

and has been used as a model of turbulence in fluid dynamics. The subscripts indicate partial derivatives and also indicate that the elementary solution will be a function of only x and t. This equation is especially amenable to the hypercomplex methods that have been developed above. Specifically, we solve the larger problem

$$\lambda\ \mathbf{W}_{xx} - \mathbf{W}\ \mathbf{W}_x - \mathbf{W}_t = 0\ , \tag{3.198}$$

with

$$\mathbf{W} = \mathbf{1}U + \mathbf{i}R + \mathbf{j}V + \mathbf{k}S\ ,$$

in the varibles x,y,z,ct and later set $y\!=\!z\!=\!0$ to obtain the $\mathbf{W}(x,t)$ solution. The process is started by replacing the partial derivatives in (3.198) with ordinary derivatives by means of (2.169):

$$\lambda\ \frac{d^2\mathbf{W}}{d\mathbf{Z}^2} - \mathbf{W}\ \frac{d\mathbf{W}}{d\mathbf{Z}} - \mathbf{k}\frac{c\,d\mathbf{W}}{d\mathbf{Z}} = 0\ ,$$

$$\lambda\ \frac{d^2\mathbf{W}}{d\mathbf{Z}^2} - \frac{1}{2}\ \frac{d\mathbf{W}^2}{d\mathbf{Z}} - \mathbf{k}\frac{c\,d\mathbf{W}}{d\mathbf{Z}} = 0\ , \tag{3.199}$$

$$\frac{d}{d\mathbf{Z}}\left[\lambda\ \frac{d\mathbf{W}}{d\mathbf{Z}} - \frac{\mathbf{W}^2}{2} - \mathbf{k}c\mathbf{W}\right] = 0\ ,$$

$$\lambda\ \frac{d\mathbf{W}}{d\mathbf{Z}} - \frac{\mathbf{W}^2}{2} - \mathbf{k}c\mathbf{W} = \mathbf{C}\ , \qquad \text{(a constant)} \tag{3.200}$$

$$\frac{d\mathbf{W}}{d\mathbf{Z}} = \frac{\lambda^{-1}}{2}\ (\mathbf{W}^2 + 2\mathbf{k}c\mathbf{W} + 2\mathbf{C})\ ,$$

with $\mathbf{C}$ a hypercomplex constant of integration. We can complete the squar on the right-hand side and rearrange to obtain

$$\frac{d\mathbf{W}}{(\mathbf{W}\mathbf{k}c)^2 + \mathbf{D}^2} = \frac{\lambda^{-1}}{2}\; d\mathbf{Z} \;, \tag{3.201}$$

where we have collected constants into a new, arbitrary constant $\mathbf{D}^2 = 2\mathbf{C} - c^2$. Form (3.201) integrates to

$$\frac{1}{\mathbf{D}}\,\mathrm{TAN}^{-1}\left[\frac{\mathbf{W} + \mathbf{k}c}{\mathbf{D}}\right] = \frac{\lambda^{-1}}{2}\,\mathbf{Z} + \mathbf{G} \;, \tag{3.202}$$

with **G** another arbitrary constant of integration. This may be solved for **W**, explicitly:

$$\mathbf{W} = -\mathbf{k}c + \mathbf{D}\,\mathrm{TAN}\;[\mathbf{D}\,(\frac{\lambda^{-1}}{2}\,\mathbf{Z} + \mathbf{G})] \;. \tag{3.203}$$

This is a general solution of (3.198) inasmuch as it contains two arbitrary constants of integration. This implies that the number of functional forms that satisfy (3.197) is limited. Because the original equation is nonlinear, we cannot use (3.203) in a linear superposition scheme (eigenfunction expansion). Perhaps a nonlinear superposition scheme could be devised. On the other hand, we could view (3.203) as a point solution giving the *variation* of the field about the origin, which we may move about at will, and use it in a numerical scheme to "bridge" a solution between the boundaries.

The elementary Cartesian solution of the original equation, (3.197), is the expression (3.203), with y and z set to zero. We can expand (3.203) by means of the general expansion formula, (2.99). In doing so, we shall use the following notation:

$$\begin{aligned}
\mathbf{D} &= \mathbf{1}d_1 + \mathbf{i}d_2 + \mathbf{j}d_3 + \mathbf{k}d_4 \;, \\
&= \xi_d\mathbf{e}_1 + \eta_d\mathbf{e}_2 \;, \qquad\qquad (3.204) \\
\mathbf{G} &= \mathbf{1}g_1 + \mathbf{i}g_2 + \mathbf{j}g_3 + \mathbf{k}g_4 \;, \\
&= \xi_g\mathbf{e}_1 + \eta_g\mathbf{e}_2 \;, \\
-\mathbf{k}c &= c\mathbf{e}_1 - c\mathbf{e}_2 \;,
\end{aligned}$$

$$\mathbf{Z} = \mathbf{1}x + \mathbf{i}y + \mathbf{j}z + \mathbf{k}ct \ ,$$
$$= \xi \mathbf{e}_1 + \eta \mathbf{e}_2 \ .$$

In these terms, and by the general definition of a hypercomplex function, the elementary solution (3.203) is

$$\mathbf{W} = \{c + \xi_d \tan[\frac{\lambda^{-1}}{2} \xi_d \xi + \xi_d \xi_g]\}\mathbf{e}_1 \tag{3.205}$$

$$+ \{-c + \eta_d \tan[\frac{\lambda^{-1}}{2} \eta_d \eta + \eta_d \eta_g]\}\mathbf{e}_2$$

Because all the eigenvalue forms in (3.205) in general can be complex, (3.205) would be relatively complicated to expand further by means of the general expansion formula, (2.99), although it can be done. Fortunately, we are not interested in the general expansion, but only the x,ct-expansion, which is considerably easier. If we are to restrict the elementary solution to the x,ct-plane (i.e., the **1**,**k**-plane), we must set $y=z=d_2=d_3=g_2=g_3=0$; then *all the eigenvalue forms in (3.205) are real*:

$$\mathbf{D} = (d_1 - d_4)\mathbf{e}_1 + (d_1 + d_4)\mathbf{e}_2 \ , \tag{3.206}$$

$$\mathbf{G} = (g_1 - g_4)\mathbf{e}_1 + (g_1 + g_4)\mathbf{e}_2 \ ,$$

$$\mathbf{W} = \{c + (d_1 - d_4) \tan[\frac{\lambda^{-1}}{2} (d_1 - d_4)(x - ct)$$
$$+ (d_1 - d_4)(g_1 - g_4)]\}\mathbf{e}_1 \tag{3.207}$$

$$+ \{-c + (d_1 + \mathrm{d}_4) \tan[\frac{\lambda^{-1}}{2} (d_1 + d_4)(x + ct)$$
$$+ (d_1 + d_4)(g_1 + g_4)]\}\mathbf{e}_2 \ .$$

Now the expansion formula (2.99) can be applied quite easily, yielding the vector form of **W**, the elementary Cartesian solution of the Burger's equation:

$$\mathbf{W} = \mathbf{1} \ \{(d_1 - d_4) \tan[\frac{\lambda^{-1}}{2} (d_1 - d_4)(x - ct) + (d_1 - d_4)(g_1 - g_4)]$$

$$+ \; (d_1 + d_4) \tan\left[\frac{\lambda^{-1}}{2}(d_1 + d_4)(x+ct) + (d_1 + d_4)(g_1 + g_4)\right]\}/2$$

$$(3.208)$$

$$+ \; \mathbf{k}\,\{-2c \; - \; (d_1 - d_4) \tan\left[\frac{\lambda^{-1}}{2}(d_1 - d_4)(x-ct) + (d_1 - d_4)(g_1 - g_4)\right]/2$$

$$+ \; (d_1 + d_4) \tan\left[\frac{\lambda^{-1}}{2}(d_1 + d_4)(x+ct) + (d_1 + d_4)(g_1 + g_4)\right]\}/2 \;,$$

This is of the form

$$\mathbf{W} = \mathbf{1}\,\{ A \tan\left[\frac{A\lambda^{-1}}{2}(x-ct) + B\right] + D \tan\left[\frac{D\lambda^{-1}}{2}(x+ct) + E\right]\}/2$$

$$(3.209)$$

$$+ \; \mathbf{k}\,\{-2c \; - \; A \tan\left[\frac{A\lambda^{-1}}{2}(x-ct) + B\right] + D \tan\left[\frac{D\lambda^{-1}}{2}(x+ct) + E\right]\}/2$$

with A, B, D, E arbitrary scalar constants, which we may easily verify as an elementary solution of the Burger's equation by direct substitution. We may as easily verify that the first component of **W**, alone, is not a solution. This is because the second term of the Burger's equation, $\mathbf{W}\,\mathbf{W}_x$, may be written $(1/2)\,(\mathbf{W}^2)_x$, and the $\mathbf{W}^2$ term has a **1**-component made up of the square of the original **1**-component plus the square of the original **k**-component. Both are necessary for the solution.

We are not conditioned by prior work to looking for a vector field solution to the Burger's equation and may not immediately see how it applies. Perhaps one way to gain understanding is to look at the field intensity, which is the vector magnitude of (3.209). We also note that (3.209) can be stated in real matrix form by replacing **1** and **k** by their matrix representations, given by (2.2).

3.3.9 Emden's Equation

The scalar del form of Emden's equation is

$$\nabla^2 U + A^2 U^n = 0 \;, \tag{3.210}$$

with A a real scalar and n a positive integer. It occurs, for example, in the hydrostatic modelling of a large, spherical cloud of hydrogen gas under the influence of its own gravity[39]. As in the example above, we complete the

D'Alembertian on the left and use (2.169) to convert the time partial derivative to an ordinary derivative with respect to the independent variable $\mathbf{Z}$:

$$\Box^2 U - \frac{\partial^2 U}{\partial (ct)^2} + A^2 U^n = 0 \ , \tag{3.211}$$

$$\frac{d^2 \mathbf{W}}{d\mathbf{Z}^2} = A^2 \mathbf{W}^n \ , \tag{3.212}$$

$$\frac{d\mathbf{W}}{d\mathbf{Z}} \frac{d^2 \mathbf{W}}{d\mathbf{Z}^2} = \frac{d\mathbf{W}}{d\mathbf{Z}} A^2 \mathbf{W}^n \ , \tag{3.213}$$

$$\frac{1}{2} \frac{d}{d\mathbf{Z}} \left[\frac{d\mathbf{W}}{d\mathbf{Z}} \right]^2 = \frac{A^2}{n+1} \frac{d}{d\mathbf{Z}} (\mathbf{W}^{n+1})$$

$$\left[\frac{d\mathbf{W}}{d\mathbf{Z}} \right]^2 = \frac{2A^2}{n+1} \mathbf{W}^{n+1} + \mathbf{C} \ , \tag{3.214}$$

where $\mathbf{C}$ is an arbitrary constant of integration. Because of $\mathbf{C}$, the final integration for the general case is not readily accomplished. We are at liberty, however, to set $\mathbf{C} = 0$ and obtain a particular solution:

$$\frac{d\mathbf{W}}{d\mathbf{Z}} = \pm \left[\frac{2A^2}{n+1} \right]^{1/2} \mathbf{W}^{\frac{n+1}{2}} \ , \tag{3.215}$$

$$\mathbf{W}^{-\frac{n+1}{2}} d\mathbf{W} = d \frac{(\mathbf{W}^{-\frac{n-1}{2}})}{-\frac{n-1}{2}} = \pm \left[\frac{2A^2}{n+1} \right]^{1/2} d\mathbf{Z} \ , \tag{3.216}$$

$$\frac{\mathbf{W}^{-\frac{n+1}{2}}}{-\frac{n-1}{2}} = \pm \left[\frac{2A^2}{n+1} \right]^{1/2} \mathbf{Z} + \mathbf{D} \ ,$$

$$\mathbf{W} = \left[\frac{n-1}{2} \left[\pm \left[\frac{2A^2}{n+1} \right]^{1/2} \mathbf{Z} + \mathbf{D} \right] \right]^{-\frac{2}{n-1}}, \quad n = 2,3,4, \ldots \tag{3.217}$$

with **D** being a single, arbitrary constant of integration, implying that we have found a particular elementary solution of (3.211). The original scalar dependent variable, U, has been expanded into the vector solution **W**, given by (3.217). Since the original equation, (3.210), is nonlinear, we cannot use (3.217) in a linear superposition scheme (eigenfunction expansion). Perhaps a nonlinear superposition scheme could be devised. On the other hand, we could view (3.217) as a point solution giving the variation of the field about the origin, which we may move about at will, and use it in a numerical scheme to "bridge" a solution between the boundaries.

The vector elementary solution (3.217) may be expanded into component form by means of (2.99). The nonlinearity of the original equation dictates that the vector components of (3.217) are not themselves solutions.

It is of interest to obtain an elementary solution of the one–dimensional Emden's equation for comparison with solutions developed by other means. We start with the one-dimensional form

$$\frac{\partial^2 U}{\partial x^2} + A^2 U^n = 0 \tag{3.218}$$

and convert to an ordinary differential equation by means of (2.169):

$$\frac{d^2 \mathbf{W}}{d\mathbf{Z}^2} = -A^2 \mathbf{W}^n , \tag{3.219}$$

where the boldface **W** indicates that now we are working with a vector dependent variable. The only difference between the vector equation for the three-dimensional case, (3.212), and that for the one-dimensional case, (3.219), is the sign in front of the A^2 factor, hence we can write down the elementary Cartesian solution immediately:

$$\mathbf{W} = \left[\frac{n-1}{2} \left[\pm \left[\frac{-2A^2}{n+1} \right]^{1/2} \mathbf{Z} + \mathbf{D} \right] \right]^{-\frac{2}{n-1}}, \quad n = 2,3,4, \ldots \tag{3.220}$$

which is of the form

$$\mathbf{W} = B(\pm\mathbf{Z} + \mathbf{G})^{-H} , \quad n = 2,3,4,\ldots \tag{3.221}$$

with $B(n,A)$ a scalar (possibly complex) quantity, $H(n) = 2/(n-1)$ a real scalar, and $\mathbf{G}$ an arbitrary hypercomplex constant. This expands into the vector canonical form,

$$\mathbf{W} = B(\pm\xi + \xi_g)^{-H}\mathbf{e}_1 + B(\pm\eta + \eta_g)^{-H}\mathbf{e}_2 , \tag{3.222}$$

with

$$\begin{aligned} \xi &= (x-ct) + \mathbf{i}(y+z) \\ \eta &= (x+ct) + \mathbf{i}(y-z) \end{aligned} \tag{3.223}$$

$$\begin{aligned} \xi_g &= (g_1-g_4) + \mathbf{i}(g_2+g_3) \\ \eta_g &= (g_1+g_4) + \mathbf{i}(g_2-g_3) \end{aligned} \tag{3.224}$$

We are after the $\mathbf{W}(x,ct)$ solution, so we must do as we did for the Burger's equation: set y=z=g_2=g_3=0; then all the eigenvalue forms in (3.222) are real, and the expansion is easily completed:

$$\begin{aligned} \mathbf{W} &= B[\pm(x-ct) + (g_1-g_4)]^{-H}\mathbf{e}_1 + B[\pm(x-ct) + (g_1+g_4)]^{-H}\mathbf{e}_2 \\ &= \mathbf{1}\; B\{[\pm(x-ct) + (g_1-g_4)]^{-H} + [\pm(x+ct) + (g_1+g_4)]^{-H}\}/2 \\ &\quad + \mathbf{k}\; B\{-[\pm(x-ct) + (g_1-g_4)]^{-H} + [\pm(x+ct) + (g_1+g_4)]^{-H}\}/2 , \end{aligned} \tag{3.225}$$

with g_i arbitrary,

$$B = \left[-\frac{n-1}{2} \left[-\frac{2A^2}{n+1} \right]^{1/2} \right]^{-H}$$

and (3.226)

$$H = 2/(n-1) , \quad n = 2,3,4,\ldots$$

3.3.10 Boundary Layer Equations

The boundary layer equations of fluid dynamics may be written

$$U\ U_x + V\ U_y = \nu\, U_{yy}\ , \tag{3.227}$$

$$U_x + V_y = 0\ ,$$

where the subscripts indicate partial derivatives and ν is a scalar. We consider this to be a system of equations in the two dependent variables U, V and convert the partial derivatives to ordinary derivatives by means of (2.169). To do so, we must allow U and V to be vector quantities, which we shall denote by boldface **U**,**V**, of which U, V will be the respective first components.

$$\mathbf{U}\ \frac{d\mathbf{U}}{d\mathbf{Z}} - \mathbf{V}\mathbf{i}\ \frac{d\mathbf{U}}{d\mathbf{Z}} = \nu\,\frac{d^2\mathbf{U}}{d\mathbf{Z}^2}$$

$$\frac{d\mathbf{U}}{d\mathbf{Z}} - \mathbf{i}\ \frac{d\mathbf{V}}{d\mathbf{Z}} = 0\ . \tag{3.228}$$

From the second equation,

$$\frac{d}{d\mathbf{Z}}\ (\mathbf{U} - \mathbf{i}\mathbf{V}) = 0\ ,$$

$$\mathbf{U} - \mathbf{i}\mathbf{V} = \mathbf{C}\ , \tag{3.229}$$

with **C** an arbitrary constant of integration. Putting this back into the first equation, one obtains

$$\mathbf{U}\ \frac{d\mathbf{U}}{d\mathbf{Z}} - (-\mathbf{i}\mathbf{U} + \mathbf{i}\mathbf{C})\ \mathbf{i}\,\frac{d\mathbf{U}}{d\mathbf{Z}} = -\nu\,\frac{d^2\mathbf{U}}{d\mathbf{Z}^2}\ , \tag{3.230}$$

$$\mathbf{U}\ \frac{d\mathbf{U}}{d\mathbf{Z}} - (\mathbf{U} - \mathbf{C})\ \frac{d\mathbf{U}}{d\mathbf{Z}} = -\nu\ \frac{d^2\mathbf{U}}{d\mathbf{Z}^2}\ ,$$

$$\mathbf{C}\ \frac{d\mathbf{U}}{d\mathbf{Z}} = -\nu\,\frac{d^2\mathbf{U}}{d\mathbf{Z}^2}\ , \tag{3.231}$$

$$\mathbf{C}\ \mathbf{U} = -\nu \frac{d\mathbf{U}}{d\mathbf{Z}} ,$$

$$\frac{d\mathbf{U}}{\mathbf{U}} = \frac{-\mathbf{C}}{\nu}\ d\mathbf{Z} ,$$

(3.232)

$$\mathrm{LN}(\mathbf{U}) = \frac{-\mathbf{C}}{\nu}\ \mathbf{Z} + \mathbf{D} , \qquad \text{(}\mathbf{D}\text{ a constant of integration)}$$

$$\mathbf{U} = \mathbf{G}\ \mathrm{EXP}\left(\frac{-\mathbf{C}}{\nu}\ \mathbf{Z}\right) , \tag{3.233}$$

with $\mathbf{G} = \mathrm{EXP}(\mathbf{D})$ for simplicity; then, from (3.229),

$$\mathbf{V} = -\mathbf{i}\mathbf{U} + \mathbf{i}\mathbf{C} \tag{3.234}$$

$$= -\mathbf{i}\mathbf{G}\ \mathrm{EXP}\left(\frac{-\mathbf{C}}{\nu}\ \mathbf{Z}\right) + \mathbf{i}\mathbf{C} ,$$

with **C** and **G** arbitrary constants of integration. Equation (3.234) implies that **U** and **V** are vector fields that are orthogonally rotated and possibly offset equivalents of each other. In this view, the boundary layer behavior is described as the interaction of two vector fields, both of which are periodic in time (we can perform an orthogonal transformation on the elementary solution such that time periodicity is exhibited). The general nature of the solution implies that the number of elementary Cartesian solutions of the boundary layer equations is limited.

3.3.11 Kidder's Equation

Kidder's equation[40] is one special case of the following nonlinear partial differential equation:

$$\nabla^2(U^2) = A^2 \frac{\partial U}{\partial t} , \tag{3.235}$$

with A a scalar constant. Kidder's special case arises in the study of unsteady gas flow through a porous medium. We can solve the more-general form as follows:

$$\Box^2 (U^2) - \frac{\partial^2 (U^2)}{\partial (ct)^2} = A^2 c \frac{\partial U}{\partial ct} , \tag{3.236}$$

$$- \frac{\partial^2 (U^2)}{\partial (ct)^2} = A^2 c \frac{\partial U}{\partial ct}$$

$$- \frac{d^2(\mathbf{U}^2)}{d\mathbf{Z}^2} = A^2 c\mathbf{k} \frac{d\mathbf{U}}{d\mathbf{Z}} \tag{3.237}$$

$$- \frac{d(\mathbf{U}^2)}{d\mathbf{Z}} = A^2 c\mathbf{k}\mathbf{U} + A^2 c\mathbf{k}\mathbf{C} , \qquad (\mathbf{C} \text{ a constant}) \tag{3.238}$$

$$- 2\mathbf{U} \frac{d\mathbf{U}}{d\mathbf{Z}} - A^2 c\mathbf{k}(\mathbf{U} + \mathbf{C}) , \tag{3.239}$$

$$\frac{2\mathbf{U}}{\mathbf{U}+\mathbf{C}} d\mathbf{U} = - A^2 c\mathbf{k} \; d\mathbf{Z} ,$$

$$(\mathbf{U}+\mathbf{C}) - \mathbf{C} \text{ LOG}(\mathbf{U}+\mathbf{C}) = -A^2 \mathbf{k}\mathbf{Z} + \mathbf{D} , \tag{3.240}$$

with **C** and **D** arbitrary constants of integration. The expression on the left cannot be solved for **U** explicitly as a function of **Z**. However, **C** is an arbitrary constant of integration that we may set equal to zero, leaving the simple special case

$$\mathbf{U} = -A^2 c\mathbf{k}\mathbf{Z} + \mathbf{D} . \tag{3.241}$$

The nonlinearity of the original equation, (3.235), dictates that the components of the elementary solution **U**, implicit in (3.240), will <u>not</u> be solutions, individually. However, the vector magnitude of **U** will indicate the scalar intensity of the field.

3.3.12 The Korteweg-DeVries Equation

This equation may be written

$$6UU_x - U_{xxx} - 2U_t = 0 \ , \tag{3.242}$$

usually coupled with the initial condition

$$U(x+1,0) = U(x,0) \ , \tag{3.243}$$

and is prominent in the soliton theories of physics. The independent variables x,t are dimensionless quantities. As in the above examples, we shall find an elementary Cartesian solution and additionally show that it satisfies at least two interesting initial value problems.

Inasmuch as there are only two independent variables, x,t, we could perform the following analysis using only classical complex variable theory. However, the four-dimensional treatment naturally produces an interesting form of the solution from a physics viewpoint. Accordingly, we define

$$\mathbf{Z} = \mathbf{1}x \quad \mathbf{i}y \quad \mathbf{j}z \quad \mathbf{k}vt \ , \tag{3.244}$$

$$\mathbf{W}(\mathbf{Z}) = \mathbf{1}U + \mathbf{i}R \quad \mathbf{j}V + \mathbf{k}S \ ,$$

where U,R,V,S are scalar, conjugate functions of the independent variables x,y,z,t, and v is a dimensionless constant of proportionality that we introduce to emphasize a certain behavior in our final result; then we solve the larger problem

$$6\mathbf{W}\mathbf{W}_x - \mathbf{W}_{xxx} - 2\mathbf{W}_t = 0 \ , \tag{3.245}$$

and set $y = z = 0$ to get the $\mathbf{W}(x,t)$ solution. We start by using (2.169) to convert (3.245) to the following ordinary differential equation:

$$6\mathbf{W}\frac{d\mathbf{W}}{d\mathbf{Z}} - \frac{d^3\mathbf{W}}{d\mathbf{Z}^3} - 2\mathbf{k}v\frac{d\mathbf{W}}{d\mathbf{Z}} = 0 \ ; \tag{3.246}$$

then

$$3\frac{d(\mathbf{W}^2)}{d\mathbf{Z}} - \frac{d^3\mathbf{W}}{d\mathbf{Z}^3} - 2\mathbf{k}v\frac{d\mathbf{W}}{d\mathbf{Z}} = 0 \ , \tag{3.247}$$

$$\frac{d}{d\mathbf{Z}}\,[\,3\mathbf{W}^2 - \frac{d^2\mathbf{W}}{d\mathbf{Z}^2} - 2\mathbf{k}\nu\mathbf{W}] = 0\ , \tag{3.248}$$

$$3\mathbf{W}^2 - \frac{d^2\mathbf{W}}{d\mathbf{Z}^2} - 2\mathbf{k}\nu\mathbf{W} = \mathbf{C}\ , \qquad (\mathbf{C}\text{ an arbitrary constant}) \tag{3.249}$$

$$\frac{d^2\mathbf{W}}{d\mathbf{Z}^2} = 3\mathbf{W}^2 - 2\mathbf{k}\nu\mathbf{W} - \mathbf{C}\ , \tag{3.250}$$

$$\left(\frac{d\mathbf{W}}{d\mathbf{Z}}\right)^2 = 2\,(\mathbf{W}^3 - \mathbf{k}\nu\mathbf{W}^2 - \mathbf{C}\mathbf{W} + \mathbf{D})\ . \tag{3.251}$$

(**C** and **D** arbitrary constants of integration)

The last equation is of a form known to have solutions involving elliptic functions. We must factor the polynomial on the right in order to be able to take advantage of known solutions. A factorization in general is not readily apparent; however, if we postulate roots of the form $a, b, -b$, where a and b may be real, complex, or hypercomplex, then a factorization is immediate:

$$(\mathbf{W} - a)\,(\mathbf{W} - b)\,(\mathbf{W} + b) = \mathbf{W}^3 - a\mathbf{W}^2 - b^2\mathbf{W} + ab^2$$

$$= \mathbf{W}^3 - \mathbf{k}\nu\mathbf{W}^2 - \mathbf{C}\mathbf{W} + \mathbf{D}\ , \tag{3.252}$$

from which

$$a = \mathbf{k}\nu\ ,$$

$$b^2 = \mathbf{C}\ , \tag{3.253}$$

$$\mathbf{D} = \mathbf{k}\nu\mathbf{C}\ .$$

The last equation shows that **D** is no longer arbitrary because of our sumption about the form of the roots. We have given up one degree of edom for the benefit of an explicit factorization. Now, the solution of the tored form of (3.251) is given by Ames[41]; our special case is

$$\mathbf{W} = b(-1 + \frac{2}{\mathrm{SN}^2(-\sqrt{b}\,\mathbf{Z},\ k)})\ , \tag{3.254}$$

with

$$k^2 = \frac{\mathbf{k}v + b}{2b}, \tag{3.255}$$

where SN(**Z**) is the hypercomplex form of the Jacobi elliptic function and k is the usual elliptic parameter. If b is real or classically complex, then the bold **k** makes the elliptic parameter k hypercomplex. This is easier to understand in the canonical form, because in that case

$$\mathbf{Z} = (x-vt)\mathbf{e}_1 \quad (x+vt)\mathbf{e}_2 , \tag{3.256}$$

$$k^2 = \frac{b-v}{2b}\mathbf{e}_1 + \frac{b+v}{2b}\mathbf{e}_2 , \tag{3.257}$$

$$\mathbf{W} = b(-1 + \frac{2}{\mathrm{sn}^2[-\sqrt{b}(x-vt), k_1]})\,\mathbf{e}_1 + b(-1 + \frac{2}{\mathrm{sn}^2[-\sqrt{b}(x+vt), k_2]})\,\mathbf{e}_2 , \tag{3.258}$$

where

$$k_1 = \sqrt{\frac{b-v}{2b}}$$

and

$$k_2 = \sqrt{\frac{b+v}{2b}}, \tag{3.259}$$

the two elliptic parameters, are complementary:

$$k_1^2 = \sqrt{1-k_2^2} \quad ; \tag{3.260}$$

and $b^2 = \mathbf{C}$ is an arbitrary constant of integration which we have implicitl limited to be real or classically complex by the eigenvalue expansion (3.258 Now we have a pair of real functions [the eigenvalues of **W**(**Z**)] that eithe one or both simultaneously as in (3.258), but not their simple sum, satisf the original equation and have the explicit form of periodic waves travellin in opposite directions. This is the reason for the earlier introduction of the constant v, because here it makes the solution more explicitly take the form of a pair of travelling waves. The function $sn(x)$ is sinelike and has the period $4\mathrm{K}(k)$, where K is the complete elliptical integral of the first kind; its square has the period $2\mathrm{K}(k)$. Consequently, our solution has singularities at

$$\sqrt{b}\,(x-vt) = \pm 2n\mathrm{K}(k)$$

and (3.261)

$$\sqrt{b}\,(x+vt) = \pm 2n\mathrm{K}(k)$$

where $n = 0,1,2, \ldots$ We can use our remaining arbitrary constant b to set the period to meet initial conditions. Our solution has the form of equally-spaced quantum mechanical potential wells as seen by a particle in uniform motion in a crystalline solid.

It is remarkable that, because of the definition of *operator* (see Section 2.3.1), each of the eigenvalues of $\mathbf{W}(x,t)$, (3.258), are themselves solutions of the original KdV equation, even though the latter is nonlinear. In the form of (3.258), we have a hypercomplex sum of two solutions. The simple sum of the two solutions is *not* a solution. This difference originates in the implicit $\mathbf{W}^2$ term in the KdV equation [see (3.247)]; squaring a hypercomplex form merely squares each eigenvalue, whereas squaring a simple sum not only squares each term, but also produces cross terms.

To summarize, we have found a solution $\mathbf{W}(x,t)$ to a specific Korteweg-deVries initial-value problem, as follows:

$$6\mathbf{W}\mathbf{W}_x - \mathbf{W}_{xxx} - 2\mathbf{W}_t = 0 \,, \qquad (3.262)$$

$$\mathbf{W}(x+1,0) = \mathbf{W}(x,0)$$

$$= b\left(-1 + \frac{2}{sn^2(-\sqrt{b}\,x,\ k_1)}\right)\mathbf{e}_1$$

$$+\ b\left(-1 + \frac{2}{sn^2(-\sqrt{b}\,x,\ k_2)}\right)\mathbf{e}_2 \,, \qquad (3.263)$$

with b, k_1, k_2 as defined above. Moreover, each of the eigenvalues of $\mathbf{W}(x,t)$ are themselves solutions of the associated KdV scalar problem

$$6UU_x - U_{xxx} - 2U_t = 0 \ , \tag{3.264}$$

$$U(x+1,0) = U(x,0) \tag{3.265}$$

$$= b(-1 + \frac{2}{sn^2(-\sqrt{b}\,x,\ k)}) \ ,$$

where k can be either k_1 or k_2 as defined above.

We indicated at the beginning that our elementary Cartesian solution, (3.258), would solve at least two KdV initial-value problems. The second problem that we had in mind is a special case of (3.265), namely the case wherein $k = 1$. The $sn(x,k)$ function becomes $tanh(x)$, which has a single zero crossing at $x = 0$, hence our solution has degenerated into a solitary singularity moving in either direction:

$$U(x,t) = b(-1 + \frac{2}{tanh^2[-\sqrt{b}\ (x-vt)]}) \ . \tag{3.266}$$

Explaining solitary wave behavior was the purpose of the original KdV equation, but it was applied to problems concerning shallow water waves that do not develop amplitude singularities. Clearly, our expression (3.258), which was derived solely from the KdV equation and not from boundary or initial conditions, is something that will never be seen in water waves, because water waves are unstable after a certain height and so break over or "cap out." Nevertheless, our solution, because it embodies the behavior of the KdV partial differential equation, must have something to do with shallow water wave physics. We reconcile the two as follows. The original description of the shallow-water phenomenon stated that the water ". . . accumulated around the prow of the vessel in a state of violent agitation, then suddenly leaving it behind, rolled forward with a great velocity, assuming the form of a large solitary elevation, a rounded, smooth and well-defined heap of water . . ."[49] I hypothesize that, at the moment of formation, the wave was attempting to build up to a singular height but was prevented from doing so by factors unaccounted for in the KdV equation, plausibly chaotic instability above a certain height. Instead, the wave reshaped itself by dissipative processes, then moved away in a dissipation-free manner with a lower height.

One other feature provides another link with existing theory. Many of the existing solutions for KdV problems either contain or have as a limiting case the square of the hyperbolic function $sech(x)$. Our degenerate solution, (3.266) is approximately proportional to a $sech^2(\ldots)$ term, as follows. We use the elementary relations

$$tanh^2(x) = 1 - sech^2(x) \tag{3.267}$$

and

$$\frac{1}{1 - sech^2(x)} = 1 + sech^2(x) + sech^4(x) + \ldots \tag{3.268}$$

(Geometric progression)

to write

$$\begin{aligned} U(x,t) &= b\left(-1 + \frac{2}{tanh^2[-\sqrt{b}\,(x-vt)]}\right) \\ &= b\{-1 + 2 + 2sech^2[-\sqrt{b}\,(x-vt)] \\ &\qquad + 2sech^4[-\sqrt{b}\,(x-vt)] + \ldots\} \\ &\simeq b\{1 + 2sech^2[-\sqrt{b}\,(x-vt)]\}\ . \end{aligned} \tag{3.269}$$

The approximation is good away from the singularity, in the leading and trailing edges of the wave. The effect of this approximation is exactly like that of the dissipative process hypothesized above: the higher-amplitude components are selected out, leaving a relatively low and wide wave moving away at uniform velocity.

3.3.13 Hypercomplex Solutions Imply Classical Complex Solutions

Section 3.3.12 brought up a point that needs emphasis. For those readers who are uncomfortable with the notion of a four-dimensional vector-valued function being a solution of a scalar-appearing PDE with real coefficients, perhaps a classically complex-valued solution is more readily acceptable. One may show that the existence of a hypercomplex solution implies the existence of classical complex-valued solutions, as follows. Recall that any analytic, hypercomplex function $F(\mathbf{Z})$ can be written in the canonical form

$$F(\mathbf{Z}) = f(\xi)\mathbf{e}_1 + f(\eta)\mathbf{e}_2\ ,$$

with

$$\mathbf{Z} = \xi \, \mathbf{e}_1 + \eta \, \mathbf{e}_2 \,, \tag{3.270}$$

$$\xi = (x-ct) + \mathbf{i}\,(y+z)$$

$$\eta = (x+ct) + \mathbf{i}\,(y-z) \;;$$

moreover, any linear or nonlinear operator, including a PDE operator, acts upon the canonical eigenfunctions $f(\xi)$ and $f(\eta)$ as separate entities, hence *the canonical eigenfunctions (which are classically complex-valued functions) of any hypercomplex solution are also solutions.* For example,

$$U = \{-\frac{n-1}{2}\,[+\left(\frac{2A^2}{n+1}\right)^{1/2} \xi + \xi_d]\,\}^{-\frac{2}{n-1}}, \; n = 2,3,4,\ldots \tag{3.271}$$

with ξ_d arbitrary, is a classically complex-valued, elementary Cartesian solution of Emden's equation, (3.210), written in the form (3.212) with an independent variable ξ.

In conclusion for Section 3.3, the above examples show that the $\mathbb{D}$-space analysis, particularly the Cauchy-Riemann conditions, allow a great simplification in the solution of many partial differential equations. A new class of objects, the hypercomplex functions, has been established as elementary Cartesian solutions of linear and nonlinear PDEs. Each hypercomplex solution is composed of a pair of classical complex solutions. A new technique for finding possible eigenfunctions of a linear partial differential operator has been established that depends only on the Cauchy-Riemann conditions. The C-R conditions, in turn, assume only that the vector field under investigation is continuous and single-valued in the region of interest. For most physics and engineering problems, this is a mild assumption. For those fields that develop shocks or discontinuities, the present mathematics will produce an elementary Cartesian solution that is indeterminate under shock conditions, but is appropriate everywhere else.

IV. APPLICATIONS TO RELATIVITY PHYSICS

The author feels the need to take the following philosophical stance before beginning any discussion of relativity: *Einstein's relativity is an experimental fact. There will be no attempt to diminish Einstein's achievements or to question his conclusions.* The author understands that special relativity is in no great need of revision, but believes that an alternate formulation in an alternate analysis system, especially one so well-suited as we shall show, can be illuminating.

Accordingly, the objective for this chapter is the restatement of the Einstein-Lorentz special relativity calculations in a new and different mathematical system, that being the $\mathbb{D}$-space system of the first half of the book. A group of four-dimensional transformations will be developed that closely resembles the classical Lorentz group, but is commutative. We shall see that certain computational advantages and possible extensions are gained from the $\mathbb{D}$-space formulation.

PLEASE NOTE: The casual reader is alerted that a reading of the first half of the book will be necessary for understanding the notation and following the developments in this chapter. The formulation is not in terms of the usual classical vector analysis, and cannot be evaluated in those terms.

4.1 Motivation For Relativity Applications

At the beginning of the work leading to this book, there was no anticipation that the present mathematics would be applicable to relativity. The author's purpose was to create a mathematical system for classical physics and engineering applications that would be clearer, more direct, and easier to use than the classical vector analysis. What has been created is a function theory and system of analysis for four-dimensional numbers, or vectors, that is an analogue of the complex analysis. But what could complex variables have to do with special relativity?

The initial thought came from examining the (at first) troubling change that occurred in going from two- to four-dimensional complex numbers: there was now an infinite number of noninvertible elements. However, the noninvertible conditions $x = \pm ct$, where c is interpreted as the speed of light and t is interpreted as time, place the noninvertible elements into precisely the regime wherein *all experimental physics becomes indeterminate*. In other words, our new system "breaks down" or is in some way different in properties under exactly the conditions (only) in which all experimental physics becomes indeterminate. This seemed more than coincidence to the author.

Moreover, under the noninvertible conditions, our four-dimensional algebraic basis collapses into a two-dimensional plane:

$$\text{e.g.,}\quad \begin{aligned} \mathbf{Z} &= \mathbf{1}x + \mathbf{i}y + \mathbf{j}z + \mathbf{k}ct \\ &\rightarrow \mathbf{1}x + \mathbf{i}(-z) + \mathbf{j}z + \mathbf{k}x \\ &= (\mathbf{1}+\mathbf{k})\,(x+\mathbf{i}z) \\ &= \text{Const X } (x+\mathbf{i}z)\ , \end{aligned} \tag{4.1}$$

just as any material body whose speed approaches c appears to flatten into a plane perpendicular to the direction of motion. Elements of the form $(x+\mathbf{i}z)$ constitute a field in the complex plane, hence the noninvertible elements make up separate subspaces, one for each set of noninvertible conditions. We shall see that this is only a small part of the relativistic aspects of the $\mathbb{D}$-space mathematical system, entirely aside from experimental considerations, and that the $\mathbb{D}$-space "field" itself seems to embody much of special relativity. We were induced to explore a statement of special relativity in the new notation.

The remainder of the chapter will examine the relativistic aspects of the $\mathbb{D}$-space system, will develop a $\mathbb{D}$-space version of the special relativistic transformation and investigate its properties, then will end with an exploration of the consequences of relativistic transformations in the $\mathbb{D}$-space. The usual special relativistic effects will be recovered, and some possible extensions suggested by the mathematics will be discussed. The reader is cautioned that the discussion will be set in the context of the $\mathbb{D}$-space mathematics, except as noted. Parallels and contrasts will be drawn with the traditional formulation of special relativity.

4.2 Relativity Aspects of the Hypercomplex Algebra

This section will show that the $\mathbb{D}$-space algebra, itself, exhibits certain relativistic-appearing characteristics, and that the relativistic behavior carries over into the function theory and analysis.

4.2.1 The Algebra Is Independent Of Spacetime Orientation

Consider the typical element $\mathbf{Z}$ of the ring $\mathbb{D}$ in matrix form

$$\mathbf{Z} = \begin{bmatrix} x & -y & -z & ct \\ y & x & -ct & -z \\ z & -ct & x & -y \\ ct & z & y & x \end{bmatrix} ,$$

and an othogonal coordinate transformation A in the form

$$\begin{aligned} x' &= a_{11}x + a_{12}y + a_{13}z + a_{14}ct , \\ y' &= a_{21}x + a_{22}y + a_{23}z + a_{24}ct , \\ z' &= a_{31}x + a_{32}y + a_{33}z + a_{34}ct , \\ ct' &= a_{41}x + a_{42}y + a_{43}z + a_{44}ct , \end{aligned} \tag{4.2}$$

where the a_{ij} are constrained by the orthogonality conditions. The original element **Z** is transformed into

$$\mathbf{Z}' = \begin{bmatrix} x' & -y' & -z' & ct' \\ y' & x' & -ct' & -z' \\ z' & -ct' & x' & -y' \\ ct' & z' & y' & x' \end{bmatrix} , \tag{4.3}$$

which is again an element of $\mathbb{D}$. One may proceed from this point with $\mathbb{D}$-space calculations in the new frame of reference.

We remarked earlier that one should not indiscriminately change frames of reference in the middle of a sequence of $\mathbb{D}$-space operations without checking whether indeterminacy complications have been introduced. One must realize also that the expression $\mathbf{Z}' = \mathrm{A}\mathbf{Z}$, where A is a 4 X 4 orthogonal matrix, has at least two different interpretations. The first is as an orthogonal transformation of the *classical vector* **Z**, hence is equivalent to (4.2). The second interpretation is as a multiplication of two 4 X 4 matrices, A and **Z**. This interpretation has little utility in $\mathbb{D}$-space calculations because A is not in general an element of $\mathbb{D}$, hence the product A**Z** will not in general be an element of $\mathbb{D}$. One exception is wherein A is an element of Λ_4, the four-dimensional orthogonal transformation group in the $\mathbb{D}$-space (Section 2.2.14).

This is a convenient place to point out that a *general* orthogonal transformation A can rotate a non-axis-plane vector **Z** into an axis plane (the planes of indeterminacy; see Section 2.2.4 for a discussion), but that a transformation from the group Λ_4 cannot. The latter half of the statement may be understood as follows: an element **A** of Λ_4 has

$$det\,(\mathbf{A}) = \xi\xi^*\eta\eta^* = 1\ ,$$

or (4.4)

$$|\xi| \neq 0$$

$$|\eta| \neq 0\ ,$$

and a non-axis-plane vector **Z** has the same conditions. The $\mathbb{D}$-space product **AZ** is then of the form

$$\mathbf{AZ} = (\mathbf{e}_1\xi_1 + \mathbf{e}_2\eta_1)(\mathbf{e}_1\xi_2 + \mathbf{e}_2\eta_2) \quad (4.5)$$

$$= (\mathbf{e}_1\xi_1\xi_2 + \mathbf{e}_2\eta_1\eta_2)\ ,$$

hence has both eigenvalues nonzero, and one concludes that the result cannot be in an axis plane. This is one more indication that a $\mathbb{D}$-space rotation takes place about both axis planes, simultaneously; see Section 2.2.16 for other indications.

4.2.2 The Axis Plane Effects Are The Same In Every Frame Of Reference

The axis planes contain the noninvertible elements. The casual reader should review Section 2.2.4 for the definition of "axis plane," keeping in mind that the named Section uses the notation "t" instead of "ct" for the fourth coordinate. It is only in science and engineering applications that "ct" makes sense.

Suppose that several observers are recording the same physical event from different frames of reference in some way that involves measuring the inverse of some distance, which indirectly is the same as measuring the inverse of some $\mathbb{D}$-space vector, $\mathbf{Z}^{-1}$. The measurement will break down under the axis plane conditions, $x = \pm ct$. The axis planes maintain a fixed orientation with respect to the chosen frame of reference. One might think that it would be possible to find some orientation in four-space in which breakdown would not occur. However, in any new orientation except the one moving along with the object to be measured, there will be relative motion, and if the speed of motion approaches c then breakdown will again occur. This means that the conditions $x = \pm ct$ will have exactly the same critical import in every frame of reference, even though each frame may orient "x" differently. This being so, one has no basis for claiming that any particular frame of reference is somehow more fundamental or preferred over the others. Relativity physics makes the same assertion.

4.2.3 The Noninvertible Elements Form Invariant Subspaces

The typical element in canonical form in $\mathbb{D}$ is

$$\mathbf{Z} = \mathbf{e}_1\xi + \mathbf{e}_2\eta,$$

where (4.6)

$$\xi = (x-ct) + \mathbf{i}(y+z)$$

$$\eta = (x+ct) + \mathbf{i}(y-z).$$

The inverse of $\mathbf{Z}$ is defined as

$$\mathbf{Z}^{-1} = \mathbf{e}_1\xi^{-1} + \mathbf{e}_2\eta^{-1}, \qquad (4.7)$$

and exists only if $\xi \neq 0$ and $\eta \neq 0$. The axis planes are defined as the sets of numbers $\mathbf{Z}$ for which $\xi = 0$ or $\eta = 0$ (see Section 2.2.4). It was shown (Section 2.2.4) that the ring $\mathbb{D}$ is isomorphic to the product ring $\mathbb{C}^2$ of pairs of complex numbers that correspond to (ξ,η), here. It is an elementary result of $\mathbb{C}^2$ ring theory that numbers of the form $(0,\eta)$ or $(\xi,0)$ constitute *fields*; i.e., closed subspaces.

The reader should keep in mind that the axis planes are invariant *with respect to the chosen reference frame*, which one may translate or rotate at will.

A consequence is that the multiplication of two *invertible* (non-axis-plane) elements can never produce a noninvertible (axis-plane) result. The result can be forced arbitrarily close to an axis plane, but can never enter it. In physics, a material body may have a speed of motion approaching that of light, but can never reach it.

4.2.4 The Invariant Subspaces Are Reached Only At A Speed *c*

Consider a body in motion in an inertial reference frame (one moving with a constant, uniform speed along a straight line with respect to the observer's reference frame). One may, without loss of generality, align the x-axis along the direction of motion. The position vector of the moving body is then

$$\mathbf{Z} = \mathbf{e}_1(x-ct) + \mathbf{e}_2(x+ct). \tag{4.8}$$

In order to enter an axis plane subspace, either $x-ct=0$ or $x+ct=0$ is required, which is the same as

$$\dot{x} = c \quad \text{or} \quad \dot{x} = -c. \tag{4.9}$$

4.2.5 The Invariant Subspaces Delimit The Reachable Universe

Special relativity has a construct called the *light cone*[28] that graphically depicts a moving system's collective past and possible future events. It is usually drawn in cross section in the x,ct plane as two cones aligned along the ct-axis in an opposed arrangement with their points at the origin. The half angle of the cone is 45 degrees. The equations of the lines of intersection of the cones and the x,ct plane are then $x=ct$ and $x=-ct$. When all three space dimensions are included, the surface of the cone structure is precisely where the *relativistic interval* is zero:

$$x^2 + y^2 + z^2 - ct^2 = 0. \tag{4.10}$$

A material body's existence traces out a *world line* which, due to c being the upper bound on the speed of motion, must stay within the cone. The forward cone, where ct is positive, therefore contains all possible future events for a body presently at the origin, or its *future*. The forward cone is also called the *reachable universe* because it contains all the points that are reachable by a moving body starting from the origin ($t=0$). In a similar way, the reverse cone contains all possible past events that may have influenced the body at the origin, or its *past*. Everything else is called *elsewhere*.

The corresponding situation in the $\mathbb{D}$-space is as follows. Suppose that one imagines some fixed "direction" for the ct-axis. This "direction" cannot be related to any real direction in the physical coordinate xyz three-space. Moreover, it was argued (Section 4.2.2) that no one orientation of the axes is preferable over the others. It follows that at any perpendicular direction off of the ct-axis one may construct an x-axis and draw the lines $x=ct$ and $x=-ct$ for the intersection with the axis planes. It was shown (Section 4.2.4) that a material body can reach an axis plane only by reaching the speed c, which is experimentally not observed in nature. The totality of all such orientations and lines $x = ct$ and $x = -ct$ makes up the light cone discussed above, hence one concludes that the invariant subspaces (axis planes) delimit the reachable universe

However, one cannot perceive a "ct-axis." Instead, if an observer is at the origin of coordinates, then the axis plane conditions $x=ct$ and $x=-ct$ indicate a front moving toward or away from the observer at the speed of light. This is true no matter how the coordinate frame is rotated about the origin (the observer's position), hence the observer will perceive the totality of all possible axis plane conditions as spherical fronts that either collapse on or expand about the observer's position at the speed of light.

4.2.6 The Axis Planes Are Invariant Under Analytic Functions

The axis planes contain the noninvertible elements. The casual reader should review Section 2.2.4 for the definition of "axis plane," keeping in mind that the named Section uses the notation "t" instead of "ct" for the fourth coordinate. It is only in science and engineering applications that "ct" makes sense.

A hypercomplex, analytical function F of one hypercomplex variable $\mathbf{Z}$ in canonical form in $\mathbb{D}$ is

$$\mathrm{F}(\mathbf{Z}) = \mathbf{e}_1 f(\xi) + \mathbf{e}_2 f(\eta),$$

where (4.11)

$$\xi = (x-ct) + \mathbf{i}(y+z)$$

$$\eta = (x+ct) + \mathbf{i}(y-z),$$

and f is an analytic function of one classical complex variable. The eigenvectors $\mathbf{e}_1$ and $\mathbf{e}_2$ lie in the axis planes and are unaffected by the analytic function operation. The analytic function operation does not change the existence or orientation of the axis planes relative to the chosen coordinate frame, but merely maps each plane onto itself, hence the axis planes are invariant.

Our observations so far are not very interesting, but let us look at the converse situation. One must conclude that *every conservative force field (analytic function) in $\mathbb{D}$, irrespective of the orientation of the coordinate frame, sees the same constraints and limitations imposed by the axis planes.* This is beginning to look like the essence of relativity. Perhaps one should ask: can one find a representation in $\mathbb{D}$ for any conservative force field that is representable in classical vector analysis terms? One cannot easily prove this in the affirmative, but may strongly suspect that it is so because the $\mathbb{D}$ analytic function space has a more general definition and a wider range of analysis techniques.

4.3 Construction Of A $\mathbb{D}$-Space Relativity Transformation Group

The purpose of this Section is to develop a group of coordinate transformations in four dimensions in the $\mathbb{D}$-space that corresponds to the proper Lorentz subgroup as formulated in a quaternion-based system (classical vector analysis). The new group, although different from the Lorentz group, will be shown to satisfy Einstein's special relativity postulates. The usual special relativistic effects will be recovered, and a later section will postulate additional effects purely from the mathematics.

4.3.1 A Brief Review Of Special Relativity

This section will review some elementary concepts from special relativity and set up some notation to be used in later sections. We will let c denote the speed of light in a vacuum, let

$$\mathbf{X} = \mathbf{1}x + \mathbf{i}y + \mathbf{j}z + \mathbf{k}ct$$

denote a *position vector* in the physical four-space, with **1,i,j,k** interpreted as unit direction vectors, and let

$$\mathbf{V} = \mathbf{1}\dot{x} + \mathbf{i}\dot{y} + \mathbf{j}\dot{z} + \mathbf{k}c \tag{4.12}$$

denote the *relative motion vector* (different from the three-space relative velocity because it always has the fourth term, $\mathbf{k}c$) for two Cartesian coordinate systems in relative motion. The coefficients of this vector are assumed to be constants when used in special relativity discussions. The dot superscript will indicate the first derivative with respect to time. A lower-case v will indicate the relative speed of motion in the real three-space, as follows:

$$v = [(\dot{x})^2 + (\dot{y})^2 + (\dot{z})^2]^{\frac{1}{2}}. \tag{4.13}$$

We will let $\underline{EL}_2(\underline{\mathbf{V}})$ (for Einstein-Lorentz) denote the subgroup of *Lorentz transformations* of one space coordinate and time of the form

$$\begin{aligned} x' &= \gamma\,[x - (v/c)ct] \\ ct' &= \gamma\,[ct - (v/c)x]\ , \end{aligned} \tag{4.14}$$

with

$$\gamma = 1/[1 - (v/c)^2]^{½} .$$

which have the usual interpretations. In this case, the relative speed is

$$v = | \dot{x} | .$$

The other two dimensions, $y'=y$ and $z'=z$, shall purposely not be considered for the time being, for reasons which will become apparent later.

The matter of primed coordinates will come up so often that the general usage conventions need to be defined. In most treatments of special relativity, the observer is considered to be fixed in a frame of reference which itself is assumed to be stationary. The observer's measurements are stated in terms of unprimed coordinates, hence the observer's frame is the unprimed frame. A second, primed, frame of reference is assumed to be moving with a constant relative velocity with respect to the first, and contains the objects or measurables that are under observation. An object can be stated to be at rest with respect to the moving frame (or in the moving frame). A zero subscript denotes a quantity that is measured while at rest within a coordinate frame (e.g., L_o is an at-rest length); such quantities may be defined with respect to either frame. The terms *observer's frame*, *rest frame*, and *unprimed frame* mean the same thing; and *moving frame* and *primed frame* mean the same thing. These conventions shall be followed unless otherwise noted.

If T denotes an element of $EL_2(\mathbf{V})$, then T can be written in the matrix form

$$\mathrm{T} = \gamma \begin{bmatrix} 1 & -(v/c) \\ -(v/c) & 1 \end{bmatrix} , \tag{4.15}$$

with $v < c$. The inverse of the typical element is

$$\mathrm{T}^{-1} = \gamma \begin{bmatrix} 1 & (v/c) \\ (v/c) & 1 \end{bmatrix} . \tag{4.16}$$

The determinant of T is +1, but T is *nonorthogonal* because the inverse is not merely the transpose of T. The group multiplication is given by

$$T_1T_2 = [1 - (v_3/c)^2]^{1/2} \begin{bmatrix} 1 & -(v_3/c) \\ -(v_3/c) & 1 \end{bmatrix} , \tag{4.17}$$

with

$$v_3 = \frac{v_1 + v_2}{1 + (v_1 v_2/c^2)} . \tag{4.18}$$

The group of transformations thus defined is *commutative*, as can be seen from (4.17) and (4.18). Equation (4.18) is the usual *Einstein addition law* for relativistic velocities. It is to be interpreted as follows: an observer in Frame 0, assumed to be at rest, observes another frame (Frame 1) in motion radially toward or away from the observer's location. Within Frame 1 and relative to Frame 1, the observer sees yet another frame (Frame 2) in motion in the same direction as for Frame 1. Equation (4.18) expresses how the at-rest observer will see the compounding, v_3, of the two motions. The main consequence is that even if v_1 and v_2 both approach c in magnitude, v_3 will still be limited to c.

As a direct consequence of the transformation (4.14), two observers in relative motion will disagree on the apparent length of an object in the system which is designated as the moving frame of reference: An observer moving along with the object in question measures its length as

$$L_o = x_2' - x_1' , \tag{4.19}$$

where the quantities on the right are the coordinates of the end points of the object in the moving system. The at-rest observer tacitly assumes $t_1 = t_2$ and measures the length as

$$\begin{aligned} L &= x_2 - x_1 \\ &= (x_2' - x_1') \, [1 - (v/c)^2]^{1/2} \\ &= L_o \, [1 - (v/c)^2]^{1/2}, \end{aligned} \tag{4.20}$$

An apparent contraction, called the *Lorentz-Fitzgerald contraction*, has occured as a result of (4.13).

The *time dilation effect* is another direct consequence of (4.14): Suppose the origins of the two coordinate systems coincide at at time $t' = t = 0$, and suppose that the origin of the moving system is observed from the rest system. Its coordinate in the rest system will be (can be, with the proper orientation) $x = vt$; and from (4.14) it follows that

$$\begin{aligned} ct' &= \gamma\ [ct - (v/c)vt] \\ &= \gamma\ ct\ [1 - (v/c)^2] \end{aligned} \tag{4.21}$$

or

$$ct = ct' \,/\, [1 - (v/c)^2]^{1/2}\ ;$$

i.e., the observer in the rest system thinks that *time runs more slowly in the moving system* than in a stationary one. Suppose that some process taking place in the moving system has a lifetime of $\Delta t'$ as measured within the moving system. By (4.21), the same process observed from the rest system appears to have a lifetime

$$\Delta t = \Delta t' \,/\, [1 - (v/c)^2]^{1/2}\ , \tag{4.22}$$

which is a larger value. This is called time dilation.

4.3.2 A $\mathbb{D}$-Space Representation Of Two-Dimensional Relativity

One may show that $EL_2(\mathbf{V})$ has a formulation in terms of the real algebra $\mathbb{D}$ as follows. Consider the multiplication operator

$$\mathbf{T} = \gamma\ [\mathbf{1} - (v/c)\mathbf{k}], \tag{4.23}$$

where $\mathbf{k}$ is the basis element in $\mathbb{D}$ such that $\mathbf{k}^2 = \mathbf{1}$. If $\mathbf{T}$ operates on a vector $\mathbf{X} = \mathbf{1}x + \mathbf{k}ct$ the result is

$$\begin{aligned} \mathbf{X}' &= \mathbf{T}\mathbf{X} \\ &= \gamma\ [\mathbf{1} - (v/c)\mathbf{k}]\ [\mathbf{1}x + \mathbf{k}ct] \\ &= \gamma\ \{\mathbf{1}[x - (v/c)\,ct] + \mathbf{k}[ct - (v/c)x]\}\ . \end{aligned} \tag{4.24}$$

Equating of coefficients of corresponding basis vectors on opposite sides of (4.24) produces precisely (4.14), hence (4.23) establishes the desired formulation in $\mathbb{D}$.

The form of (4.23) gives us little indication as to how it might be extended to four dimensions. For that purpose one may use the elementary algebraic and functional rules on $\mathbb{D}$ to rearrange (4.23) into the canonical form:

$$\begin{aligned}\mathbf{T} &= [\mathbf{1} - (v/c)\mathbf{k}] \;/\; [1 - (v/c)^2]^{1/2} \\ &= [\mathbf{1} - (v/c)\mathbf{k}] \;/\; \{[\mathbf{1} - (v/c)\mathbf{k}]\,[\mathbf{1} + (v/c)\mathbf{k}]\}^{1/2} \\ &= \{[\mathbf{1} - (v/c)\mathbf{k}] \;/\; [\mathbf{1} + (v/c)\mathbf{k})]\}^{1/2} \;;\end{aligned}$$

and, multiplying both numerator and denominator under the square root by $\mathbf{k}c$ and simplifying,

$$\begin{aligned}\mathbf{T} &= [(-\mathbf{1}v + \mathbf{k}c) \;/\; (\mathbf{1}v + \mathbf{k}c)]^{1/2} \\ &= \{[(-v-c)\mathbf{e}_1 + (-v+c)\mathbf{e}_2] \;/\; [(v-c)\mathbf{e}_1 + (v+c)\mathbf{e}_2]\}^{1/2} \\ &= \{[-\eta\mathbf{e}_1 - \xi\mathbf{e}_2] \;/\; [\xi\mathbf{e}_1 + \eta\mathbf{e}_2]\}^{1/2} \qquad (4.25) \\ &= [-\eta/\xi]^{1/2}\mathbf{e}_1 + [-\xi/\eta]^{1/2}\mathbf{e}_2 \;,\end{aligned}$$

where ξ, η are the eigenvalues of the relative motion vector $\mathbf{V} = \mathbf{1}v + \mathbf{k}c$:

$$\begin{aligned}\xi &= (v-c) \qquad (4.26) \\ \eta &= (v+c) \;.\end{aligned}$$

4.3.3 Construction Of A Four-Dimensional Relativity Group In $\mathbb{D}$

We shall now construct a four-dimensional group of transformations in $\mathbb{D}$, which we shall name $\underline{EL_4}(\underline{\mathbf{V}})$, to be the counterpart in $\mathbb{D}$ of the group of proper Lorentz transformations (having determinant +1 but allowing space and time inversions). The approach that we shall take is exactly that of Einstein: we shall assume only his two special relativity postulates, develop a formulation in $\mathbb{D}$ which satisfies them, then merely explore the consequences and differences, if any, from classical relativity.

We do not have to start from scratch because we already have a two-dimensional $\mathbb{D}$-space formulation, above, which we have named $EL_2(\mathbf{V})$. This group embodies Einstein's postulates in one space dimension and time. All we have to do is extend it to four dimensions. We shall take a different approach than Einstein did on the handling of the two coordinates lying transverse to the line of motion. He assumed that they might be affected in magnitude but not direction and went on to deduce *under those circumstances* that magnitude was not affected. This type of behavior, in which two coordinates are treated qualitatively differently from the others by a functional transformation, is not possible in the $\mathbb{D}$-space function theory. Nevertheless, the relativistic-like properties of the algebraic and analysis systems in the $\mathbb{D}$-space and the conservative property of the function theory, have convinced us that relativity may have a very simple and natural expression entirely within the $\mathbb{D}$-space mathematics. Accordingly, we shall allow the transverse coordinates to be changed in both direction and magnitude, in order to effect equal standing among the four coordinates and to maintain four-space continuity.

One may deduce that if $EL_4(\mathbf{V})$ is to retain $EL_2(\mathbf{V})$ as a subgroup, then the canonical form in (4.25) must be retained. Secondly, a transformation $\mathbf{T}$ belonging to $EL_4(\mathbf{V})$ should be an *analytic* function of the relative motion vector $\mathbf{V}$; otherwise, special relativistic effects would exhibit qualitatively discontinuous behavior as the relative speed is changed from one fixed value to another. Recall that $EL_2(\mathbf{V})$ had

$$\mathbf{V} = \mathbf{1}\dot{x} + \mathbf{k}c$$

for a relative motion vector. For the four-dimensional case, an obvious means of extension such that an element $\mathbf{T}$ has the *form* of an analytic function of a four-dimensional $\mathbf{V}$ is to merely add in the two missing components of velocity to get

$$\begin{aligned}
\mathbf{V} &= \mathbf{1}\dot{x} + \mathbf{i}\dot{y} + \mathbf{j}\dot{z} + \mathbf{k}c \\
\xi &= (\dot{x} - c) + \mathbf{i}(\dot{y} + \dot{z}) \\
\eta &= (\dot{x} + c) + \mathbf{i}(\dot{y} - \dot{z}) \\
\mathbf{T} &= [-\eta/\xi]^{1/2}\mathbf{e}_1 + [-\xi/\eta]^{1/2}\mathbf{e}_2
\end{aligned} \tag{4.27}$$

Naturally, one restricts attention to those elements $\mathbf{T}$ for which

$$\det(\mathbf{V}) = \xi\ \eta\ \xi^*\ \eta^*$$

$$= [(\dot{x}-c)^2 + (\dot{y}+\dot{z})^2]\ [(\dot{x}+c)^2 + (\dot{y}-\dot{z})^2] \neq 0\ . \qquad (4.28)$$

Note that $\mathbf{V}$ has a fourth component c that is a constant in special-relativistic discussions, hence $\mathbf{T}(\mathbf{V})$ will require some interpretation as an analytic function. We shall show below that we have an analytic function of such form that its argument $\mathbf{V}$ can always have its fourth component normalized to c without changing any final results or consequences.

One may verify that $EL_4(\mathbf{V})$ is a group as follows. The element

$$\mathbf{T} = 1\mathbf{e}_1 + 1\mathbf{e}_2 = \mathbf{1}$$

is the identity. Closure is assured, because

$$\mathbf{T}_1\mathbf{T}_2 = [(\eta_1\eta_2)\ /\ (\xi_1\xi_2)]^{1/2}\mathbf{e}_1 + [(\xi_1\xi_2)\ /\ (\eta_1\eta_2)]^{1/2}\mathbf{e}_2\ . \qquad (4.29)$$

Every element has an inverse as a result of (4.28) and the hypercomplex function definition:

$$\mathbf{T}^{-1} = [-\xi/\eta]^{1/2}\mathbf{e}_1 + [-\eta/\xi]^{1/2}\mathbf{e}_2\ . \qquad (4.30)$$

Associativity follows from the associativity of the underlying algebra on $\mathbb{D}$; hence $EL_4(\mathbf{V})$ is a group.

The elements of $EL_4(\mathbf{V})$, being elements of $\mathbb{D}$, have explicit matrix representations. This is developed as follows: if one uses the notation

$$\mathbf{T} = \alpha\mathbf{e}_1 + \beta\mathbf{e}_2\ , \qquad (4.31)$$

with

$$\alpha = [-\eta/\xi]^{1/2}$$

$$\beta = [-\xi/\eta]^{1/2}\ , \qquad (4.32)$$

$$\xi = (\dot{x} - c) + \mathbf{i}(\dot{y} + \dot{z}) \qquad (4.33)$$

$$\eta = (\dot{x} + c) + \mathbf{i}(\dot{y} - \dot{z})\ ,$$

$$U = [Re(\alpha) + Re(\beta)]/2$$

$$R = [Im(\alpha) + Im(\beta)]/2 \qquad (4.34)$$

$$W = [Im(\alpha) - Im(\beta)]/2$$

$$S = [-Re(\alpha) + Re(\beta)]/2\ ,$$

then by the arguments leading up to (2.99) the typical element **T** can be represented as

$$\mathbf{T} = \mathbf{1}U + \mathbf{i}R + \mathbf{j}W + \mathbf{k}S. \qquad (4.35)$$

Now, by Section 2.1.3, the matrix representation of **T** is

$$\mathbf{T} = \begin{bmatrix} U & -R & -W & S \\ R & U & -S & -W \\ W & -S & U & -R \\ S & W & R & U \end{bmatrix} . \qquad (4.36)$$

The matrix inverse of **T** is easy to calculate. Recall that in the canonical form one merely takes the reciprocal of each eigenvalue of **T**, and this action merely interchanges the eigenvalues [compare (4.27) and (4.30)]. In the algebra $\mathbb{D}$, the operation that interchanges the canonical form eigenvalues for any element **Z** or **T** is the mere changing of sign of the coefficients of the **j** and **k** components:

$$\mathbf{T}^{-1} = \mathbf{1}U + \mathbf{i}R - \mathbf{j}W - \mathbf{k}S \qquad \text{(Vector form)}$$

$$\mathbf{T}^{-1} = \begin{bmatrix} U & -R & W & -S \\ R & U & S & W \\ -W & S & U & -R \\ -S & -W & R & U \end{bmatrix} . \qquad \text{(Matrix form)} \qquad (4.37)$$

A large part of the simplicity of (4.37) from a matrix viewpoint arises from the fact that the matrix inverse is of the form *adjoint* (**T**) / *det* (**T**), and *det* (**T**) = 1.

One last point of interest concerning the matrix form of **T** is as follows: It is known from the corresponding canonical forms, (4.27) and (4.30), that $\mathbf{T}\mathbf{T}^{-1} = \mathbf{1}$; but if one forms the matrix product, then diagonal terms $U^2 - R^2 + W^2 - S^2$ and off-diagonal terms $2(UR + WS)$ are obtained, hence one concludes

$$\begin{aligned} U^2 - R^2 + W^2 - S^2 &= 1 \\ UR + WS &= 0. \end{aligned} \tag{4.38}$$

Before continuing, let us more formally state the eigenvalue exchange action that was mentioned above. If

$$\begin{aligned} \mathbf{Z} &= \mathbf{1}x + \mathbf{i}y + \mathbf{j}z + \mathbf{k}ct \\ &= \xi\mathbf{e}_1 + \eta\mathbf{e}_2 , \end{aligned}$$

then the *eigenvalue exchange operation* is denoted by

$$\begin{aligned} \mathrm{EXCH}(\mathbf{Z}) &= \mathbf{1}x + \mathbf{i}y - \mathbf{j}z - \mathbf{k}ct \\ &= \eta\mathbf{e}_1 + \xi\mathbf{e}_2 . \end{aligned} \tag{4.39}$$

In these terms,

$$\mathbf{T}^{-1} = \mathrm{EXCH}(\mathbf{T}). \tag{4.40}$$

The EXCH operation affords us a third way to find a vector perpendicular to any given **Z** [see (2.163) and (2.164) for the others]:

$$\begin{aligned} \mathbf{Z} \bullet (\mathbf{k}\,\mathrm{EXCH}(\mathbf{Z})) &= \mathbf{Z} \bullet \mathbf{k}(\mathbf{1}x + \mathbf{i}y - \mathbf{j}z - \mathbf{k}ct) \\ &= \mathbf{Z} \bullet (-\mathbf{1}ct + \mathbf{i}z - \mathbf{j}y + \mathbf{k}x) \\ &= -xct + yz - yz + xct \\ &= 0 . \end{aligned} \tag{4.41}$$

■ *Comparison With The Classical Four-Dimensional Lorentz Group*—A commonly-used representation of the typical element in the group of four dimensional Lorentz transformations is given in the form

$$\begin{aligned} x' &= \gamma\,(x - vt) \\ y' &= y \\ z' &= z \\ t' &= \gamma\,[t - (v/c^2)x]\ . \end{aligned} \tag{4.42}$$

One may give (4.42) a more symmetrical appearance by transforming *ct* instead of merely *t*:

$$\begin{aligned} x' &= \gamma\,[x - (v/c)ct] \\ y' &= y \\ z' &= z \\ ct' &= \gamma\,[ct - (v/c)x]\ . \end{aligned} \tag{4.43}$$

The transformation matrix associated with (4.43) is

$$\mathrm{T} = \begin{bmatrix} \gamma & 0 & 0 & -(v/c)\gamma \\ 0 & 1 & 0 & 0 \\ 0 & 0 & 1 & 0 \\ -(v/c)\gamma & 0 & 0 & \gamma \end{bmatrix}, \tag{4.44}$$

with

$$\gamma = 1 \,/\, [1 - (v/c)^2]^{1/2}\ .$$

NOTE: If we had not rearranged (4.42) so as to transform *ct* instead of merely *t*, then (4.44) would have been the following more commonly-used form:

$$\mathrm{T} = \begin{bmatrix} \gamma & 0 & 0 & -v\gamma \\ 0 & 1 & 0 & 0 \\ 0 & 0 & 1 & 0 \\ -(v/c^2)\gamma & 0 & 0 & \gamma \end{bmatrix}, \tag{4.45}$$

Both (4.44) and (4.45) assume a relative velocity v along the positive x-axis. The more general case of a relative velocity in an arbitrary direction is available[29], and our own $\mathbb{D}$-space representation, (4.27), allows a velocity in an arbitrary direction. However, no loss of generality in the comparison will occur if one chooses a coordinate orientation such that the relative velocity is along the x-axis. We argued in Section 4.2.2 that no one coordinate frame is preferable to any other, so one is free to make a choice that will provide clarity and simplicity in the comparison. Accordingly, we shall restrict our four-dimensional form, (4.27), to velocity along the $+x$-axis. To do so, we return to the starting point of our four-dimensional derivation, (4.23), which concerned itself with the restricted case:

$$\mathbf{T} = \gamma\,[\mathbf{1} - (v/c)\mathbf{k}] \qquad \text{(Vector representation)}$$

$$= \begin{bmatrix} \gamma & 0 & 0 & -\gamma(v/c) \\ 0 & \gamma & \gamma(v/c) & 0 \\ 0 & \gamma(v/c) & \gamma & 0 \\ -\gamma(v/c) & 0 & 0 & \gamma \end{bmatrix} \qquad \text{(Matrix representation)} \qquad (4.46)$$

Compare (4.46) with the traditional form (4.44). Clearly, there is a wide difference in effect because if we apply the transformation (4.46) to a four-dimensional vector we shall find that the x and ct components transform as expected but that the y and z components do not remain unchanged:

$$\begin{aligned} x' &= \gamma\,[x - (v/c)ct] \\ y' &= \gamma\,[y + (v/c)z] \\ z' &= \gamma\,[(v/c)y + z] \\ ct' &= \gamma\,[-(v/c)x + ct] \end{aligned} \qquad (4.47)$$

This difference will be investigated in later sections. For now, notice carefully what has happened. In deriving the two-dimensional group $EL_2(\mathbf{V})$, we applied the transformations to vectors of only two dimensions (x,ct). When we constructed a $\mathbb{D}$-space representation $\mathbf{T}$ [see (4.23)], we continued to apply it to vectors of only two dimensions (x,ct) and obtained the traditional results for x and ct. In effect, we said nothing about what might be happening to y and z. Recall that Einstein's relativity leaves them unaffected. However, (4.23) is an element of $\mathbb{D}$, hence has a four-dimensional matrix representation, (4.46). When applied to a four-dimensional vector, (4.23) will always have some effect on the y and z components.

4.3.4 The Relativity Transform As A Hypercomplex Function

We shall use the following notation:

$$\begin{aligned} \mathbf{V} &= \mathbf{1}\dot{x} + \mathbf{i}\dot{y} + \mathbf{j}\dot{z} + \mathbf{k}c \\ &= \xi\mathbf{e}_1 + \eta\mathbf{e}_2 , \end{aligned} \tag{4.48}$$

and

$$\begin{aligned} \mathbf{U} &= \mathbf{1}\dot{x} + \mathbf{i}\dot{y} - \mathbf{j}\dot{z} - \mathbf{k}c \\ &= \eta\mathbf{e}_1 + \xi\mathbf{e}_2 , \end{aligned} \tag{4.49}$$

where

$$\xi = (\dot{x} - c) + \mathbf{i}(\dot{y} + \dot{z}) ,$$

$$\eta = (\dot{x} + c) + \mathbf{i}(\dot{y} - \dot{z}) .$$

Now the typical element $\mathbf{T}$, (4.27), in the $\mathbb{D}$-space Lorentz group may be rearranged as follows:

$$\begin{aligned} \mathbf{T} &= [-\eta/\xi]^{1/2}\mathbf{e}_1 + [-\xi/\eta]^{1/2}\mathbf{e}_2 \\ &= \{[-\eta]^{1/2}\mathbf{e}_1 + [-\xi]^{1/2}\mathbf{e}_2\} \\ &\quad \times \{[\xi]^{-1/2}\mathbf{e}_1 + [\eta]^{-1/2}\mathbf{e}_2\} \\ &= [-\mathbf{U}]^{1/2}\mathbf{V}^{-1/2} , \end{aligned}$$

or

$$\boxed{\mathbf{T} = [-\mathbf{U}/\mathbf{V}]^{1/2}} \tag{4.50}$$

One may assert that $\mathbf{U}$ and $\mathbf{V}$ are independent variables, as follows. The relationship between $\mathbf{U}$ and $\mathbf{V}$ is a classical vector transformation: if

$$\mathbf{V} = \mathbf{1}\dot{x} + \mathbf{i}\dot{y} + \mathbf{j}\dot{z} + \mathbf{k}c$$

and (4.51)

$$\mathbf{U} = \mathbf{1}\dot{x}' + \mathbf{i}\dot{y}' + \mathbf{j}\dot{z}' + \mathbf{k}c',$$

then

$$\begin{bmatrix} \dot{x}' \\ \dot{y}' \\ \dot{z}' \\ c' \end{bmatrix} = \begin{bmatrix} 1 & 0 & 0 & 0 \\ 0 & 1 & 0 & 0 \\ 0 & 0 & -1 & 0 \\ 0 & 0 & 0 & -1 \end{bmatrix} \begin{bmatrix} \dot{x} \\ \dot{y} \\ \dot{z} \\ c \end{bmatrix}, \tag{4.52}$$

yielding

$$\mathbf{U} = \mathbf{1}\dot{x} + \mathbf{i}\dot{y} - \mathbf{j}\dot{z} - \mathbf{k}c.$$

The operation (4.52) is not one that will occur within the $\mathbb{D}$-space system of analysis, because the transformation matrix is not an element of $\mathbb{D}$. Equation (4.52) shows that **U** is not a scalar multiple of **V**, but instead is a partial reflection of **V** through the origin. **U** and **V** are related by an orthogonal transformation, (4.52), that is outside the $\mathbb{D}$-space system. Moreover, **U** can never be identical to **V** because of the **k**-component, c; equality would require $c=-c$, contrary to our original assumptions. One may conclude that **U** *and* **V** *are independent hypercomplex variables* within the $\mathbb{D}$-space, with coordinates

$$(\dot{x},\dot{y},-\dot{z},-c) \text{ and } (\dot{x},\dot{y},\dot{z},c),$$

respectively. It follows that **T** *is a function of two independent hypercomplex variables* in the $\mathbb{D}$-space system.

4.3.5 Some Required Properties Of The Four-Dimensional Transform

The elements of $EL_4(\mathbf{V})$ have several mathematical properties in common with the subgroup of proper Lorentz transformations. This section will examine the commonality and note some differences to be addressed in later sections.

■ *The Determinant Is Always* $+1$

The canonical form of the typical element **T** is

$$\mathbf{T} = [-\eta/\xi]^{1/2}\mathbf{e}_1 + [-\xi/\eta]^{1/2}\mathbf{e}_2 ,$$

hence the eigenvalues are

$$\begin{aligned}
\alpha &= [-\eta/\xi]^{1/2} \\
\beta &= [-\xi/\eta]^{1/2} \\
\beta^* &= \{ [-\xi/\eta]^{1/2} \}^* \\
\alpha^* &= \{ [-\eta/\xi]^{1/2} \}^* \ ,
\end{aligned} \tag{4.53}$$

and the determinant is

$$det(\mathbf{T}) = \alpha \ \beta \ \alpha^* \ \beta^* = 1 \ . \tag{4.54}$$

The eigenvalues always occur in complex conjugate pairs in the classical complex variable sense. We conclude that $EL_4(\mathbf{V})$ must correspond to the subgroup of proper Lorentz transformations[30]. Moreover, in the matrix form $EL_4(\mathbf{V})$ is a group which can be applied outside of the $\mathbb{D}$-space mathematical system.

■ *Zero Spatial Velocity Produces An Identity Transform*

This is most easily shown using the functional form of **T**, as defined in Section 4.3.4: If

$$\mathbf{U} = -\mathbf{k}c$$

and (4.55)

$$\mathbf{V} = +\mathbf{k}c,$$

(spatial parts zero) then

$$\begin{aligned}
\mathbf{T} &= \{ [-(-\ \mathbf{k}c)] \ / \ [(\mathbf{k}c)] \}^{1/2} \qquad (4.56) \\
&= [\mathbf{k}c/\mathbf{k}c]^{1/2} \\
&= \mathbf{1} \ .
\end{aligned}$$

■ *Time Reversal Causes No Effect*

Consider a vector $\mathbf{X}$ in the rest system which connects the origins of the moving and rest systems. The motion is uniform along a fixed line (in the special relativity case), meaning that the spatial components of the connecting vector are simple linear functions of time:

$$\mathbf{X} = \mathbf{1}at + \mathbf{i}bt + \mathbf{j}et + \mathbf{k}ct, \tag{4.57}$$

where a,b,e are real scalars. Let a superscript bar indicate the time-reversed version of the various quantities under discussion; then

$$\begin{aligned} \overline{\mathbf{X}} &= \mathbf{1}a(-t) + \mathbf{i}b(-t) + \mathbf{j}e(-t) + \mathbf{k}c(-t) \\ &= -(\mathbf{1}at + \mathbf{i}bt + \mathbf{j}et + \mathbf{k}ct) \\ &= -\mathbf{X}\ . \end{aligned} \tag{4.58}$$

The relative motion vector $\overline{\mathbf{V}}$ in the time-reversed case is the time derivative of $\overline{\mathbf{X}}$:

$$\overline{\mathbf{V}} = \frac{d\overline{\mathbf{X}}}{dt} = \frac{-d\mathbf{X}}{dt} = -\mathbf{V}\ . \tag{4.59}$$

Similarly,

$$\overline{\mathbf{U}} = -\mathbf{U}\ ;$$

then

$$\begin{aligned} \overline{\mathbf{T}} &= [-(-\mathbf{U})\ /\ (-\mathbf{V})]^{1/2} \\ &= [-\mathbf{U}/\mathbf{V}]^{1/2} = \mathbf{T}\ . \end{aligned} \tag{4.60}$$

We conclude in the $\mathbb{D}$-space theory that we are unable to determine whethe[r] time is running "forward" or "backward." This observation is supported b[y] physics experimentation.

■ *Reversing The Spatial Velocity Yields The Inverse Transformation*

This is easiest to see in the restricted case of velocity v along the $+x$-direction, expressed in the vector form (4.23):

$$\mathbf{T}(v) = \gamma\ [\mathbf{1} - (v/c)\mathbf{k}]\ ;$$

then (4.61)

$$\mathbf{T}(-v) = \gamma\ [\mathbf{1} - (-v/c)\mathbf{k}]$$

$$= \gamma\ [\mathbf{1} + (v/c)\mathbf{k}]\ ;$$

and

$$\begin{aligned} \mathbf{T}(v)\mathbf{T}(-v) &= \gamma\ [\mathbf{1} - (v/c)\mathbf{k}]\ \gamma\ [\mathbf{1} + (v/c)\mathbf{k}] \\ &= \gamma^2\ \{(\mathbf{1})^2 - [(v/c)\mathbf{k}]^2\} \\ &= \gamma^2\ [\mathbf{1} - (v/c)^2\mathbf{1}] \\ &= \mathbf{1}\ \gamma^2\ [1 - (v/c)^2] \\ &= \mathbf{1}\ . \end{aligned} \tag{4.62}$$

This assertion is not true, however, for the case of a relative velocity in n arbitrary direction. Reversing the spatial velocity in the general case gives

$$\begin{aligned} \mathbf{T} &= [-(-\mathbf{1}\dot{x} - \mathbf{i}\dot{y} + \mathbf{j}\dot{z} - \mathbf{k}c)\ /\ (-\mathbf{1}\dot{x} - \mathbf{i}\dot{y} - \mathbf{j}\dot{z} + \mathbf{k}c)]^{1/2} \\ &\neq [-(\mathbf{1}\dot{x} + \mathbf{i}\dot{y} + \mathbf{j}\dot{z} + \mathbf{k}c)\ /\ (\mathbf{1}\dot{x} + \mathbf{i}\dot{y} - \mathbf{j}\dot{z} - \mathbf{k}c)]^{1/2}\ , \end{aligned} \tag{4.63}$$

e latter of which is the inverse of **T**. This is the first major break with xisting treatments of special relativity, and this difference will be fully explored the later section on unorthodox consequences. For the moment, let us nderstand under what circumstances the $\mathbb{D}$-space and traditional Lorentz eatments agree about the reverse velocity yielding the inverse transformation.

The restricted case of the Lorentz transformation concerns two frames of reference in relative motion with each other at a constant relative velocity. The x-axes of the two systems are collinear, and at some time t the origins of the two systems will coincide. What is not always understood is that *the spatial relative velocity and the observer's line of sight lie along a common line* in the traditional restricted treatment (the area of agreement). It is when the spatial relative velocity has off-axis components with respect to the observer's line of sight that the proposition fails.

The Relativity Transform Is Orthogonal

The traditional Lorentz transformation, (4.44), is not orthogonal, per se, because the inverse of the transformation matrix is not simply the transpose. One may show that an invariant of the transformation is

$$x^2 + y^2 + z^2 - c^2t^2 .$$

However, by the device of changing the time coordinate from ct to $c\bar{t}=ict$, then the four-space length is preserved; i.e.,

$$x^2 + y^2 + z^2 + (c\bar{t})^2$$

becomes an invariant, and from this viewpoint the Lorentz transformation is orthogonal. The rotation is hyperbolic, with a complex angle of rotation[31].

A similar situation holds for transformations $\mathbf{T}$ from $EL_4(\mathbf{V})$. It is clear from (4.36) and (4.37) that the inverse of $\mathbf{T}$ is not merely the transpose of $\mathbf{T}$ in the matrix form. One may use (4.36) and (4.38) and a transformation equation $\mathbf{X}'=\mathbf{T}\mathbf{X}$ to show by direct substitution that

$$x'^2 - y'^2 + z'^2 - c^2t'^2 = x^2 - y^2 + z^2 - c^2t^2 , \tag{4.64}$$

hence the quadratic, length-related invariant form for $\mathbf{T}$ differs only in the sign of the y-term from the corresponding traditional Lorentz quantity.

Continuing the parallel with the analysis of the traditional case, we next consider the unitary matrix

$$A = \begin{bmatrix} 1 & 0 & 0 & 0 \\ 0 & -i & 0 & 0 \\ 0 & 0 & 1 & 0 \\ 0 & 0 & 0 & i \end{bmatrix} , \tag{4.65}$$

where "i" is the classical complex imaginary, and apply it as a similarity transformation to the relativity transform equation $\mathbf{X}' = \mathbf{T}\mathbf{X}$:

$$A\mathbf{X}' = ATA^{-1}\ (A\mathbf{X})$$

or

$$\begin{bmatrix} x' \\ -iy' \\ z' \\ ict' \end{bmatrix} = \begin{bmatrix} U & -iR & -W & -iS \\ -iR & U & iS & W \\ W & -iS & U & iR \\ iS & -W & iR & U \end{bmatrix} \begin{bmatrix} x \\ -iy \\ z \\ ict \end{bmatrix} . \tag{4.66}$$

If we form the product

$$(AT^{-1}A^{-1})\ (ATA^{-1}) , \tag{4.67}$$

we clearly should obtain an identity matrix. In actuality, we obtain a result with the principal diagonal elements all of the form

$$U^2 - R^2 + W^2 - S^2 , \tag{4.68}$$

with secondary diagonal elements all of the form

$$2i(UR + WS) \text{ or } -2i(UR + WS) ; \tag{4.69}$$

but we already have

$$U^2 - R^2 + W^2 - S^2 = 1$$
$$UR + WS = 0 \quad (4.70)$$

in (4.38). Now one may use (4.66) and (4.70) to show by direct substitution that

$$x'^2 + y'^2 + z'^2 + c^2t'^2 = x^2 + y^2 + z^2 + c^2t^2 \quad (4.71)$$

is an invariant, hence transformations **T** from $EL_4(\mathbf{V})$ are orthogonal in the same sense as are the Lorentz transformations. The rotation is hyperbolic and has a complex angle of rotation. The major difference is that, in the $EL_4(\mathbf{V})$ restricted case, the y and z coordinates, also, suffer a hyperbolic rotation, as shown by (4.47).

Once again, we emphasize that a transformation of coordinates, such as (4.65), can be used beforehand to set a frame of reference or afterwards to aid interpretation of results, but should never be indiscriminately mixed with $\mathbb{D}$-space operations, because (4.65), for example, is not an element of $\mathbb{D}$.

As an aside, the transformation matrix $\mathbf{ATA}^{-1}$ expressly satisfies the classic orthogonality condition: if

$$\overline{\mathbf{T}} = \mathbf{ATA}^{-1} , \quad (4.72)$$

then

$$(\overline{\mathbf{T}})^{-1} = (\overline{\mathbf{T}})^{\mathrm{T}} , \quad (4.73)$$

where the superscript T indicates the transpose of the matrix. Notice that although $\overline{\mathbf{T}}$ contains complex-valued elements, no complex conjugation is needed to obtain the inverse. Transformations of this type are not hermitian or unitary but *complex orthogonal.* Real-valued vectors will always be transformed into complex-valued vectors by $\overline{\mathbf{T}}$, yet the inner product of any vector, whether complex-valued or not, with itself will be preserved. The latter assertion may be explicitly demonstrated as follows:

let

$$\mathbf{X} = \begin{bmatrix} x \\ y \\ z \\ ct \end{bmatrix} \tag{4.74}$$

$$\mathbf{X}^{\mathrm{T}} = [\ x\ \ y\ \ z\ \ ct\ ] \qquad \text{(transpose)} \ ;$$

then by matrix methods one has

$$\begin{aligned} (\mathbf{X}')^{\mathrm{T}}\,\mathbf{X}' &= (\overline{\mathbf{T}}\mathbf{X})^{\mathrm{T}}\,(\overline{\mathbf{T}}\mathbf{X}) \\ &= \mathbf{X}^{\mathrm{T}}\,(\overline{\mathbf{T}})^{\mathrm{T}}\,(\overline{\mathbf{T}})\mathbf{X} = \mathbf{X}^{\mathrm{T}}\mathbf{X}\ . \end{aligned} \tag{4.75}$$

The same argument may be used to assert that the inner product of any two vectors, not necessarily the same, is preserved. We shall call the unitary similarity transformation (4.72), using (4.65), the *observer's bias* transformation, inasmuch as it appears to convert certain 𝔻-space expressions involving special relativity into more readily-recognized forms that can be related directly to the results of physics experimentation.

■ *The Transformation Group Is Commutative*

The group $EL_4(\mathbf{V})$ is commutative because it is composed within the 𝔻-space algebra, an inherently commutative system. The restricted case subgroup of the full Lorentz group is commutative, also.

The $EL_4(\mathbf{V})$ group has a 4 X 4 real matrix representation which allows it to be used in all ways that the Lorentz group is employed, irrespective of any 𝔻-space considerations. The unitary transformation (4.65) is especially useful inasmuch as it produces explicitly orthogonal forms of the elements of $EL_4(\mathbf{V})$. However, the greatest gain is made by using the elements of $EL_4(\mathbf{V})$ in the functional form (4.50) within the 𝔻-space system and using the wide array of complex analysis techniques available in the new system.

.3.6 Einstein's Special Relativity Postulates Are Obeyed

Section 4.3.5 has shown that $EL_4(\mathbf{V})$ and the subgroup of proper Lorentz transformations have many mathematical properties in common, but differ in that a transformation **T** from $EL_4(\mathbf{V})$ causes the coordinates that are transverse to the relative motion to be affected, while one from the Lorentz group does not. That would seem to dismiss any applicability of $EL_4(\mathbf{V})$ to relativity matters, except that the two groups have an even more important consideration in common: Einstein's special relativity postulates are satisfied. The proof is as follows.

Einstein's first postulate of special relativity states that the laws of physics and the results of all experiments performed within a given coordinate system are independent of the translational motion of the system as a whole. This is usually demonstrated in the existing treatments (see, for example, Jackson[32], Goldstein[33], Bergmann[34], and Aharoni[35]) by writing the equations of physics in covariant form and showing that such forms remain invariant under the classical Lorentz transformations. It is also true that such forms remain invariant under any orthogonal transformation of the frame of reference. In (4.72) we have an explicitly-orthogonal form of the typical element of $EL_4(\mathbf{V})$, hence the form of physics equations will be preserved. In a later section, we will give several explicit examples of transformations of some important physics and vector analysis expressions, such as the wave equation.

To those who will say "But the Lorentz group is the sole invariance group for physics . . .", one might complete their statement with ". . . as stated in the classical system of vector analysis."

Einstein's second postulate states that the speed of light is a constant, regardless of the motion of the light source or of the translational motion of the observer. In existing treatments, it is shown that a Lorentz transformation (relative motion) does not affect the apparent speed of light by showing that

$$x'^2 + y'^2 + z'^2 - c^2t'^2 = x^2 + y^2 + z^2 - c^2t^2 \tag{4.76}$$

is a Lorentz invariant. In the present case, if one considers the unitary matrix

$$A = \begin{bmatrix} 1 & 0 & 0 & 0 \\ 0 & -i & 0 & 0 \\ 0 & 0 & 1 & 0 \\ 0 & 0 & 0 & 1 \end{bmatrix}, \tag{4.77}$$

where "i" is the classical complex imaginary, and the similarity transformation

$$\overline{\mathbf{T}} = \mathrm{ATA}^{-1}, \tag{4.78}$$

one can show by direct substitution that (4.76) holds for transformations in $EL_4(\mathbf{V})$, hence the concept of an invariant speed for light is not violated by the $\mathbb{D}$-space formulation.

We shall spend an entire section, below, showing how some of the more important vector analysis operators transform under $EL_4(\mathbf{V})$. For now, the following example is given for illustration. The *gradient* is a particularly important operator in the description of physical phenomena, and should retain its form under a relativistic transformation of the independent variables. If $Q(x,y,z,ct)$ is any scalar analytic function of four independent variables, then its gradient is

$$\Box Q = \mathbf{1}\frac{\partial Q}{\partial x} + \mathbf{i}\frac{\partial Q}{\partial y} + \mathbf{j}\frac{\partial Q}{\partial z} + \mathbf{k}\frac{\partial Q}{\partial ct} \,. \tag{4.79}$$

Form (4.79) is known to be a covariant, first-rank tensor, but we want to show explicitly how it transforms. First, consider the relativistic transformation of coordinates

$$\begin{bmatrix} x' \\ y' \\ z' \\ ct' \end{bmatrix} = \begin{bmatrix} U & -R & -W & S \\ R & U & -S & -W \\ W & -S & U & -R \\ S & W & R & U \end{bmatrix} \begin{bmatrix} x \\ y \\ z \\ ct \end{bmatrix} . \tag{4.80}$$

After a change of variables $Q(x,y,z,ct) \rightarrow Q(x',y',z',ct')$ is made, the chain rule for differentiation yields

$$\begin{aligned}
\frac{\partial Q}{\partial x} &= \frac{\partial Q}{\partial x'}\frac{\partial x'}{\partial x} + \frac{\partial Q}{\partial y'}\frac{\partial y'}{\partial x} + \frac{\partial Q}{\partial z'}\frac{\partial z'}{\partial x} + \frac{\partial Q}{\partial ct'}\frac{\partial ct'}{\partial x} \\
\frac{\partial Q}{\partial y} &= \frac{\partial Q}{\partial x'}\frac{\partial x'}{\partial y} + \frac{\partial Q}{\partial y'}\frac{\partial y'}{\partial y} + \frac{\partial Q}{\partial z'}\frac{\partial z'}{\partial y} + \frac{\partial Q}{\partial ct'}\frac{\partial ct'}{\partial y} \\
\frac{\partial Q}{\partial z} &= \frac{\partial Q}{\partial x'}\frac{\partial x'}{\partial z} + \frac{\partial Q}{\partial y'}\frac{\partial y'}{\partial z} + \frac{\partial Q}{\partial z'}\frac{\partial z'}{\partial z} + \frac{\partial Q}{\partial ct'}\frac{\partial ct'}{\partial z} \\
\frac{\partial Q}{\partial ct} &= \frac{\partial Q}{\partial x'}\frac{\partial x'}{\partial ct} + \frac{\partial Q}{\partial y'}\frac{\partial y'}{\partial ct} + \frac{\partial Q}{\partial z'}\frac{\partial z'}{\partial ct} + \frac{\partial Q}{\partial ct'}\frac{\partial ct'}{\partial ct}
\end{aligned} \tag{4.81}$$

This can be written in vector-matrix form as

$$\begin{bmatrix} \dfrac{\partial Q}{\partial x} \\ \dfrac{\partial Q}{\partial y} \\ \dfrac{\partial Q}{\partial z} \\ \dfrac{\partial Q}{\partial ct} \end{bmatrix} = \begin{bmatrix} \dfrac{\partial x'}{\partial x} & \dfrac{\partial y'}{\partial x} & \dfrac{\partial z'}{\partial x} & \dfrac{\partial ct'}{\partial x} \\ \dfrac{\partial x'}{\partial y} & \dfrac{\partial y'}{\partial y} & \dfrac{\partial z'}{\partial y} & \dfrac{\partial ct'}{\partial y} \\ \dfrac{\partial x'}{\partial z} & \dfrac{\partial y'}{\partial z} & \dfrac{\partial z'}{\partial z} & \dfrac{\partial ct'}{\partial z} \\ \dfrac{\partial x'}{\partial ct} & \dfrac{\partial y'}{\partial ct} & \dfrac{\partial z'}{\partial ct} & \dfrac{\partial ct'}{\partial ct} \end{bmatrix} \begin{bmatrix} \dfrac{\partial Q}{\partial x'} \\ \dfrac{\partial Q}{\partial y'} \\ \dfrac{\partial Q}{\partial z'} \\ \dfrac{\partial Q}{\partial ct'} \end{bmatrix}, \qquad (4.82)$$

Now we use (4.80) on the elements of the 4 X 4 matrix in (4.82) to obtain

$$\begin{bmatrix} \dfrac{\partial Q}{\partial x} \\ \dfrac{\partial Q}{\partial y} \\ \dfrac{\partial Q}{\partial z} \\ \dfrac{\partial Q}{\partial ct} \end{bmatrix} = \begin{bmatrix} U & -R & -W & S \\ R & U & -S & -W \\ W & -S & U & -R \\ S & W & R & U \end{bmatrix} \begin{bmatrix} \dfrac{\partial Q}{\partial x'} \\ \dfrac{\partial Q}{\partial y'} \\ \dfrac{\partial Q}{\partial z'} \\ \dfrac{\partial Q}{\partial ct'} \end{bmatrix}, \qquad (4.83)$$

One observes that the 4 X 4 matrix has the form of an element of $EL_4(\mathbf{V})$ hence

$$\Box Q = \mathbf{T}\,\Box_1 Q\,,$$

with (4.84)

$$\Box_1 = \mathbf{1}\frac{\partial}{\partial x'} + \mathbf{i}\frac{\partial}{\partial y'} + \mathbf{j}\frac{\partial}{\partial z'} + \mathbf{k}\frac{\partial}{\partial ct'}$$

and form invariance is concluded. Moreover, suppose that we have a position vector

$$\mathbf{Z} = \mathbf{1}x + \mathbf{i}y + \mathbf{j}z + \mathbf{k}ct$$

and a vector function

$$\mathrm{F}(\mathbf{Z}) = \mathbf{1}X + \mathbf{i}Y + \mathbf{j}Z + \mathbf{k}T \tag{4.85}$$

with components X, Y, Z, T each of which is a scalar analytic function of the independent variables (coordinates) x, y, z, ct. If one now applies a relativistic transformation

$$\mathbf{Z}' = \mathbf{T}\mathbf{Z} \tag{4.86}$$

to the independent variable, then by (3.88), (4.84), and distributivity in $\mathbb{D}$,

$$\Box\,\mathrm{F} = \mathbf{T}\,\Box_1\,\mathrm{F} = 0\ . \tag{4.87}$$

4.3.7 The Special Relativistic Effects Are Produced

We mean to say that the special relativistic effects in the classical form are reproduced in the $\mathbb{D}$-space system *under certain conditions*. Specifically, we refer to the restricted case in the traditional Lorentz treatments: two frames of reference with collinear x-axes are in constant relative motion along the x- axis of the observer's frame. Under these conditions, the typical element of $EL_4(\mathbf{V})$ reduces to

$$\mathbf{T} = \begin{bmatrix} \gamma & 0 & 0 & -\gamma(v/c) \\ 0 & \gamma & \gamma(v/c) & 0 \\ 0 & \gamma(v/c) & \gamma & 0 \\ -\gamma(v/c) & 0 & 0 & \gamma \end{bmatrix}, \tag{4.88}$$

and if we use this to transform the coordinates we obtain

$$
\begin{aligned}
x' &= \gamma \, [x - (v/c)ct] \\
y' &= \gamma \, [y + (v/c)z] \\
z' &= \gamma \, [(v/c)y + z] \\
ct' &= \gamma \, [-(v/c)x + ct] \, .
\end{aligned}
\qquad (4.89)
$$

The x and ct coordinates transform exactly as in the traditional Lorentz treatments, hence the observer will see all the special relativistic effects associated with x and ct; specifically, length contraction, time dilation, and velocity compounding in such a way that the speed of light is an upper limit.

Consider, for a moment, the geometry of the restricted case. The observer is assumed to be at the origin of the designated observer's frame of reference and motion is assumed to be along the observer's $+x$-axis, hence *the restricted case is concerned with relative velocities directed radially inward or outward from the observer.* We have perfect agreement with the traditional Lorentz treatments in such a case, but the next section will show that clear disagreement exists in the case of relative velocities having components transverse to the observer's line of sight.

4.4 Additional Effects Are Postulated

The effects presented in this section are natural consequences of the mathematical structure of the transformation group, $EL_4(\mathbf{V})$. Whether or not they represent any physical or experimental reality will have to be determined by physical experiment.

4.4.1 Distant Transverse Motion Appears To Be Newtonian

The $\mathbb{D}$-space mathematics suggest that motion transverse to the line of sight, if viewed from large enough distances, *will appear to be unaffected by relativity.* In particular, no foreshortening along the line of motion will be observed and relative velocities will appear to compound by simple vector addition. *The speed of light will appear to be violated*, if the compounding velocities are high enough. One may verify the foregoing statements as follows.

Transverse linear motion is a straight-line motion that approaches the observer, has a point of closest approach, then recedes from the observer. We shall be concerned with that portion of the motion near and at the point of closest approach, at such large viewing distances that any component of motion toward or away from the observer is small compared to the transverse motion. We shall use the same orientation of coordinates as in the restricted Lorentz case: collinear x-axes with the observer's line of sight along the $+x$-axis, except that now the observer's coordinates will be aligned so that the relative velocity will be along the $+z$-axis. This can always be done without loss of generality. Under these conditions we have, referring to (4.45)–(4.47),

$$\begin{aligned} \mathbf{V} &= \mathbf{j}\dot{z} + \mathbf{k}c \\ \mathbf{U} &= -\mathbf{j}\dot{z} - \mathbf{k}c, \end{aligned} \tag{4.90}$$

and

$$\begin{aligned} \mathbf{T} &= [-\mathbf{U}/\mathbf{V}]^{1/2} \\ &= [-(-\mathbf{j}\dot{z} - \mathbf{k}c) \,/\, (\mathbf{j}\dot{z} + \mathbf{k}c)]^{1/2} \\ &= [(\mathbf{j}\dot{z} + \mathbf{k}c) \,/\, (\mathbf{j}\dot{z} + \mathbf{k}c)]^{1/2} \\ &= [\mathbf{1}]^{1/2} = \mathbf{1}\ . \end{aligned} \tag{4.91}$$

This result occurs only *at* the point of closest approach. Off to either side, there will always be a component of the motion toward or away from the observer. That is why we have specified distant observing, because for the current discussion we want the radial component of the motion to be proportionally insignificant. We conclude that, with an identity relativity transform, distant transverse motion must appear to be Newtonian. Apparently, the relativity effects shade off from the Einstein-Lorentz effects for radial motion to the near absence of effects for transverse motion viewed from great distances. Everything in between will exhibit some effects of both cases.

If distant transverse motion appears to be Newtonian, then the possibility of *the appearance* of the speed of light being exceeded will occur. For example, if two astronomical bodies are each moving away from some fixed reference point in opposing directions at three-fourths the speed of light, then a distant observer in a transverse direction will claim that the two bodies are separating at a relative speed greater than the speed of light. It is only an effect of the observer's viewpoint, however, because an observer on either body will perceive that the other body is moving away at a speed less than the speed of light in agreement with Einstein-Lorentz theory.

There are numerous examples from astronomy wherein two bodies appear to be separating at up to several times the speed of light. These superluminal cases are currently thought to be instances of strobe effects, colliding wavefronts, gravitational lens effects, and others, and some cases have been satisfactorily explained in those ways. Others, however, remain enigmatic. I submit that the $EL_4(\mathbf{V})$ transformation theory provides a direct explanation of certain cases in a way that leaves the Einstein-Lorentz theory intact.

A little more explanation is needed for the result (4.91) and what it seems to imply: a constant relative velocity along a line not passing through the observer's position produces *no relativistic effects*. What is wrong? The answer is in the phrase "constant relative velocity." Under the specified transverse geometry conditions, with the line of motion not through the observer's position, it is not possible to set up a constant relative velocity *as perceived by the observer* by a rectilinear motion of an inertial frame. The observer will see th moving object approach nearly radially from infinity with a speed $|\mathbf{V}|$. The radial component of velocity will decelerate to zero at the point of closest approach, then will accelerate back to $|\mathbf{V}|$ at infinity in the opposite, outgoing side. The relative velocity is decidedly not constant, hence *relative motion along any line not intersecting the observer's position is in the domain of general relativity* in the 𝔻-space system. It is only at astronomical distances that the observed body stays in the vicinity of the point of closest approach long enough for an observer to perceive nearly rectilinear motion. Truly constant relative motion can take place only along a radial direction with respect to the observer, and in this view special relativity might be more-descriptively labeled as *radial relativity*. Nevertheless, $EL_4(\mathbf{V})$ can serve as a first-order model for relative motion along lines of action that do not intersect the observer's position. One would use the radial component of the relative motion vector as **V**.

4.4.2 Relative Velocity Compounding Depends On Viewing Angle

The problem for this section is to determine how two relative velocities in arbitrary directions compound to produce an equivalent resultant velocity We proceed as follows. The typical element of $EL_4(\mathbf{V})$ is of the form

$$\mathbf{T} = [-\mathbf{U}/\mathbf{V}]^{1/2} ,$$

with (4.92)

$$\mathbf{V} = \mathbf{1}\dot{x} + \mathbf{i}\dot{y} + \mathbf{j}\dot{z} + \mathbf{k}c$$

$$\mathbf{U} = \mathbf{1}\dot{x} + \mathbf{i}\dot{y} - \mathbf{j}\dot{z} - \mathbf{k}c .$$

If two of these are applied successively, effectively compounding the two velocities, the result is of the form

$$\mathbf{T}_1\mathbf{T}_2 = [\mathbf{U}_1\mathbf{U}_2/\mathbf{V}_1\mathbf{V}_2]^{\frac{1}{2}}. \tag{4.93}$$

Now we must rearrange (4.93) into the fundamental form (4.92), taking care that the **k**-component is c, the speed of light. By the usual multiplication rule in $\mathbb{D}$,

$$\begin{aligned}\mathbf{V}_1\mathbf{V}_2 = {} & \mathbf{1}\ (\dot{x}_1\dot{x}_2 - \dot{y}_1\dot{y}_2 - \dot{z}_1\dot{z}_2 + cc) \\ & + \mathbf{i}\ (\dot{y}_1\dot{x}_2 + \dot{x}_1\dot{y}_2 - c\dot{z}_2 - \dot{z}_1c) \\ & + \mathbf{j}\ (\dot{z}_1\dot{x}_2 - c\dot{y}_2 + \dot{x}_1\dot{z}_2 - \dot{y}_1c) \\ & + \mathbf{k}\ (c\dot{x}_2 + \dot{z}_1\dot{y}_2 + \dot{y}_1\dot{z}_2 + \dot{x}_1c)\ ;\end{aligned} \tag{4.94}$$

similarly,

$$\begin{aligned}\mathbf{U}_1\mathbf{U}_2 = {} & \mathbf{1}\ (\dot{x}_1\dot{x}_2 - \dot{y}_1\dot{y}_2 - \dot{z}_1\dot{z}_2 + cc) \\ & + \mathbf{i}\ (\dot{y}_1\dot{x}_2 + \dot{x}_1\dot{y}_2 - c\dot{z}_2 - \dot{z}_1c) \\ & + \mathbf{j}\ (-\dot{z}_1\dot{x}_2 + c\dot{y}_2 - \dot{x}_1\dot{z}_2 + \dot{y}_1c) \\ & + \mathbf{k}\ (-c\dot{x}_2 - \dot{z}_1\dot{y}_2 - \dot{y}_1\dot{z}_2 - \dot{x}_1c) \\ = {} & \mathbf{1}\ (\dot{x}_1\dot{x}_2 - \dot{y}_1\dot{y}_2 - \dot{z}_1\dot{z}_2 + cc) \\ & + \mathbf{i}\ (\dot{y}_1\dot{x}_2 + \dot{x}_1\dot{y}_2 - c\dot{z}_2 - \dot{z}_1c) \\ & - \mathbf{j}\ (\dot{z}_1\dot{x}_2 - c\dot{y}_2 + \dot{x}_1\dot{z}_2 - \dot{y}_1c) \\ & - \mathbf{k}\ (c\dot{x}_2 + \dot{z}_1\dot{y}_2 + \dot{y}_1\dot{z}_2 + \dot{x}_1c)\ .\end{aligned} \tag{4.95}$$

These products have the proper corresponding terms and signs, but have two problematical features: the dimensional units are length squared, and the **k**-component is not the constant c. However, one may factor both products in exactly the same way, as follows: Let

$$\mathbf{P} = \mathbf{k}\,\frac{(\dot{x}_1\dot{x}_2 - \dot{y}_1\dot{y}_2 - \dot{z}_1\dot{z}_2 + cc)}{c}\;; \tag{4.96}$$

then **P** is nonzero so long as the magnitude of the three-space velocities $(\dot{x}_1, \dot{y}_1, \dot{z}_1)$ and $(\dot{x}_2, \dot{y}_2, \dot{z}_2)$ are both less than c.

Next, factor **P** out of each product to obtain

$$\begin{aligned} \mathbf{V}_1\mathbf{V}_2 = \mathbf{k}\,[\mathbf{1}\,&(c\dot{x}_2 + \dot{z}_1\dot{y}_2 + \dot{y}_1\dot{z}_2 + \dot{x}_1 c) \\ - \mathbf{i}\,&(\dot{z}_1\dot{x}_2 - c\dot{y}_2 + \dot{x}_1\dot{z}_2 - \dot{y}_1 c) \\ - \mathbf{j}\,&(\dot{y}_1\dot{x}_2 + \dot{x}_1\dot{y}_2 - c\dot{z}_2 - \dot{z}_1 c) \\ + \mathbf{k}\,&(\dot{x}_1\dot{x}_2 - \dot{y}_1\dot{y}_2 - \dot{z}_1\dot{z}_2 + cc)\,] \end{aligned} \tag{4.97}$$

$$\begin{aligned} = \mathbf{P}\Bigg[\mathbf{1}\,&\frac{c(c\dot{x}_2 + \dot{z}_1\dot{y}_2 + \dot{y}_1\dot{z}_2 + \dot{x}_1 c)}{\dot{x}_1\dot{x}_2 - \dot{y}_1\dot{y}_2 - \dot{z}_1\dot{z}_2 + cc} \\ - \mathbf{i}\,&\frac{c(\dot{z}_1\dot{x}_2 - c\dot{y}_2 + \dot{x}_1\dot{z}_2 - \dot{y}_1 c)}{\dot{x}_1\dot{x}_2 - \dot{y}_1\dot{y}_2 - \dot{z}_1\dot{z}_2 + cc} \\ - \mathbf{j}\,&\frac{c(\dot{y}_1\dot{x}_2 - \dot{x}_1\dot{y}_2 + c\dot{z}_2 - \dot{z}_1 c)}{\dot{x}_1\dot{x}_2 - \dot{y}_1\dot{y}_2 - \dot{z}_1\dot{z}_2 + cc} \\ + \mathbf{k}\,&c\Bigg]\;; \end{aligned} \tag{4.98}$$

similarly,

$$\mathbf{U}_1\mathbf{U}_2 = -\mathbf{P}\left[\mathbf{1}\,\frac{c(c\dot{x}_2 + \dot{z}_1\dot{y}_2 + \dot{y}_1\dot{z}_2 + \dot{x}_1 c)}{\dot{x}_1\dot{x}_2 - \dot{y}_1\dot{y}_2 - \dot{z}_1\dot{z}_2 + cc}\right.$$

$$- \mathbf{i}\,\frac{c(\dot{z}_1\dot{x}_2 - c\dot{y}_2 + \dot{x}_1\dot{z}_2 - \dot{y}_1 c)}{\dot{x}_1\dot{x}_2 - \dot{y}_1\dot{y}_2 - \dot{z}_1\dot{z}_2 + cc}$$

$$- \mathbf{j}\,\frac{c(\dot{y}_1\dot{x}_2 + \dot{x}_1\dot{y}_2 - c\dot{z}_2 - \dot{z}_1 c)}{\dot{x}_1\dot{x}_2 - \dot{y}_1\dot{y}_2 - \dot{z}_1\dot{z}_2 + cc} \tag{4.99}$$

$$\left. + \mathbf{k}\; c\right] ;$$

Now, if one forms the quotient $\mathbf{U}_1\mathbf{U}_2/\mathbf{V}_1\mathbf{V}_2$, the overall factor **P** cancels out of the numerator and denominator, leaving a resultant transform having exactly the form as either original transform; i.e., the same as (4.92). It follows that the resultant (compounded) velocity is

$$\mathbf{V}_3 = \mathbf{1}\,\frac{c(c\dot{x}_2 + \dot{z}_1\dot{y}_2 + \dot{y}_1\dot{z}_2 + \dot{x}_1 c)}{\dot{x}_1\dot{x}_2 - \dot{y}_1\dot{y}_2 - \dot{z}_1\dot{z}_2 + cc}$$

$$- \mathbf{i}\,\frac{c(\dot{z}_1\dot{x}_2 - c\dot{y}_2 + \dot{x}_1\dot{z}_2 - \dot{y}_1 c)}{\dot{x}_1\dot{x}_2 - \dot{y}_1\dot{y}_2 - \dot{z}_1\dot{z}_2 + cc}$$

$$- \mathbf{j}\,\frac{c(\dot{y}_1\dot{x}_2 + \dot{x}_1\dot{y}_2 - c\dot{z}_2 - \dot{z}_1 c)}{\dot{x}_1\dot{x}_2 - \dot{y}_1\dot{y}_2 - \dot{z}_1\dot{z}_2 + cc} \tag{4.100}$$

$$+ \mathbf{k}\; c \;;$$

We shall call (4.100) the *generalized Einstein addition law for velocities*.

We point out that $\mathbf{V}_1$ and $\mathbf{V}_2$ are defined in parallel frames of reference. Otherwise, one would have to include in (4.94) and (4.95) a similarity transform which might be outside the $\mathbb{D}$-space system of analysis. If frame one is the observer's frame, then frame two is assumed to be moving with a velocity $\mathbf{V}_1$ with respect to frame one, and the body under observation is assumed to be moving with velocity $\mathbf{V}_2$ with respect to frame two. With a parallel-frame geometry as assumed here, $\mathbf{V}_2$ has exactly the same value if referred back to frame one, but will have a parallel, but offset, line of action in frame one.

There are two special cases of (4.100) that are easily examined and illustrate the variation with viewing angle. First, we know, a priori, that the Einstein-Lorentz velocity compounding formula is implicit in (4.100) because $EL_2(\mathbf{V})$ is a subgroup in $EL_4(\mathbf{V})$. If we set

$$\dot{y}_1 = \dot{y}_2 = \dot{z}_1 = \dot{z}_2 = 0, \tag{4.101}$$

then (4.100) reduces to

$$\begin{aligned} \mathbf{V}_3 &= \mathbf{1}\,\frac{c(c\dot{x}_2 + \dot{x}_1 c)}{\dot{x}_1\dot{x}_2 + cc} \\ &= \mathbf{1}\,\frac{\dot{x}_1 + \dot{x}_2}{1 + \dfrac{\dot{x}_1\dot{x}_2}{c^2}}\,, \end{aligned} \tag{4.102}$$

which is the Einstein addition law. The second special case is the distant transverse velocity case. In that case,

$$\dot{x}_1 = \dot{y}_1 = \dot{x}_2 = \dot{y}_2 = 0, \tag{4.103}$$

and

$$\begin{aligned} \mathbf{V}_3 &= -\,\mathbf{j}\,\frac{c(-c\dot{z}_2 - \dot{z}_1 c)}{-\dot{z}_1\dot{z}_2 + cc} \\ &= \mathbf{j}\,\frac{\dot{z}_2 + \dot{z}_1}{1 - \dfrac{\dot{z}_1\dot{z}_2}{c^2}} = \mathbf{U}_3\,. \end{aligned} \tag{4.104}$$

This is, at first glance, a bizarre-looking result. It says that the equivalent single velocity $\mathbf{V}_3$ obtained by compounding two transverse velocities, $\mathbf{V}_1$ and $\mathbf{V}_2$, has a magnitude that increases faster than simple vector addition, quite contrary to Einstein-Lorentz theory. The only difference in the compounding formula, (4.104), and the Einstein addition formula is one minus sign that is due to the algebraic basis and the multiplication rule in $\mathbb{D}$. However, it is not the expression for the compounded velocities that affects our actual perception of distant transverse motion, but the transformation of coordinate that results from the motion. We have seen in (4.91) that distant transverse motion will produce an identity transformation, and the product of two identity transforms is an identity transform. In the latter case, $\mathbf{U}_3$ is equal to the negative of $\mathbf{V}_3$ in (4.93), and they cancel. One must then perceive such scenarios as being unaffected by relativity. Physical dimensions and time intervals will have their rest-system values regardless of which system is used as a reference. Consequently, *distant, transverse velocities will appear to compound by simple vector addition.* The possibility then arises that *the appearance* of the speed of light being exceeding can occur. There would not even be any apparent wavelength shift of light due to the motion because the motion is assumed to have an insignificant component toward or away from the observer!

Again, we emphasize that the transverse effects are merely functions of the observer's viewpoint, inasmuch as one could turn the same actions end-on to the observer (collinear with the observer's line of sight) and see the familiar Einstein-Lorentz effects. Clearly, it is not space that is nonisotropic, but the observer's perceptions of actions and events in space.

4.4.3 Length Distortion Results From Time Interval Assumptions

We intend to show that the Lorentz (length) contraction is dependent on the viewing angle and is a result of our inability to assign correlated time intervals to the measurement process. Consider the distance vector

$$\begin{aligned}\Delta\mathbf{X} &= \mathbf{1}(x_1 - x_2) + \mathbf{i}(y_1 - y_2) + \mathbf{j}(z_1 - z_2) + \mathbf{k}c(t_1 - t_2) \\ &= \mathbf{1}\Delta x + \mathbf{i}\Delta y + \mathbf{j}\Delta z + \mathbf{k}c\Delta t\ .\end{aligned} \qquad (4.105)$$

Let L_0 denote some four-vector length for a vector of form (4.105) measured at rest in the moving system, and let L denote the same quantity measured from the observer's system. By (4.75),

$$\begin{aligned}\mathrm{L}^2 &= (\Delta\mathbf{X})^{\mathrm{T}}(\Delta\mathbf{X}) \\ &= (\Delta\mathbf{X}')^{\mathrm{T}}\ (\Delta\mathbf{X}') = \mathrm{L}_0^2\ ,\end{aligned} \qquad (4.106)$$

which predicts *no contraction effect* in four dimensions. In the three spatial dimensions we see a length contraction effect. I submit that it is a result of our implicit assumption that

$$\Delta t' = \Delta t = 0\ . \qquad (4.107)$$

For illustration, consider the transformation

$$\Delta \mathbf{X}' = \mathbf{T} \Delta \mathbf{X} ,$$

or

$$\begin{bmatrix} \Delta x' \\ \Delta y' \\ \Delta z' \\ c\Delta t' \end{bmatrix} = \begin{bmatrix} U & -R & -W & S \\ R & U & -S & -W \\ W & -S & U & -R \\ S & W & R & U \end{bmatrix} \begin{bmatrix} \Delta x \\ \Delta y \\ \Delta z \\ c\Delta t \end{bmatrix} . \tag{4.108}$$

If we a priori, arbitrarily set $\Delta t' = \Delta t = 0$, we are left with

$$\begin{bmatrix} \Delta x' \\ \Delta y' \\ \Delta z' \\ 0 \end{bmatrix} = \begin{bmatrix} U & -R & -W & S \\ R & U & -S & -W \\ W & -S & U & -R \\ S & W & R & U \end{bmatrix} \begin{bmatrix} \Delta x \\ \Delta y \\ \Delta z \\ 0 \end{bmatrix} . \tag{4.109}$$

This gives a nonsensical fourth equation, so we drop it; also, the fourth terms in the three remaining equations drop out because of the zero fourth element of the independent vector, leaving

$$\begin{bmatrix} \Delta x' \\ \Delta y' \\ \Delta z' \end{bmatrix} = \begin{bmatrix} U & -R & -W \\ R & U & -S \\ W & -S & U \end{bmatrix} \begin{bmatrix} \Delta x \\ \Delta y \\ \Delta z \end{bmatrix} . \tag{4.110}$$

Now, if an at-rest observer in the moving system measures a dimensio of an at-rest body in the moving system as

$$L^2_o = (\Delta x')^2 + (\Delta y')^2 + (\Delta z')^2 ,$$

then an observer in the unprimed system will measure the same quantity as

$$L^2_o = (U\Delta x - R\Delta y - W\Delta z)^2 \qquad (4.111)$$
$$+ (R\Delta x + U\Delta y - S\Delta z)^2$$
$$+ (W\Delta x - S\Delta y + U\Delta z)^2 \ ,$$

with U,R,W,S defined by (4.31)–(4.34). We shall call (4.111) the *generalized Lorentz contraction law*. Formula (4.111) gives us a means to back-calculate the at-rest dimension from observed data.

We observe length contraction effects in three-space, so they must be implicit in (4.111). We can recover the Lorentz contraction formula as follows. Consider the restricted case of the relativistic transform, with

$$v = \dot{x}$$
$$\dot{y} = \dot{z} = 0 \ ; \qquad (4.112)$$

and let the dimension of the moving body to be measured be aligned along the x-axis of the observer (the direction of motion), so that

$$L = \Delta x \ ,$$

and (4.113)

$$\Delta y = \Delta z = \Delta y' = \Delta z' = 0 \ .$$

Now refer back to (4.31)–(4.34) to calculate

$$\xi = v - c \qquad (4.114)$$
$$\eta = v + c \ ,$$

$$\alpha = [-\eta/\xi]^{1/2}$$
$$= [(c + v) / (c - v)]^{1/2}$$
$$= (c + v) / (c^2 - v^2)^{1/2} \qquad (4.115)$$

$$\beta = [-\xi/\eta]^{1/2}$$
$$= [(c - v) / (c + v)]^{1/2}$$
$$= (c - v) / (c^2 - v^2)^{1/2} \ ,$$

$$U = [Re(\alpha) + Re(\beta)] / 2$$
$$= c / [c^2 - v^2]^{1/2}$$

$$R = [Im(\alpha) + Im(\beta)] / 2 = 0 \tag{4.116}$$

$$W = [Im(\alpha) - Im(\beta)] / 2 = 0$$

$$S = [-Re(\alpha) + Re(\beta)] / 2$$
$$= -v / [c^2 - v^2]^{1/2} ,$$

and, going back to (4.111),

$$\mathrm{L}_o^2 = (U\Delta x)^2 + (R\Delta x)^2 + (W\Delta x)^2 \tag{4.117}$$
$$= U^2 (\Delta x)^2 ;$$

then

$$\mathrm{L}_o = U\Delta x$$

$$= c / [c^2 - v^2]^{1/2} \mathrm{L} \tag{4.118}$$

$$= 1 / [1 - (v/c)^2]^{1/2} \mathrm{L}$$

or

$$\mathrm{L} = \mathrm{L}_o [1 - (v/c)^2]^{1/2} , \tag{4.119}$$

which is the Lorentz contraction formula. As for the transverse effect, it is indicated from Section (4.4.1) that pure transverse motion will produce an identity transform in the $\mathbb{D}$-space mathematics, hence will cause no Lorentz contraction. Nevertheless, we must verify that our Lorentz contraction formula is in agreement. Let

$$v = \dot{z} \tag{4.120}$$

$$\dot{x} = \dot{y} = 0 ,$$

let the $+x$-axes of the two systems be collinear, let the observer's line of sight be the $+x$-axis, and let the dimension of the moving body to be measured be aligned along the z-axis of the moving system (the direction of motion, also parallel to the observer's z-axis), so that

$$\mathrm{L} = \Delta z$$

and (4.121)

$$\Delta x = \Delta y = \Delta x' = \Delta y' = 0 \ .$$

Again refer back to (4.31)–(4.34) to calculate

$$\xi = -c + \mathbf{i}v \qquad (4.122)$$

$$\eta = c - \mathbf{i}v \ ,$$

$$\begin{aligned} \alpha &= [-\eta/\xi]^{1/2} \\ &= [\,(c - \mathbf{i}v)\,/\,(c - \mathbf{i}v)\,]^{1/2} \\ &= (1)^{1/2} = 1 \end{aligned} \qquad (4.123)$$

$$\begin{aligned} \beta &= [-\xi/\eta]^{1/2} \\ &= [\,(c - \mathbf{i}v)\,/\,(c - \mathbf{i}v)\,]^{1/2} \\ &= (1)^{1/2} = 1 \end{aligned}$$

$$\begin{aligned} U &= [\,Re(\alpha) + Re(\beta)]\,/\,2 \\ &= [1 + 1]\,/\,2 = 1 \end{aligned}$$

$$R = [\,Im(\alpha) + Im(\beta)\,]\,/\,2 = 0 \qquad (4.124)$$

$$W = [\,Im(\alpha) - Im(\beta)]\,/\,2 = 0$$

$$\begin{aligned} S &= [-Re(\alpha) + Re(\beta)\,]\,/\,2 \\ &= [-1 + 1]\,/\,2 = 0 \end{aligned}$$

and, going back to (4.111),

$$L_o^2 = (W\Delta z)^2 + (-S\Delta z)^2 + (U\Delta z)^2$$
$$= U^2(\Delta z)^2 = (\Delta z)^2 ;$$

then (4.125)

$$L_o = \Delta z = L ,$$

and no longitudinal contraction due to purely transverse motion (with respect to the observer's line of sight) will be perceived. The same result is obtained if one chooses a transverse velocity along the y-axis. Again, we emphasize that this apparent no-contraction result is due to the nonisotropic nature of an observer's perceptions. If the same motion were viewed along the line of action, a contraction effect would be observed.

4.4.4 Time Dilation Depends On Viewing Angle

The formula for the time dilation effect may also be generalized, as follows. Let a_1,a_2,a_3 be spatial direction cosines such that

$$(a_1)^2 + (a_2)^2 + (a_3)^2 = 1 , \tag{4.126}$$

and let the relative motion vector be

$$\mathbf{V} = v(\mathbf{1}a_1 + \mathbf{i}a_2 + \mathbf{j}a_3) + \mathbf{k}c . \tag{4.127}$$

Assume the appropriate initial conditions such that in the rest system the origin of the moving system will have the coordinates

$$x_1 = a_1 vt$$

$$y_1 = a_2 vt \tag{4.128}$$

$$z_1 = a_3 vt .$$

From (4.80),

$$ct' = Sx_1 + Wy_1 + Rz_1 + Uct \tag{4.129}$$

$$= S(a_1 vt) + W(a_2 vt) + R(a_3 vt) + Uct$$

$$= [(Sa_1 + Wa_2 + Ra_3)(v/c) + U]\,ct ,$$

or

$$ct = ct' / [(Sa_1 + Wa_2 + Ra_3)(v/c) + U] , \tag{4.130}$$

with U, R, W, S defined by (4.31)–(4.34). Equation (4.130) is the *generalized time dilation relation*. It implicitly contains the Einstein time dilation formula, which may be recovered as follows. For the restricted case of the Lorentz transform, one has a relative motion vector

$$\mathbf{V} = \mathbf{1}v + \mathbf{k}c , \tag{4.131}$$

which has direction cosines

$$a_1 = 1, a_2 = a_3 = 0; \tag{4.132}$$

then by (4.116) and (4.130),

$$ct = ct' / [Sa_1(v/c) + U]$$

$$= ct' / \{-(v/c)^2 / [1 - (v/c)^2]^{1/2} + 1 / [1 - (v/c)^2]^{1/2}\}$$

$$= ct' / [1 - (v/c)^2]^{1/2} , \tag{4.133}$$

which is the Einstein formula. We may also check the pure transverse velocity case, and we expect no time dilation in that case because the overall transform **T** is an identity matrix. The relative motion vector (one choice) is

$$\mathbf{V} = \mathbf{j}v + \mathbf{k}c , \tag{4.134}$$

which has direction cosines

$$a_1 = a_2 = 0 , \qquad a_3 = 1 ; \tag{4.135}$$

then by (4.124) and (4.130),

$$\begin{aligned} ct &= ct' \,/\, [\, Ra_3 (v/c) \,+\, U] \\ &= ct' \,/\, [0 \,+\, 1] = ct' \,. \end{aligned} \tag{4.136}$$

This result and the length contraction result for the transverse velocity case are perfectly explained in the same way as are the more-established Lorentz contraction effects: they result from the finite, constant speed of light and the differing (or in the present case, equal) distances that the measurement impulses have to travel, hence preserving simultaneity. For example, if an experimenter in the moving system is measuring the length of a rod fixed in the moving system and sets off simultaneous light flashes from the ends of the rod as part of the process, then any observer in a rest system viewing along a line perpendicular to the rod and through the center of the rod will see the flashes simultaneously, as well, because the distances that the two light flashes must traverse to the observer are equal.

4.4.5 The Observer's Bias Is Needed For Transverse Alignments

For the restricted case of the Lorentz transform, wherein one considers relative velocities radially inward or outward from the observer, certain measurements may give surprising results. For example, suppose that the observer is viewing a rod lying transverse to the line of sight (said line going through the center of the rod), and the rod is moving away from the observer. The mathematical particulars are:

$$\begin{aligned} &v = \dot{x} \\ &\dot{y} = \dot{z} = 0 \,; \\ &\mathrm{L} = \Delta y \\ &\Delta x = \Delta z = \Delta x' = \Delta z' = 0 \,. \end{aligned} \tag{4.137}$$

Now use (4.111) and (4.116) to calculate

$$L^2_o = (-R\Delta y)^2 + (U\Delta y)^2 + (-S\Delta y)^2$$

$$= (R^2 + U^2 + S^2)(\Delta y)^2 \tag{4.138}$$

$$= \{0 + 1/[1 - (v/c)^2] + (v/c)^2/[1 - (v/c)^2]\}\, L^2 ,$$

or

$$L = L_o \{[1 - (v/c)^2]/[1 + (v/c)^2]\}^{1/2}. \tag{4.139}$$

This implies that a transverse alignment of the object under measurement will cause the length contraction effect to be more pronounced, by the factor

$$1/[1 + (v/c)^2]^{1/2},$$

which is hardly plausible. However, if one uses the observer's bias transformation one obtains the expected result, that *no* contraction occurs as follows. If the derivation of the contraction formula is started over at (4.108) and the observer's bias is included, one obtains

$$L^2_o = (U\Delta x - iR\Delta y - W\Delta z)^2 \tag{4.140}$$

$$+ (-iR\Delta x + U\Delta y + iS\Delta z)^2$$

$$+ (W\Delta x - iS\Delta y + U\Delta z)^2 ,$$

with U, R, W, S defined by (4.31)–(4.34), and "i" denotes the classical complex imaginary. We repeat the calculation in (4.138) to obtain

$$L^2_o = (-iR\Delta y)^2 + (U\Delta y)^2 + (-iS\Delta y)^2$$

$$= (-R^2 + U^2 - S^2)(\Delta y)^2$$

$$= \{0 + 1/[1 - (v/c)^2] - (v/c)^2/[1 - (v/c)^2]\}\, L^2 ,$$

$$= \{[1 - (v/c)^2]/[1 - (v/c)^2]\}\, L^2 ,$$

or

$$L_o = L . \tag{4.141}$$

This is far more plausible, because if an experimenter at rest with respect to the rod sets off simultaneous light flashes at the ends of the rod, then the observer at the origin of the rest system will see the light flashes as simultaneous, inasmuch as each must travel the same distance to the observer.

4.4.6 Constant Motion Produces A Rotational Offset About The Direction Of Motion

This is most easily seen by use of the restricted case of the Lorentz transform, with a relative velocity vector along the x-axis of the observer and parallel frames of reference. In that case, (4.47) gives the transformation of coordinates. One observes that the relativistic effect is decoupled between the x,ct coordinates and the y,z coordinates:

$$\begin{aligned} x' &= \gamma\,[x - (v/c)\,\mathrm{ct}] \\ ct' &= \gamma\,[-(v/c)\,\mathrm{x} + \mathrm{ct}] \\ y' &= \gamma\,[y + (v/c)\,\mathrm{z}] \\ z' &= \gamma\,[(v/c)\,\mathrm{y} + \mathrm{z}]\ . \end{aligned} \tag{4.142}$$

The determinant of each transformation pair is +1, leading us to believe that a rotation may be taking place. However, the coefficient γ is always real and above unity in magnitude in the velocity regime that we are considering, hence we are dealing with a hyperbolic rotation. Consider the y,z transformation: it is of the form

$$\begin{aligned} y' &= y\,cosh(\Phi) + z\,sinh(\Phi) \\ z' &= y\,sinh(\Phi) + z\,cosh(\Phi)\ , \end{aligned} \tag{4.143}$$

with Φ real. The determinant remains unity due to a common hyperbolic relationship:

$$cosh^2(\Phi) - sinh^2(\Phi) = 1\ .$$

In special relativistic discussions, the relative velocity v is fixed and constant hence the y,z components will be rotated by some fixed amount as indicated in (4.143).

As noted in Section 2.2.16, a rotation in four dimensions takes place about a plane. Here, we have the *y,z* plane rotating about the *x,ct* plane, and vice versa. In the spatial *x,y,z* three-space, we perceive the rotation to be taking place about the *x*-axis, which is the direction of relative motion, and our thesis for this section is established.

It was also shown that it is a matter of a unitary similarity transformation to get to a viewpoint in which length is preserved by the transformation [see (4.65) and (4.66)]. In the present special case, the observer's bias transformation causes (4.142) to become

$$\begin{aligned} x' &= \gamma\,[x + \mathrm{i}(v/c)\,\mathrm{ct}] \\ ct' &= \gamma\,[-\mathrm{i}(v/c)\,\mathrm{x} + \mathrm{ct}] \\ y' &= \gamma\,[y - \mathrm{i}(v/c)\mathrm{z}] \\ z' &= \gamma\,[\mathrm{i}(v/c)\,\mathrm{y} + \mathrm{z}]\;, \end{aligned} \tag{4.144}$$

from which one can establish by direct substitution that, separately,

$$x'^2 + c^2t'^2 = x^2 + c^2t^2$$

and (4.145)

$$y'^2 + z'^2 = y^2 + z^2\;;$$

thus one sees that, with the proper viewpoint, transverse length is preserved. With length preserved, the transformation will look like a simple rotational offset about the *x*-axis.

4.4.7 Reconciliation With The Einstein-Lorentz Theories

We shall now address the most delicate issue of all: if the D-space theories are subjected to experiment and prove to have merit, where are the fundamental points of divergence with the Einstein-Lorentz theories? I propose that the key differences lie in two assumptions used in the mathematical derivation and application of the Lorentz transformation: (1) that the transverse coordinates would not be affected by the motion, and (2) that length contraction would look the same no matter from whatever angle it is viewed, after simple geometry is taken into account.

Concerning the first assumption, Einstein, in his 1905 paper, included the possibility of a scale change for the transverse coordinates (which did not manifest itself), but did not consider rotations. Later authors implicitly assume (sometimes explicitly assume) that the transverse coordinates will be unaffected. This is understandable, because there was nothing known from experiment to prompt toward any other conclusion. We have hypothesized above that, under the proper viewpoint, the magnitude of the transverse coordinates will not be affected, but that they will be rotated about the line of motion.

Einstein and later authors point to the apparent isotropy of space to support the second assumption. In the present work, we distinguish between the isotropy of space, itself, and the (non)isotropy of the observer's perceptions of events in space. On the one hand, we agree that space is fundamentally isotropic, because one could take a relativistic experiment and an observer at some fixed angular position in relation to the experiment and rotate the whole affair as a unit to any orientation in space without affecting the observer's measurements or perceptions. On the other hand, we calculate that if the experiment is fixed in space while the observer is moved to different positions, then the observer will see variations in measurements even after geometry is taken into account. Modern authors basically take the Einstein relativity formulation and use orthogonal transformations to produce a general angular orientation for the observer. By doing so, they are implicitly assuming that measurable effects are propagated uniformly in all directions.

The $\mathbb{D}$-space theory predicts, as a side result, the rotation of the transverse components. The rotation occurs because of the casting of the relativistic transformation as an analytic function [see (4.27)]. An analytic transformation seems extremely advisable and desirable, inasmuch as its application must not change the inherent analyticity of, for example, electric and magnetic field formulations for free space. A non-analytic distortion of a material body can result in an inexplicable disappearance of part of the material. An analytic distortion is "conservative" of space and its contents.

Lastly, if the $\mathbb{D}$-space theory has merit, should we not expect to see an occasional formula or mathematical result that is not rooted strongly in classical vector theory and that takes the form of a $\mathbb{D}$-space expression? In fact, such a thing occurs: Aharoni[36] gives a series of relativistic transformation equations for the components of an electromagnetic field. A particular four-equation subset of those that are given may be rewritten in matrix form as follows:

$$\begin{bmatrix} E_{y'} \\ E_{z'} \\ H_{y'} \\ H_{z'} \end{bmatrix} \doteq \begin{bmatrix} \gamma & 0 & 0 & -\gamma(v/c) \\ 0 & \gamma & \gamma(v/c) & 0 \\ 0 & \gamma(v/c) & \gamma & 0 \\ -\gamma(v/c) & 0 & 0 & \gamma \end{bmatrix} \begin{bmatrix} E_y \\ E_z \\ H_y \\ H_z \end{bmatrix} \tag{4.146}$$

If we define

$$\mathbf{E} = \mathbf{1}E_y + \mathbf{i}E_z + \mathbf{j}H_y + \mathbf{k}H_z \ , \tag{4.147}$$

then we immediately recognize (4.146) as being of the form

$$\mathbf{E}' = \mathbf{T}\mathbf{E} \ , \tag{4.148}$$

with **T** an element of $EL_4(\mathbf{V})$; this is a $\mathbb{D}$-space relativistic expression. Moreover, (4.146) is just a notational variation of a subset of the electrodynamical transformation equations stated by Einstein in his 1905 paper[37]. We provide a matrix form of his equations for comparison with (4.146), for the reader's convenience:

$$\begin{bmatrix} Y' \\ Z' \\ M' \\ N' \end{bmatrix} =. \begin{bmatrix} \beta & 0 & 0 & -\beta(v/c) \\ 0 & \beta & \beta(v/c) & 0 \\ 0 & \beta(v/c) & \beta & 0 \\ -\beta(v/c) & 0 & 0 & \beta \end{bmatrix} \begin{bmatrix} Y \\ Z \\ M \\ N \end{bmatrix} \tag{4.149}$$

where his β corresponds to the γ that we have been using, (X, Y, Z) is the electric field vector in Einstein's formulation, and (L, M, N) is the magnetic field vector. The (Y, Z, M, N) vector components transform exactly as in (4.146). The fact that they take this form is not due to vector mathematics or the relativistic transformation formulas, but is primarily due to a symmetry argument[38].

4.5 Transformation Effects For The Field Equations Of Physics

This Section will provide the transformation relations for several of the more fundamental physics field theory equations and operators under the transformation group $EL_4(\mathbf{V})$. We shall use the notation

$$\begin{aligned} \mathbf{Z} &= \mathbf{1}x + \mathbf{i}y + \mathbf{j}z + \mathbf{k}ct \\ \mathbf{X} &= \mathbf{1}x + \mathbf{i}y + \mathbf{j}z + \mathbf{k}ct \end{aligned} \tag{4.150}$$

for the independent variable and position vector, respectively;

$$\mathbf{W}(\mathbf{Z}) = \mathbf{1}X + \mathbf{i}Y + \mathbf{j}Z + \mathbf{k}T \tag{4.151}$$

for an analytic field or vector function;

$$\mathbf{Z}' = \mathbf{T}\mathbf{Z} \tag{4.152}$$

or

$$\mathbf{X}' = \mathbf{T}\mathbf{X}$$

for the transformation of the independent variable(s);

$$\Box = \mathbf{1}\frac{\partial}{\partial x} + \mathbf{i}\frac{\partial}{\partial y} + \mathbf{j}\frac{\partial}{\partial z} + \mathbf{k}\frac{\partial}{\partial ct} \tag{4.153}$$

for the four-dimensional gradient operator;

$$\Box_1 = \mathbf{1}\frac{\partial}{\partial x'} + \mathbf{i}\frac{\partial}{\partial y'} + \mathbf{j}\frac{\partial}{\partial z'} + \mathbf{k}\frac{\partial}{\partial ct'} , \tag{4.154}$$

for the gradient operator in the transformed coordinates;

$$\begin{aligned} \mathbf{V} &= \mathbf{1}\dot{x} + \mathbf{i}\dot{y} + \mathbf{j}\dot{z} + \mathbf{k}c \\ \mathbf{U} &= \mathbf{1}\dot{x} + \mathbf{i}\dot{y} - \mathbf{j}\dot{z} - \mathbf{k}c \end{aligned} \tag{4.155}$$

for the relative motion vector and its EXCH counterpart;

$$\begin{aligned} \mathbf{T} &= [-\mathbf{U}/\mathbf{V}]^{1/2} \\ &= [-\eta/\xi]^{1/2}\,\mathbf{e}_1 + [-\xi/\eta]^{1/2}\,\mathbf{e}_2 \\ &= \mathbf{1}U + \mathbf{i}R + \mathbf{j}W + \mathbf{k}S \end{aligned} \tag{4.156}$$

for the typical transformation from $EL_4(\mathbf{V})$; and

$$\Psi = \Psi(x, y, z, ct) \tag{4.157}$$

for a scalar analytic function. We already have from Section 4.3.6 that

$$\Box \Psi = \mathbf{T} \Box_1 \Psi \tag{4.158}$$

and

$$\Box \mathrm{F} = \mathbf{T} \Box_1 \mathrm{F} = 0 \ , \tag{4.159}$$

which shows the form invariance of the four-gradient of an analytic vector function. In the following, we give several additional, representative examples. The reader may see Eisele[29] for a detailed presentation and analysis of physics equations in classical vector notation, especially the D'Alembertian, in forms that are easily translated into $\mathbb{D}$-space notation.

4.5.1 Increment Of Four-Dimensional Volume

The increment of four-dimensional volume in rectangular coordinates is *dxdydzcdt*. Because we are considering a transformation of the independent variable of the form

$$\mathbf{X}' = \mathbf{TX}, \tag{4.160}$$

the Jacobian of the transformation, commonly denoted as follows, is the determinant of $\mathbf{T}$:

$$\frac{\partial (x',y',z',t')}{\partial (x,y,z,t)} = \begin{bmatrix} U & -R & -W & S \\ R & U & -S & -W \\ W & -S & U & -R \\ S & W & R & U \end{bmatrix} = +1 \ . \tag{4.161}$$

In terms of the Jacobian, the transformation relation for the four-dimensional element of volume is

$$\begin{aligned} dx'\,dy'\,dz'\,cdt' &= \frac{\partial (x',y',z',t')}{\partial (x,y,z,t)}\, dx\,dy\,dz\,cdt \\ &= dx\,dy\,dz\,cdt \ . \end{aligned} \tag{4.162}$$

We emphasize that (4.162) is a four-dimensional result involving elements from $EL_4(\mathbf{V})$, which embody the $\mathbb{D}$-space mathematics, hence (4.162) is, in one sense, a $\mathbb{D}$-space statement. In another view, an element of $EL_4(\mathbf{V})$ is just a familiar- looking, 4 X 4, real-valued transformation matrix that preserves the four-dimensional volume increment.

The volume element is not preserved if only the three spatial dimensions are considered because, in that case,

$$\frac{\partial(x',y',z')}{\partial(x,y,z)} = \begin{bmatrix} U & -R & -W \\ R & U & -S \\ W & -S & U \end{bmatrix} \neq 1 , \qquad (4.163)$$

except in certain instances. It follows that we shall see relativistic effects associated with three-space volume integrals, but not with four-space integrals in the $\mathbb{D}$-space mathematics.

4.5.2 Four-Dimensional Differential Increment

The differential increment associated with a position vector $\mathbf{X}$ in the observer's system is $d\mathbf{X}$. For a fixed relative motion vector $\mathbf{V}$, the associated transformation $\mathbf{T}$ is a constant in the $\mathbb{D}$-space, and

$$\begin{aligned} \mathbf{X}' &= \mathbf{T}\ \mathbf{X} \\ d\mathbf{X}' &= \mathbf{T}\ d\mathbf{X}. \end{aligned} \qquad (4.164)$$

4.5.3 $\mathbb{D}$-Space Derivatives

Suppose $\mathrm{F}(\mathbf{Z})$ and $\mathrm{G}(\mathbf{Z})$ are analytic functions in $\mathbb{D}$. One may compose a third analytic function $\mathrm{F}(\mathrm{G}(\mathbf{Z}))$ from the first two; then the chain rule for derivatives yields

$$\frac{d\mathrm{F}}{d\mathbf{Z}} = \frac{d\mathrm{F}}{d\mathrm{G}}\frac{d\mathrm{G}}{d\mathbf{Z}} \qquad (4.165)$$

$$= \frac{d\mathrm{G}}{d\mathbf{Z}}\frac{d\mathrm{F}}{d\mathrm{G}} . \qquad \text{(Commutativity)}$$

Now, let

$$G(\mathbf{Z}) = \mathbf{Z}' = \mathbf{T}\ \mathbf{Z}; \tag{4.166}$$

then

$$\frac{dG}{d\mathbf{Z}} = \mathbf{T}$$

and

$$\frac{dF}{d\mathbf{Z}} = \mathbf{T}\,\frac{dF}{d\mathbf{Z}'}\ . \tag{4.167}$$

4.5.4 Vector Integrals

We are considering analytic vector functions F(**Z**) in $\mathbb{D}$ and their indefinite integrals

$$G(\mathbf{Z}) = \int F(\mathbf{Z})\, d\mathbf{Z}\ . \tag{4.168}$$

Assuming the integrability of F(**Z**) (which can be checked by means of the classical complex theory), then the integral is representable as

$$G(\mathbf{Z}) = \int \frac{dG}{d\mathbf{Z}}\, d\mathbf{Z}\ . \tag{4.169}$$

Now one may use (4.164) and (4.167) to assert that

$$\int \frac{dG}{d\mathbf{Z}}\, d\mathbf{Z} = \int \left[\mathbf{T}\,\frac{dG}{d\mathbf{Z}'}\right] \mathbf{T}^{-1} d\mathbf{Z}' = \int \frac{d\mathbf{G}}{d\mathbf{Z}'}\, d\mathbf{Z}'\ ; \tag{4.170}$$

i.e.,

$$\int F(\mathbf{Z})\, d\mathbf{Z} = \int F(\mathbf{Z}')\, d\mathbf{Z}'\ . \tag{4.171}$$

4.5.5 The Wave Equation

Section 3.1.7 showed that the wave equation is preserved under analytic transformations of the independent variables. Here, we merely note that $\mathbf{X}' = \mathbf{T}\mathbf{X}$ is an analytic transformation, inasmuch as $\mathbf{T}$ is a $\mathbb{D}$-space constant in special relativistic discussions. By a notational variation of (3.98),

$$\begin{aligned} \Box^2 U &= |\Box x'|^2 \, \Box_1^2 U \\ &= |\mathbf{T}|^2 \Box_1^2 U = 0 \ . \end{aligned} \tag{4.172}$$

The magnitude of $\mathbf{T}$ is nonzero, hence the desired result is obtained. The $\Box^2$ operator has a plus sign in front of the time derivative, here, but it is only a matter of a unitary transformation to change it to the negative, yielding the classical D'Alembertian form.

4.5.6 Maxwell's Equations

Section 3.2.2 showed that one can take the three-dimensional magnetic potential $\mathbf{A}$ and the scalar electric potential Φ and form a four-dimensional electromagnetic potential function

$$\Gamma = \mathbf{A} + \mathbf{k}\Phi \ . \tag{4.173}$$

If it is further required that

$$\Box \Gamma = 0 \ , \tag{4.174}$$

then not only is the *Lorentz condition* (3.122) satisfied, but Γ is an analytic function, as well. Consequently, from analytic function theory,

$$\Box^2 \mathbf{A} = 0 \quad \text{and} \quad \Box^2 \Phi = 0 \tag{4.175}$$

in free space. Others have shown that Equations (4.175) are equivalent to Maxwell's equations in free space. That being so, the single equation (4.174) is a more fundamental form of Maxwell's equations. By (4.159), equation (4.174) transforms as follows:

$$\Box \Gamma = \mathbf{T} \, \Box_1 \Gamma = 0 \ . \tag{4.176}$$

The determinant of **T** is nonzero, hence the desired result is obtained. Conversely, if one starts with the assumption that Maxwell's equations can be reduced to wave equations, then (4.172) shows that they are unchanged by a transformation **T** from $EL_4(\mathbf{V})$.

4.5.7 Helmholtz's Equation

The Helmholtz equation for a scalar function U is

$$\nabla^2 U + \kappa^2 U = 0 \;, \tag{4.177}$$

where κ is a scalar. In order to show form invariance under a relativistic transformation **T**, we resort to a simple device that will allow us to use our previous results. We first broaden the equation to operate on a vector function:

$$\mathbf{W} = \mathbf{1}U + \mathbf{i}R + \mathbf{j}V + \mathbf{k}S \;. \tag{4.178}$$

The Helmholtz operator is linear and we have distributivity in $\mathbb{D}$, hence

$$\nabla^2 \mathbf{W} + \kappa^2 \mathbf{W} = 0 \;. \tag{4.179}$$

Equation (4.177) is implicit in (4.179) as the first vector component. We add and subtract the same time derivative quantity to complete a D'Alembertian operator from the scalar del operator and obtain

$$\Box^2 \mathbf{W} - \frac{1}{c^2}\frac{\partial^2 \mathbf{W}}{\partial t^2} + \kappa^2 \mathbf{W} = 0 \;. \tag{4.180}$$

We now assume that we are dealing with an *analytic* function **W**. This is a reasonable assumption for most physical problems, inasmuch as it merely requires that **W** shall be continuous and single-valued within some region of interest. By (2.169), taking account that ct is the time coordinate here, the isolated time partial derivative term converts directly to a full derivative of the hypercomplex variable **Z**:

$$\Box^2 \mathbf{W} - \frac{d^2 \mathbf{W}}{d\mathbf{Z}^2} + \kappa^2 \mathbf{W} = 0 \;. \tag{4.181}$$

By the transformational rules that we have developed, above,

$$|\mathbf{T}|^2 \Box_1^2 \mathbf{W} - \mathbf{T}^2 \frac{d^2\mathbf{W}}{d\mathbf{Z}'^2} + \kappa^2 \mathbf{W} = 0 \ . \tag{4.182}$$

The untransformed (4.181) and transformed (4.182) equations do not look alike, but they are. The D'Alembertian term drops off because it is uniformly zero for any analytic function. For the two equations, this leaves

$$\frac{d^2\mathbf{W}}{d\mathbf{Z}^2} - \kappa^2 \mathbf{W} = 0 \tag{4.183}$$

and

$$\mathbf{T}^2 \frac{d^2\mathbf{W}}{d\mathbf{Z}'^2} - \kappa^2 \mathbf{W} = 0 \ . \tag{4.184}$$

Equation (4.184) may be rewritten as

$$\frac{d^2\mathbf{W}}{d\mathbf{Z}'^2} - (\mathbf{T}^{-1}\kappa)^2 \ \mathbf{W} = 0 \ , \tag{4.185}$$

and since **T** is a hypercomplex constant (in special relativistic cases) embodying the effects of the relative motion, one may view the result as the scalar κ having been modified for different directions in space, especially in the direction of motion. For those cases wherein the independent variable **Z** represents the real, physical four-space, the scalar κ has units of (1 / length), and we know that our perception of length is altered by relative motion. We conclude that the Helmholtz equation retains the same form, except with modified constant coefficients, under a transformation **T** of the coordinates. For the low relative speeds encountered in the macroscopic world, **T** is essentially unity and no effect is noticed.

4.5.8 The Klein-Gordon Equation

The Klein-Gordon equation for a free particle of spin zero has the form

$$\Box^2 \Psi - \kappa^2 \Psi = 0 \ , \tag{4.186}$$

where κ is a scalar. Classically, the D'Alembertian in (4.186) has a minus sign in front of the time derivative; but it is only a matter of a unitary transformation to change the sign to the positive. By the transformation rule (4.172), equation (4.186) becomes

$$|\mathbf{T}|^2 \Box_1^2 \Psi - \kappa^2 \Psi = 0 , \tag{4.187}$$

or

$$\Box_1^2 \Psi - (\kappa/|\mathbf{T}|)^2 \Psi = 0 . \tag{4.188}$$

Equations (4.186) and (4.188) have the same form, but the scalar parameter κ has been modified by the transformation. This is reasonable because

$$\kappa = \text{Const X mass} , \tag{4.189}$$

and it is known from physics experiments that the apparent mass of a particle is modified by motion.

4.5.9 The Diffusion Equation

The diffusion equation is of the form

$$\nabla^2 U - \kappa \frac{\partial U}{\partial t} = 0 , \tag{4.190}$$

where κ is a scalar. The symbol U represents a scalar field, often representing temperature in a solid. One may use the Cauchy-Riemann conditions (2.156) and the scalar function U to construct an analytic, hypercomplex function $\mathbf{W}$ such that

$$\nabla^2 \mathbf{W} - \kappa \frac{\partial \mathbf{W}}{\partial t} = 0 . \tag{4.191}$$

Equation (4.190) is implicit in (4.191) as the first vector component. As we did for the Helmholtz equation, we complete the D'Alembertian from the scalar del term to obtain

$$\Box^2 \mathbf{W} - \frac{\partial^2 \mathbf{W}}{\partial (ct)^2} - \kappa c \frac{\partial \mathbf{W}}{\partial (ct)} = 0 \ . \tag{4.192}$$

We eliminate the D'Alembertian term because it is uniformly zero for an analytic function, then convert the partial derivatives to full hyper-complex derivatives by means of (2.169):

$$\frac{d^2 \mathbf{W}}{d\mathbf{Z}^2} + \kappa c \mathbf{k} \frac{d\mathbf{W}}{d\mathbf{Z}} = 0 \ . \tag{4.193}$$

This reduces to

$$\frac{d}{d\mathbf{Z}} \left[\frac{d\mathbf{W}}{d\mathbf{Z}} + \kappa c \mathbf{k} \mathbf{W} \right] = 0 \ ,$$

$$\frac{d\mathbf{W}}{d\mathbf{Z}} + \kappa c \mathbf{k} \mathbf{W} = \kappa c \mathbf{k} \mathbf{G} \ , \qquad \text{(a constant)} \tag{4.194}$$

with **G** being a convenient hypercomplex constant. This transforms to

$$\mathbf{T} \frac{d\mathbf{W}}{d\mathbf{Z}'} + \kappa c \mathbf{k} \mathbf{W} = \kappa c \mathbf{k} \mathbf{G} \ , \tag{4.195}$$

which can be rearranged to

$$\frac{d\mathbf{W}}{d\mathbf{Z}'} + \mathbf{T}^{-1} \kappa c \mathbf{k} \mathbf{W} = \mathbf{T}^{-1} \kappa c \mathbf{k} \mathbf{G} \ . \tag{4.196}$$

For problems in the real, physical four-space, the constant κc has dimensions of (1 / length), hence one way to interpret (4.196) is that the (apparent) constant κ is modified by the motion, preferentially in some directions. The resultant constant is a four-vector. For those cases wherein the independent variable **Z** represents the real, physical four-space, the scalar κ has units of (1 / length) and we know that our perception of length is altered by relative motion. We conclude that the diffusion equation retains the same form, except with modified constant coefficients, under a transformation **T** of the coordinates. For the low relative speeds encountered in the macroscopic world, **T** is essentially unity and no effect is noticed.

4.5.10 The Vector Field Continuity Equation

The basic continuity equation for a vector field is of the form

$$\frac{\partial \rho}{\partial t} + \nabla \cdot (\rho \mathbf{v}) = 0 \ . \tag{4.197}$$

An example of its application is for compressible fluid flow, wherein ρ is the mass per unit volume at a point and **v** is the vector point velocity of the moving fluid. The continuity equation is a mass conservation formula, inasmuch as it requires the divergence of the mass field (excess mass entering or leaving a volume element) to be balanced by the change of mass density per unit time in the volume element. Another example of application is for the law of conservation of electric charge, with ρ representing the charge per unit volume. Lastly, it also applies for the Poynting vector electromagnetic energy conservation equation in free space, with the correspondences

$$\rho \mathbf{v} \rightarrow \mathbf{E} \times \mathbf{H}$$

and (4.198)

$$\rho \rightarrow (\varepsilon_0 E^2 + \mu_0 H^2)/2 \ .$$

Before transforming (4.197), we rearrange and convert the time element t into ct, as follows:

$$\nabla \cdot (\rho \mathbf{v}) + \frac{\partial(\rho c)}{\partial(ct)} = 0 \ . \tag{4.199}$$

This is immediately recognizable as

$$\Box \cdot (\rho \mathbf{V}) = 0 \ , \tag{4.200}$$

and by (4.159),

$$\Box \cdot (\rho \mathbf{V}) = \mathbf{T} \Box_1 \cdot (\rho \mathbf{V}') = 0 \ . \tag{4.201}$$

One concludes that the continuity equation is invariant in form under a transformation **T** of the independent variables (x,y,z,ct).

Moreover, we know that (4.200) is, within an orthogonal transformation of (x,y,z,ct), the same as the first component of

$$\Box(\rho\mathbf{V}) = 0 \; ; \tag{4.202}$$

i.e., *the continuity equation forces the flux field to be a conservative field and to satisfy the requirements of an analytic function of one hypercomplex variable*. Another interpretation is that the continuity equation is a conservation of momentum formula for a compressible fluid, with $\rho\mathbf{v}$ being interpreted as the momentum per volume increment or "momentum at a point."

4.5.11 Schrödinger's Equation For A Particle In A Cubic Box

If a subatomic particle, such as an electron, is constrained to motion in a perfect cube-shaped space whose walls are perfectly repelling, then the Schrödinger equation for the probability density function Ψ is

$$\nabla^2\Psi + i\kappa^2 \frac{\partial\Psi}{\partial(ct)} = 0 \, , \tag{4.203}$$

with

$$\kappa^2 = 2mc/\hbar ,$$

where m is the mass of the particle and $\hbar$ is a constant, proportional to Planck's constant. The function Ψ is known to be complex-valued. Before we attack the full equation, (4.203), let us consider a special case:

$$\frac{\partial^2\Psi}{\partial x^2} + i\kappa^2 \frac{\partial\Psi}{\partial(ct)} = 0 \, , \tag{4.204}$$

and assume Ψ in the form

$$\Psi = u + iv, \tag{4.205}$$

with u,v real, scalar functions. With this notation, Equation (4.204) becomes

$$\frac{\partial^2}{\partial x^2}(u+\mathrm{i}v) + \mathrm{i}\kappa^2 \frac{\partial}{\partial(ct)}(u+\mathrm{i}v)$$

$$= \left[\frac{\partial^2 u}{\partial x^2} - \kappa^2 \frac{\partial v}{\partial(ct)}\right] + \mathrm{i}\left[\frac{\partial^2 v}{\partial x^2} + \kappa^2 \frac{\partial u}{\partial(ct)}\right] = 0 \ , \tag{4.206}$$

or

$$\frac{\partial^2 u}{\partial x^2} - \kappa^2 \frac{\partial v}{\partial(ct)} = 0$$

$$\frac{\partial^2 v}{\partial x^2} + \kappa^2 \frac{\partial u}{\partial(ct)} = 0 \ . \tag{4.207}$$

We have reduced the original equation to its complex components. We can now see that the "i" in (4.203) acts as a rotation operator, and the component equations (4.207) indicate some kind of exchange (a "current"?) between the components of Ψ. We want to preserve this vector-operator behavior in four dimensions.

If we replace the "i" in (4.203) with the four-dimensional "**i**," we shall see that the desired behavior is preserved in the higher-dimensional case. (The four-dimensional "**i**" has all the properties of the classical imaginary). We complete the D'Alembertian as we did for the Helmholtz equation and expand our equation to consider a four-dimensional field **W**, of which Ψ corresponds to the first two components, then eliminate the D'Alembertian term to obtain

$$\frac{-\partial^2 \mathbf{W}}{\partial (ct)^2} + \mathbf{i}\kappa^2 \frac{\partial \mathbf{W}}{\partial (ct)} = 0 \ . \tag{4.208}$$

We next use (2.169) to convert the partial derivatives to ordinary derivatives:

$$\frac{d^2\mathbf{W}}{d\mathbf{Z}^2} - \mathbf{i}\kappa^2\,\mathbf{k}\frac{d\mathbf{W}}{d\mathbf{Z}} \tag{4.209}$$

$$= \frac{d^2\mathbf{W}}{d\mathbf{Z}^2} + \mathbf{j}\kappa^2 \frac{d\mathbf{W}}{d\mathbf{Z}}$$

$$= \frac{d}{d\mathbf{Z}}\left[\frac{d\mathbf{W}}{d\mathbf{Z}} + \mathbf{j}\kappa^2\mathbf{W}\right] = 0 \ , \tag{4.210}$$

which is the same as

$$\frac{d\mathbf{W}}{d\mathbf{Z}} + \mathbf{j}\kappa^2\mathbf{W} = \mathbf{j}\kappa^2\mathbf{G} \ . \qquad \text{(a convenient constant)} \tag{4.211}$$

In exactly the way we did for the reduced form of the diffusion equation, we transform (4.211) to obtain

$$\frac{d\mathbf{W}}{d\mathbf{Z}'} + \mathbf{T}^{-1}\kappa^2\mathbf{j}\mathbf{W} = \mathbf{T}^{-1}\kappa^2\mathbf{j}\mathbf{G} \ , \tag{4.212}$$

Again, as in the case of the diffusion equation, the scalar κ^2 has the dimension of (1 / length), hence will have its apparent value changed into a vector $\mathbf{T}^{-1}\kappa^2$ due to the relative motion. We conclude that the equation is invariant in form, up to a distortion of the scalar in the original equation.

V. CONCLUSIONS

We now have a new system of analysis for one hypercomplex variable of four dimensions. We have defined functions, derivatives, integrals and other analysis concepts that have all the same properties as the corresponding complex analysis operations and concepts. The new analysis may be interpreted and applied as a vector analysis for four-dimensional vectors, or may be interpreted as a "complex-like" analysis of a four-component variable. All the same notation as for the complex analysis is carried over into the new system. For example, the complex function expression $sin(z)$ becomes $\mathrm{SIN}(\mathbf{Z})$ in the new system and has the same definition and properties as the classical complex form.

The basis algebra is a commutative ring with unity, but under a slightly broadened viewpoint it is an analogue of the complex field, as follows. The basis ring is isomorphic to $\mathbb{C}^2$, the direct product of complex fields, with complex pair elements (ξ,η). The set O of all elements of the form $(0,\eta)$ or $(\xi,0)$ contains all the zero divisors of the algebra. Only one element of the set, (0,0,0,0), is a "true zero." Nevertheless, the *set O* plays the part of a *zero element* in four dimensions. The fact of multitudinous zero divisors is cited as the probable reason that the founders of vector analysis did not use this particular basis algebra, instead opting for the quaternion system with its single zero divisor, (0,0,0,0). By doing so, they predicated a noncommutative system of analysis that has little of the appearance of complex analysis and will not support the concepts of function, derivative and integral in the classical sense.

The basis algebra and system of analysis may be alternatively stated completely in terms of real 4 X 4 matrices, which puts everything on solid and well-understood mathematical ground. All of the analysis operators, such as the derivative operator, may be stated in matrix form in a simple and straightforward way. The only matrix elements with determinant zero are in the set O of zero divisors, meaning that the matrix eigenvalues are always nonzero outside of the set O. We use this fact in the definition of the analysis operations: functions and other analysis operators act solely on the matrix eigenvalues, hence are well-defined outside the set O and leave the set O invariant with respect to the chosen coordinate system.

We have shown that the real, the complex, and the hypercomplex algebras are but the first three elements in an infinite sequence of commutative algebras of dimension one, two, four, etc., upon which completely analogous systems of analysis may be based.

The new system of analysis thus far described might be dismissed as uninteresting, even trivial, except that it admits the definition of the Cauchy-Riemann conditions in four dimensions. As in the two-dimensional case, the four-dimensional C-R conditions have extensive consequences in the function theory. All the previous effects are included because the classical complex analysis is a proper subset of the present system. For example, all the components of an analytic function obey Laplace's equation (the wave equation) in four dimensions. Especially, all of the gradient and scalar del effects are reproduced (more properly: extended) in four dimensions. However, many new effects are introduced because of the more general definition of the zero element which results in regions of the four-space being left invariant and because of the matrix formulation. For example, most pairs of the components X, Y, Z, T of an analytic function have four-gradients that are mutually orthogonal, and those that are not mutually orthogonal have gradient inner products that are rotational invariants.

The set O of zero divisors composes two orthogonal hyperplanes and constitutes a closed subspace in the x, y, z, ct space. The inverse of an algebraic element becomes indeterminate in the zero set hyperplanes. The presence of a certain region of the real four-space that is somehow "different" in properties would seem to render the present system of analysis useless for scientific and engineering calculations, except for one thing: in precisely the same region *all experimental physics* becomes indeterminate! All the zero set elements have a coordinate $x=ct$ or $x=-ct$, implying motion at the speed of light when physical phenomena are being described. Moreover, the orientation of the zero set hyperplanes is fixed by the observer's (arbitrary) choice of coordinate reference frame, not by anything having to do with space itself. Our new analysis seems to have reserved a spot for a building block labeled "Special Relativity." We have shown that the algebraic basis embodies many properties of relativistic nature, and allows an immediate formulation of Einstein's special relativity.

A group of relativistic transformations was devised that (1) is not the Lorentz group; (2) meets Eintein's two special relativity postulates; (3) predicts the expected relativistic effects for motion radially inward or outward from the observer; and (4) predicts that the relativistic effects will vary as the line of motion moves away from a radial line from the observer, even after simple geometry is taken into account. In particular, distant motion transverse to the radial will show no relativistic effects, allowing the *appearance* (only!) of the speed of light being exceeded. There are many examples of apparently superluminal speeds in astronomy. The new theory, however, preserves Einstein's special relativity in any interaction between two objects.

The elements of the transformation group have determinant +1 but are not explicitly orthogonal. The elements have many properties in common with the elements of the restricted case of the Lorentz group, but have one fundamental difference: the coordinates aligned transversely to the motion are not left unaffected, but are given an increment of hyperbolic rotation, of the same character as that given the longitudinal coordinates. The main consequence is that distant transverse relative motion may produce the appearance of no relativistic effects, as discussed above. A unitary similarity transformation was devised that converts the group elements into complex orthogonal matrices, with the consequence that any covariant formulation of physics is left invariant in form by the new (similarity-transformed) group.

In final summary: we have created a new and powerful mathematical analysis out of the most elementary building blocks at our disposal. The building blocks have the status and familiarity of folklore, and we have all tripped over them for years. In answer to the question of "Why haven't we discovered this, sooner?," I submit that we have been standing too close to our subject. We have been seeing a random-looking collection of rather elementary, overly-familiar concepts because we have considered them individually. One must step back a bit to see the greater pattern and harmony. The reader is invited to test the claims and hypotheses of this work in his or her own area of specialization.

REFERENCES

1. M. J. Crowe, *A History of Vector Analysis* (University of Notre Dame Press, South Bend, 1967; reprinted by Dover, New York, 1985).
2. W. R. Hamilton, "On a New Species of Imaginary Quantities Connected With the Theory of Quaternions," *Proceedings of the Royal Irish Academy*, 2 (1844), pp. 424–434.
3. W. R. Hamilton, *Lectures on Quaternions* (Dublin, 1853) and *Elements of Quaternions* (London, 1866); reprinted by the Chelsea Publishing Co., New York, 1989.
4. J. C. Maxwell, *The Scientific Papers of James Clerk Maxwell*, 2 vols. bound as 1, ed. W. D. Niven (New York, 1965)
5. J. C. Maxwell, *Treatise on Electricity and Magnetism*, 2 vols., 3rd ed. (Dover, New York, 1954).
6. J. W. Gibbs, *Elements of Vector Analysis* (privately printed at New Haven in 1881 and 1884). Included in *The Scientific Papers of J. Willard Gibbs* (Longmans Green & Company, New York, 1906), vol 2. See also: E. B. Wilson, *Vector Analysis of J. W. Gibbs* (Charles Scribner's Sons, New York, 1901).
7. O. W. Heaviside, *Electromagnetic Theory*, vol I (London, 1893).
8. Ref. (1), pp. 150–181 (Dover ed.).
9. R. J. Stephenson, "Development of Vector Analysis From Quaternions," *J. Phys.*, 34 (1966), pp. 194–201.
10. Ref. (1), pp. 182–220 (Dover ed.).
11. H. G. Grassmann, *Die lineal Ausdehnungslehre, ein neuer Zweig der Mathematik dargestellt und durch Anwendungen auf die Übrigen Zweige der Mathematik, wie auch auf die Statik, Mechanik, die Lehre vom Magnetismus und die Krystallonomie erläutert* (privately printed, 1844). Included in: H. G. Grassman, *Hermann Grassmans Gesammelte mathe-*

matische und physikalische Werke, 3 vols. in 6 pts. (Leipzig, 1894–1911). Reprinted by Chelsea Publishing Co., New York, 1969.
12. G. Frobenius, "Über Lineare Substitutionen und Bilineare Formen," *J. für Die Reine and Angewandte Mathematik* 84 (1877), pp. 59–63. For a sketch of a proof of Frobenius' theorem, see T. W. Hungerford, *Algebra* (Holt, Rinehart, and Winston, New York, 1974), p. 461.
13. G. Scheffers, "Verallgemeinerung der Grundlagen der gewöhnlich complexen Functionen," *Berichte der Gesellschaft der Wissenschaften zu Leipzig*, 45 (1893), pp. 829–848.
14. F. Hausdorff, "Zur Theorie der Systeme complexer Zahlen," *Berichte der Gesellschaft der Wissenschaften zu Leipzig*, 52 (1900), pp. 43–61.
15. J. A. Ward, "A Theory of Analytic Functions in Linear Associative Algebras," *Duke Math. J.*, 7 (1940), pp. 233–248.
16. S. Agmon and L. Bers, "The Expansion Theorem for Pseudo-Analytic Functions," *Proc. Amer. Math Soc.*, 3 (1952), pp. 757–764.
17. A. Douglis, "A Function-Theoretic Approach to Elliptic Systems of Equations in Two Variables," *Comm. Pure Appl. Math.*, 6 (1953), pp. 259–289.
18. I. Vekua, *Generalized Analytic Functions* (Addison-Wesley, Reading, 1962).
19. P. W. Ketchum, "Analytic Functions of Hypercomplex Variables," *Trans. Amer. Math. Soc.*, 30 (1928), pp. 641–667.
20. M. Futagawa, "On the Theory of Functions of a Quaternary Variable," I & II, *Tohoku Math. J.*, 29(1928), pp. 175–222 and 35(1932), pp. 69–120.
21. R. A. Frazer, W. J. Duncan, and A. R. Collar, *Elementary Matrices* (Cambridge University Press, London, 1957), p. 35.
22. H. W. Turnbull, *The Theory of Determinants, Matrices, and Invariants* (Blackie and Son, London, 1928; reprinted by Dover, New York, 1960), p. 166 (Dover ed.).
23. H. P. Manning, *Geometry of Four Dimensions* (The Macmillan Company, New York, 1914; reprinted by Dover, New York, 1956).
24. H. P. Manning, Ed., *The Fourth Dimension Simply Explained* (Munn & Company, 1910; reprinted by Dover, New York, 1960).
25. R. Bellman, *Introduction to Matrix Analysis* (McGraw-Hill, New York, 1960), pp. 89–109, 159–181.
26. C. C. MacDuffee, *The Theory of Matrices* (Chelsea Publishing Company, New York, 1946).
27. J. D. Jackson, *Classical Electrodynamics* (John Wiley & Sons, New York, 1962), p. 180.
28. Ref. (27), p. 370.
29. J. A. Eisele, *Modern Quantum Mechanics With Applications To*

Elementary Particle Physics (John Wiley & Sons, New York, 1969), p. 47.
30. J. Aharoni, *The Special Theory of Relativity* (Oxford University Press, London, 1965), p. 47.
31. Ref. (30), pp. 35–36.
32. Ref. (27), pp. 374–386.
33. H. Goldstein, *Classical Mechanics* (Addison-Wesley, Reading, 1950), pp. 194–205.
34. P. G. Bergmann, *Introduction To The Theory Of Relativity* (Prentice-Hall, Englewood Cliffs, New Jersey, 1942; reprinted by Dover, New York, 1976), pp. 111–115 (Dover Ed.).
35. Ref. (30), pp. 85–88.
36. Ref. (30), p. 66.
37. A. Einstein, H. A. Lorentz, H. Weyl, H. Minkowski, *The Principle Of Relativity* (Methuen & Co., London, 1923; reprinted by Dover, New York, 1923), p. 54 (Dover Ed.).
38. Ref. (37), p. 53 (Dover Ed.).
39. H. T. Davis, *Introduction To Nonlinear Differential And Integral Equations* (Dover, New York, 1962), pp. 371–372.
40. Ref. (39), p. 410.
41. W. F. Ames, *Nonlinear Ordinary Differential Equations in Transport Processes*, (Academic Press, New York, 1968), p. 55.
42. G. L. Shpil'ker, "O kommutativnoy giperkompleksnoy sisteme chetvertogo poryadka" ("A Fourth-Order Commutative Hypercomplex System"), *Doklady Akademii Nauk. SSSR*, 1985, Vol. 282, No. 5, pp. 1090–1093.
43. R. C. Tolman, *Relativity, Thermodynamics, and Cosmology*, (Dover, New York, 1987), p. 96.
44. B. Peirce, "Linear Associative Algebras," *American Journal of Math.*, 4(1881), p. 97–215.
45. E. Study, "Über Systeme von complexen Zahlen," *Nachrichten Ges. der Wiss. Göttingen*, 1889, p. 237–268.
46. R. Dedekind, "Zur Theorie der aus n Haupteinheiten gebildeten complexen Größen," *Nachrichten Ges. der Wiss. Göttingen*, 1885, p. 141–159.
47. B. L. van der Waerden, *A History of Algebra*, (Springer-Verlag, Berlin, 1985).
48. R. Hermann, *Groups For Physicists*, (W. A. Benjamin, New York, 1966), pp. 4–7.
49. Scott-Russell, 1844, quoted in Scott, Chu, and McLaughlin, "The Soliton: A New Concept In Applied Physics," *Proc. IEEE* 61(10), 1973, pp. 1443–83.

INDEX

A

absolute value, complex 39, 70
addition
  of hypercomplex elements 13, 16, 19
  of relativistic velocities 148, 175
Agmon, S. 4
Aharoni, J. 166, 188
algebra
  classical complex 7, 27, 36
  D-space 13, 15, 17, 23
  group 5
  Lie 61
  linear associative 5
  nested complex 11, 32, 37
  quaternion 5, 63, 64, 67, 68
algebraic operations
  for D-space elements 15–16, 19
  for quaternion elements 64–67
Ames, W. F. 133
analogy
  field 27
  extended zero 26
analytic function 39
Argand's representation 45
argument, hypercomplex 45
axioms, complex 1, 2
axis planes
  definition 24
  as invariants 41, 49
  as zero elements 26
  fixed by reference frame 142
  orthogonality of 25
  rotation about 35–36, 187

B

basis group 9
  structure of 17
basis vectors 8, 9
  matrix representation 10, 12
  as rotation operators 56
Bellman, R. 41
Bergmann, P. G. 166
Bers, L. 4
boundary layer equations 129

branch cuts 49, 100
Burger's equation 121

C

canonical form 18, 19
Cartesian solutions 102
Cauchy-Riemann conditions
two-dimensional 50
four-dimensional 51, 53, 80
consequences of 58, 61, 80, 82, 83, 84, 87, 89, 90, 94
commutativity
of multiplication 2
necessity of 2, 4, 63, 68
complex conjugate 20, 21, 29, 30, 32, 38, 68, 70
conjugate functions 41, 90, 92, 132
conservative field 66, 81, 95–98, 136, 145, 151
continuity equation, vector 199
cross product 65, 67
Crowe, M. J. 2, 3
curl
classical vector 3, 66, 68, 95, 96
in quaternion multiplication 66

D

D'Alembertian
of a scalar function 80
of a hypercomplex function 77
operator 77, 182
related to second derivative 77–78
Davis, H. T. 209
Dedekind, R. 23
DeMoivre's Theorem, four-dimensional
for hyperbolic functions 44
for trigonometric functions 43
derivative
along a line 57, 59, 89
definition 48
chain rule for 59, 95
determinant, $\mathbb{D}$-space 15, 16, 30, 35, 87, 158
diagonalized matrix form 31
diffusion equation 109, 112
divergence
classical vector 3, 68
in quaternion multiplication 66
division 14, 16
divisors, zero 7
dot product 19, 25, 56, 66, 67, 68, 82, 95
Douglis, A. 4
$\mathbb{D}$-space 8
as direct sum of fields 23
duplex-space 8

E

eigenfunction 102
eigenvalue, $\mathbb{D}$-space 20
exchange operation (EXCH) 153–154, 190
matrix representation 21
vector representation 20
functions of 41
eigenvector, $\mathbb{D}$-space 21
degeneracy of 29
invariance of 22, 41
matrix representation 22
vector representation 21
Einstein, A. 139, 150, 151, 156, 166, 183, 188, 189
special relativity postulates 166
Einstein addition law 148
generalized form 175
Eisele, J. A. 103, 191
$EL_2(\mathbf{V})$ group 146, 147
$EL_4(\mathbf{V})$ group 151
comparison with Lorentz group 154

$EL_4(\mathbf{V})$ element
canonical form 151
hypercomplex function form 157
inverse of canonical form 152
inverse of matrix form 153
matrix form 153
properties of 158–165
vector form 153
element
canonical form 18
matrix form 11
of group basis 10
of quaternion algebra 12
of quaternion group basis 12
relativistic transformation 151
unity 16, 22
vector form 8
zero 26, 27, 42
elementary Cartesian solutions 102
elsewhere 144
Emden's equation 125
equations
Burger's 121
boundary layer 129
diffusion (heat) 109, 112, 197
Emden's 125
Helmholtz 104, 195
Kidder's 130
Klein-Gordon 108, 196
Korteweg-deVries 132
Maxwell's 98, 194
Schrödinger's 116, 119, 200
vector continuity 199
wave 88, 104, 194
Euclidean norm 27, 34, 38, 46

F

field
analogy for $\mathbb{D}$-space elements 27
complex 23, 24, 140
conservative 66, 81, 95, 136, 145, 151
direct sum of fields 23
hypercomplex 27
nonexistence for 4-D elements 4
numerical solution 100
frame
at-rest 147
inertial reference 144
moving 147
observer's 147
parallel 175
primed 147
unprimed 147
Frazer, R. A. 12
Frobenius, G. 4
functions, hypercomplex
analytic, definition 39
conjugate 41
eigenvalues of 41
exponential 41
square root 42
canonical form 39, 41
vector expansion 40, 41, 42
function theory
classical complex 40
in the $\mathbb{D}$-space 39
over a noncommutative algebra 4
Futagawa, M. 5
future 144

G

Gibbs, J. W. 3, 66
Goldstein, H. 166
gradient
classical vector 68, 71, 73
component four-gradients 81, 83, 84, 93
hypercomplex function 71, 72, 74, 89
scalar function 72

and divergence and curl 66, 73
and hypercomplex derivative 75
transformations of 71, 169, 191
Grassman, H. G. 4
ground state
energy 121
wave function 121
group
Abelian 10, 17, 33
cyclic 17, 33
𝔻-space basis 9, 17
Einstein-Lorentz 146, 150–154
invariance 35, 166
orthogonal transformation 33, 140
quaternion 12

H

Hamilton, W. R. 2, 6, 8, 15
Hausdorff, F. 4
heat equation 109, 112
Heaviside, O. W. 3, 66
Helmholtz equation 104
Hermann, R. 61
hyperbolic rotation 162, 186
hypersurfaces 82

I

ideal
as axis plane 24
maximal 23, 24
principal 23
idempotent 19
identity
additive 13, 16
multiplicative 9, 14, 16
increment, volume 191
inner product 28, 68
integral, definition 48
invariance group 35
invariant, absolute
axis planes 41, 49, 143, 145
eigenvectors 41, 145
subspaces 23, 41, 143, 144
invariant, rotational
axis planes 41, 49
determinant 30, 87
eigenvalue magnitude 36
eigenvector 22
elements 35
form ZZ^T 30
modulus 30, 46
quantities 87
trace of matrix form 35
vector magnitude 30, 35
inverse, additive 13
inverse, multiplicative 14, 16
isomorphism 23, 43, 80

J

Jackson, J. D. 99, 166
Jacobi elliptic function 134

K

Ketchum, P. W. 4
Kidder's equation 130
Klein-Gordon equation 108
Korteweg-DeVries equation 132

L

length, vector 68
at-rest 147
Lie algebra 61
light cone 49, 144
limit, definition 46
Lorentz condition 98, 194
Lorentz-Fitzgerald contraction 148
177–182
generalized formula 179

variation with viewing angle 182, 187–188
Lorentz transformation, 𝔻-space
for arbitrary velocity 151
for radial velocity 157, 169–170
for transverse velocity 170–171

M

MacDuffee, C. C. 41
magnitude, vector 30, 36, 38, 39, 70, 84
Manning, H. P. 36
matrix
classical complex 11, 36, 69
classical Lorentz 147
complex orthogonal 164
𝔻-space, complex form 12
𝔻-space Lorentz 153
𝔻-space, real form 11
diagonalized 31
orthogonal 10, 31
quaternion, complex form 13
quaternion, real form 12
unitary 31, 163
matrix analysis 3
matrix representation
of basis vectors 10, 13
of element of 𝔻 11, 12
of element of ℂ 11, 36, 69
of quaternions 12
Maxwell, J. C. 3
Maxwell's equations 3, 98, 194
measurables 147
metric
ℂ X ℂ 27
𝔻-space 28
R^4 28
modulus, hypercomplex 30, 38, 46
properties of 38, 46
motion
Newtonian 170
of inertial frame 144
radial 170, 172
transverse 170
moving frame 147–149
multiplication
basis group for 9, 14
𝔻-space 14, 16, 19, 65
quaternion 64
multiplicative inverse 14, 16, 19

N

nested algebra 11, 32, 36
Newtonian motion 170
noninvertible elements 139, 140, 142, 143

O

observer's bias transformation 165, 184–187
observer's frame 147
operation
derivative 48
function 39
general definition 37
gradient 72
integral 48
limit 46
unary 37, 39
operator, vector
classical curl 3, 66, 68, 95, 96
classical D'Alembertian 77, 80
classical divergence 3, 68
classical gradient 71
hypercomplex D'Alembertian 77, 80, 103, 104
hypercomplex gradient 71, 103
orthogonal matrix 10
orthogonal 31, 33, 35, 71, 74, 90, 97, 141, 142, 158, 162, 166, 200

orthogonality conditions 34, 154, 164
outer product 65

P

past 144
Peirce, B. 23
point solution 117
position vector 146
postulates, special relativity 166
potential
  electromagnetic 95, 98
  generalized 99
primed frame 147

Q

quaternions 2
  real matrix form 12
  complex matrix form 13
multiplication rules 64

R

radial motion 170, 172
radial relativity 170, 172
reachable universe 144
relative motion vector 146, 151
relative speed 146, 147
relativistic interval 144
relativistic form invariance
  derivative 193
  differential element 192
  diffusion equation 197–198
  four-gradient form 167
  Helmholtz's equation 195–196
  increment of volume 191
  integrals 193
  Klein-Gordon equation 196–197
  Maxwell's equations 194
  Schrödinger's equation 200
  vector continuity equation 199
  wave equation 194
relativity transformation
  in $\mathbb{D}$ 150–153, 155–157, 169–170, 188
  classical Lorentz formulation 146, 154–155
rest frame 147, 149
Riemann surface 49
ring
  commutative 17
  $\mathbb{D}$-space 17, 19
  principal ideal 23
  product, $\mathbb{C} \times \mathbb{C}$ 22
rotation
  about axis planes 35, 187
  about direction of motion 186–187
  and **1**, **k** plane 30, 39, 46
  hyperbolic 162, 186
  of eigenvalues 36
  operators 36, 56, 83

S

Scheffers, G. 4
Schrödinger's equation
  particle in a box 116
  hydrogen atom 119
solutions
  boundary layer equation 130
  Burger's equation 123, 125
  complex-valued 102, 138
  diffusion equation 110, 111, 113, 115
  elementary Cartesian 102
  Emden's equation 127, 128
  Helmholtz equation 105, 107
  Klein-Gordon equation 109
  Korteweg-deVries equation 133–137
  Schrödinger's equation 117, 119, 120
  wave equation 104
Shpil'ker, G. L. 6
space
  $\mathbb{C}$ 26
  $\mathbb{C}^2$ 22, 27, 37

duplex ($\mathbb{D}$)
real four-space 8, 27
special relativity
formulation 146, 154–155
postulates 165, 166
Stephenson, R. J. 3
Study, E. 23
subrings, maximal ideal 24
subtraction 14, 16, 19
superluminal speeds 171

T

tensor 100
time dilation 149, 182
generalized formula 183
variation with viewing angle 183–184
time reversal 160
Tolman, R. C. 99
topological equivalence 27
transformation
analytic function 90, 101
complex orthogonal 164
Einstein-Lorentz 146
observer's bias 166, 184–187
orthogonal 31, 33, 35, 71, 74, 90, 97, 141, 142, 158, 162, 166, 200
similarity 68, 163, 165, 166, 187
unitary 31, 72, 78, 89, 165, 166
transpose 26, 29, 69, 76
effect on eigenvalues 29
product $\mathbf{XX}^{\mathrm{T}}$ 30
transverse coordinates 151, 187–188
transverse motion 170–172, 176–177, 180–186
Turnbull, H. W. 13

U

unity
additive 16, 22
multiplicative 16, 22
unprimed frame 147

V

van der Waerden, B. L. 23
variables
classical complex 7, 11
$\mathbb{D}$-space 8
hypercomplex 8, 18
quaternion 12
vector
basis 8
canonical form 18
distance 177
Euclidean norm 27
four-component form 8
length 68, 162
magnitude (scalar length) 30, 36, 38, 39, 70, 84
modulus 38
position 146
relative motion 146, 151
unit 8, 34, 46
vector analysis 1, 2, 3, 145, 166
vector-matrix notation 53, 55, 61, 94
velocity compounding 172–177
velocity reversal 161
vector space 1
Vekua, I. 4

W

Ward, J. A. 4
wave equation 88–90, 104, 194
world line 144

Z

zero
element 26, 27, 42
set 26, 42